COMPREHENSIVE
INORGANIC CHEMISTRY

COMPREHENSIVE INORGANIC CHEMISTRY

VOLUME I

PRINCIPLES OF ATOMIC AND MOLECULAR STRUCTURE
THEORETICAL AND APPLIED NUCLEAR CHEMISTRY
THE ACTINIDE SERIES

VOLUME II

COPPER, SILVER, AND GOLD

VOLUME III

THE HALOGENS

VOLUME IV

ZINC, CADMIUM, AND MERCURY
SCANDIUM, YTTRIUM, AND THE LANTHANIDE SERIES

VOLUME V

NITROGEN; PHOSPHORUS, ARSENIC, ANTIMONY,
AND BISMUTH; NONAQUEOUS CHEMISTRY

FORTHCOMING VOLUMES

HYDROGEN—THE ALKALI METALS

THE TRANSITION ELEMENTS OF GROUPS IV, V, VI, AND VII—
COORDINATION COMPOUNDS—CATALYSIS

IRON, COBALT, AND NICKEL—THE PLATINUM METALS

BERYLLIUM, MAGNESIUM, AND THE ALKALINE EARTH
METALS—BORON—ALUMINUM, GALLIUM, INDIUM, AND
THALLIUM

CARBON—SILICON—THE METALLIC BORIDES, CARBIDES,
SILICIDES, AND RELATED COMPOUNDS—GERMANIUM,
TIN, AND LEAD

OXYGEN—SULFUR, SELENIUM, AND TELLURIUM—THE
INERT GASES

COMPREHENSIVE
INORGANIC CHEMISTRY

M. CANNON SNEED
Professor Emeritus of Chemistry, School of Chemistry
University of Minnesota

ROBERT C. BRASTED
Associate Professor of Chemistry, School of Chemistry
University of Minnesota

VOLUME FIVE

NITROGEN, PHOSPHORUS, ARSENIC,
ANTIMONY, AND BISMUTH
HARRY H. SISLER

NONAQUEOUS CHEMISTRY
ALFRED R. PRAY

D. VAN NOSTRAND COMPANY, INC.
PRINCETON, NEW JERSEY
TORONTO   LONDON
NEW YORK

D. VAN NOSTRAND COMPANY, INC.

120 Alexander St., Princeton, New Jersey
257 Fourth Avenue, New York 10, New York
25 Hollinger Rd., Toronto 16, Canada
Macmillan & Co., Ltd., St. Martin's St., London, W.C. 2, England

*All correspondence should be addressed to the
principal office of the company at Princeton, N. J.*

PRINTED IN THE UNITED STATES OF AMERICA

PREFACE

Comprehensive Inorganic Chemistry is an eleven-volume reference work on the chemical elements and their inorganic compounds. It is comprehensive in the extensiveness of the fields covered rather than in the fullness of their treatment; hence, the volumes are offered individually as a *vade mecum* for the advanced worker—whether industrial or academic—not as an encyclopedic work. Their purpose, therefore, is to serve as a ready reference to those engaged in chemical manufacture and development and to those in advanced studies in chemistry in institutions of higher learning. To meet the requirements of these groups, emphasis has been placed largely on chemical properties and relationships and their interpretation in terms of theoretical concepts of atomic and molecular structure, the deductions from the periodic system, and the basic ideas relating to electrolytes. As a consequence, chapters on the elements are supplemented by special topics, as coordination compounds, catalysis, and reactions in nonaqueous solutions.

The various volumes of Comprehensive Inorganic Chemistry have certain usefulness in courses, especially advanced courses in colleges and universities. Nevertheless, the organization and manner of presentation of these books are not primarily pedagogic. Each chapter is essentially an independent unit, not based upon another coming before or after it. Terms are used with or without definition and statements are made with or without previous background for their understanding, for readers are assumed to be equipped with such knowledge of mathematics, physics, and chemistry to understand what is written. Indeed, the level at which the subject is presented is not too high for the average senior in chemistry or the recent graduate in this field. Notwithstanding the independence of the separate topics, there is a general unity in the treatment brought about by adhering very closely to the relationships in the periodic system and to the interpretations derived from atomic and molecular investigations. However, the transition elements, with the exception of the halogens, are treated before the regular elements.

Another feature is the presentation in tabular form of the chief physical constants of the elements. Chemical properties and the uses of the elements and their compounds are severally stressed for the most part according to their relative importance. Many inorganic compounds are not mentioned at all, and for a description of these substances the

v

literature may be consulted.   From this source also may be obtained fuller treatment of the history, occurrence, physical properties, and methods of production of the elements.   Selected references are given as footnotes where they are easily available when one wishes to consult the original literature.   Throughout, the nomenclature used is that recommended by the committee of the International Union of Chemistry.

Many contributing authors have not only made these volumes possible, but have also added much to their usefulness and value.   Such success as may come to this endeavor will in no small measure be the result of the efforts of these chemists.   Acknowledgment is made to these contributors at chapter headings.

M. C. Sneed
Robert C. Brasted

Minneapolis, Minn.

CONTENTS

PART I

vii

PART II

PART I

NITROGEN, PHOSPHORUS, ARSENIC, ANTIMONY AND BISMUTH

BY H. H. SISLER

University of Florida

INTRODUCTION

The importance of the chemistry of the nitrogen family of elements—from both the practical and theoretical points of view—is not exceeded by that of any other family of the periodic system. In the present chapter the general characteristics of the nitrogen family and, in particular, the chemistry of nitrogen and its compounds are considered; in the chapter which follows, the chemistry of the other members of the family, viz., phosphorus, arsenic, antimony, and bismuth, are discussed.

General Characteristics of the Nitrogen Family. The electronic configurations of the elements of the nitrogen family are listed in Table I.1.

TABLE I.1. ELECTRONIC CONFIGURATIONS

	1 s	2 s p	3 s p d	4 s p d f	5 s p d	6 s p
Nitrogen	2	2, 3				
Phosphorus	2	2, 6	2, 3			
Arsenic	2	2, 6	2, 6, 10	2, 3		
Antimony	2	2, 6	2, 6, 10	2, 6, 10	2, 3	
Bismuth	2	2, 6	2, 6, 10	2, 6, 10, 14	2, 6, 10	2, 3

In accordance with the well-known trend toward increasing ionization potentials within a given period as the outer electron shells fill, it is not surprising to find that these elements have fairly high ionization potentials, as shown in Table I.2.

TABLE I.2. IONIZATION POTENTIALS

	1st	2nd	3rd	4th	5th	6th
N	14.54	29.605	47.426	77.450	97.863	551.925
P	11.0	19.65	30.156	51.354	65.007	220.414
As	~10	20.1	28.0	49.9	62.5	—
Sb	8.64	~18	24.7	44.0	55.5	—
Bi	~8	16.6	25.42	45.1	55.7	—

The electronegativities on the Pauling scale, for the lighter members at least, are likewise fairly high: N, 3.0; P, 2.1; As, 2.0; Sb, 1.8. There is little tendency, therefore, for the lighter numbers of this family to lose

3

electrons to form positive ions. Bismuth, however, and, to a small extent, antimony and arsenic do form triply charged positive ions. Nitrogen, on the other hand, can take up electrons to form the triply charged nitride ion, N^{-3}, and phosphorus somewhat less readily forms the phosphide ion, P^{-3}. There is less tendency for the other members of this family to form such negative ions. These facts are in accord with the general trend in the family toward increasingly metallic—or decreasingly nonmetallic—characteristics with increasing atomic number.

The principal oxidation states exhibited by the elements of the nitrogen family are -3, $+3$, and $+5$. These states are readily correlated with the electronic configurations of the elements in which each atom has five valence electrons, of which two are s electrons and three are p electrons. The stability of the $+3$ state for all members is suggested by the p^3 electrons. Other oxidation states are also exhibited, particularly by nitrogen. All the elements form compounds of the general electronic formula H:M̈:H. They also form oxides of the empirical formula, M_2O_3, which change from acidic to basic character with increasing atomic number. Acidic oxides of the empirical formula, M_2O_5, are likewise formed; the acidic character of these oxides decreases with increasing atomic number. The changes in properties of the trihalides, MX_3, and the pentahalides, MX_5 (nitrogen does not form pentahalides), in passing from lighter to heavier members of the family likewise reflect the increase in metallic nature of the elements. Compounds of Bi(III) are largely covalent in the solid but polar-covalent in certain polar solvents. The physical properties of the free elements themselves show a regular gradation from nonmetallic to metallic properties in passing from nitrogen to bismuth. These trends are discussed in more detail in the paragraphs which follow.

TABLE I.3. SUMMARY OF NUMERICAL PROPERTIES OF GROUP VA ELEMENTS

	N	P	As	Sb	Bi
Outer e^- configuration	$2s^2p^3$	$3s^23p^3$	$4s^24p^3$	$5s^25p^3$	$6s^26p^3$
Molecular state of gas	N_2	$P_4 = P_2$	$As_4 = As_2$	$Sb_4 = Sb_2$	$Bi_2 = Bi$
Atomic volume, ml	15.95	16.9 (white)	13.13 (metal)	18.50 (metal)	21.32
Melting point, °C	−210.0	44.1	814.5	630.5	271
Boiling point, °C	−195.8	280.5	610 (sub.)	1440	1420
Density, g/ml	0.808 (liq.)	1.82 (white)	5.7 (met.)	6.58 (met.)	9.8
	1.2506 (gas)	2.34 (violet)	3.9 (yellow)	5.3 (yellow)	
Radius, covalent, A	0.74	1.10	1.21	1.41	1.52
Radius, crystal, A					
M^{-3}	1.71	2.12	2.22	2.45	—
M^{+3}	—	—	0.69	0.90	1.20
$M^{+5} (MO_3^-)$	0.11	0.34	0.47	0.62	0.74
Ionization potential, ev	14.54	11.0	~10	8.64	~8
Electronegativity	3.0	2.1	2.0	1.8	—
E^0, $M + 3H_2O$	−1.44	0.49	−0.25	−0.21	−0.32
$= H_3MO_3 + 3H^+ + 3e^-$	(HNO_2)	(H_3PO_3)	$(HAsO_2)$	(SbO^+)	(BiO^+)
Heat of fusion,	0.1732	0.15 (white)	—	4.8	2.63
kcal/mole	(−210°C)	(44°C)		(630°C)	(271°C)
Heat of vaporization,	1.333	2.97	—	—	—
kcal/mole	(−196°C)	(280°C)			
Heat of dissociation,	226	—	—	—	—
kcal/mole					
Heat capacity, cal/g	—	0.189	0.082	0.050	0.029

TABLE I.4.   ISOTOPES OF NITROGEN, PHOSPHORUS, ARSENIC, ANTIMONY AND BISMUTH*

Isotopes	Class	Type of Decay	Half-life	Energy of Radiation	Method of Production and Genetic Relationships
$^{12}_{7}N$	A	β^+, $\beta^+3\alpha$	0.0125 s	β^+: 16.6 abs	C-p-n; ^{12}C-p-n; N-γ-$2n$
^{13}N	A	β^+	9.93 m	1.24 spect.	B-α-n; C-d-n; C-p-γ; ^{13}C-p-n; N-n-$2n$; N-d-t; N-γ-n; O-n-$p3n$; O-γ-$p2n$; spall Al
^{14}N : % abundance = 99.635					
^{15}N : % abundance = 0.365					
^{16}N	A	β^-	7.35 s	10.3 (20%), 4.3 (40%), 3.8 (40%) cl ch	N-n-γ; N-d-p; O-n-p; F-n-α
^{17}N	A	β^-, n	4.14 s	β^-: 3.7 β-recoil coinc abs	spall O, F, Na, Mg, Al, Si, P, S, Cl, K; ^{14}C-α-p; O-n-p; ^{18}O-γ-p; F-γ-$2p$
$^{29}_{15}P$	B	β^+	4.57 s	3.6 cl ch	Si-p-n, Si-d-n; P-γ-$2n$ (?)
^{30}P	A	β^+	2.55 m	3.5 spect.	Al-α-n, Si-p-n; Si-^{3}He-p; P-n-$2n$; P-γ-n; S-d-α; Cl-γ-αn
^{31}P : % abundance = 100					
^{32}P	A	β^-	14.30 d	1.701 spect.	Si-d-γ; Si-α-p; Si-^{3}He-p; P-d-p; P-n-γ; S-n-p; S-d-α; Cl-n-α; Cl-γ-αn; Cl-γ-t; Cl-d-$p\alpha$; spall Fe, Cu
^{33}P	A	β^-	25.4 d	0.27 spect.	S-n-p; S-γ-p; Cl-γ-α; Cl-γ-$2p$
^{34}P	B	β^-	12.4 s	5.1 (75%), 3.2 (25%) abs	S-n-p; Cl-n-α
$^{70}_{33}As$	D	β^+	52 m		As-d-$p6n$; daughter ^{70}Se; not found: ^{70}Ge-p

* A Element and mass number certain.
  B Element and mass number probable.
  C Element probable and mass number certain or probable.
  D Element certain and mass number not well established.
  E Element probable and mass number not well established (mass number not
      listed means that it is unknown).
  F Insufficient evidence.
  G Assignment probably in error.

TABLE I.4—*Continued*

Isotopes	Class	Type of Decay	Half-life	Energy of Radiation	Method of Production and Genetic Relationships
^{71}As	A	EC	60 h		Ga-α-2n; Ge-d-n; As-d-p5n; parent ^{71}Ge
^{72}As	A	EC, β^+	26 h	3.34 (19%), 2.50 (62%), 1.84 (12%), 0.67 (5%), 0.27 (2%) spect.	Ga-α-n; Ge-p-n; As-d-p4n; ^{74}Se-d-α; daughter ^{72}Se
^{73}As	A	EC	76 d		Ge-d-n; ^{70}Ge-α-p; Ge-α-p; As-d-p3n; ^{76}Se-p-α
^{74}As	A	β^- 53%, β^+ 47%	17.5 d	β^-: 1.36 (51%), 0.69 (49%) spect.	Ga-α-n; Ge-d-n; Ge-p-n; As-n-2n; As-d-p2n; Se-d-α; Br-γ-αn; spall-fission Bi
^{75}As: % abundance = 100					
^{76}As	A	β^-	26.8 h	3.04 (60%), 2.49 (25%), 1.29 (15%) spect.	Ge-p-n; As-d-p; As-n-γ; Se-n-p; Se-γ-p; Se-d-α; Br-n-α; Br-γ-αn; Br-γ-α; Br-γ-αn
^{77}As	A	β^-	38 h	0.700 spect.	Br-γ-α; spall-fission Bi; fission Th, U, ^{233}U; daughter ^{77}Ge; daughter ^{77m}Ge; not parent ^{77m}Se
^{78}As	B	β^-	90 m	4.1 ($\sim$70%); 1.4 ($\sim$30%) abs	Br-n-α; Br-γ-^{3}He; Se-n-p; fission U, daughter ^{78}Ge
^{78}As	F		40 m		fission U, daughter (?) ^{78}Ge
^{79}As	D	β^-	9 m	2.1 abs	Se-γ-p; Se-n-pn
$^{116}_{51}$Sb	A	β^+	60 m	$\sim$1.45 spect.	In-α-3n
^{117}Sb	A	EC	2.8 h		In-α-2n; Sn-d-n; Sn-p-n; spall I(π)
^{118}Sb	B	β^+	3.5 m	3.1 abs spect.	In-α-n; Sn-p-n; daughter ^{118}Te
^{118}Sb	A	EC	5.1 h	e $\sim$2 abs	In-α-n; Sn-d-n
^{119}Sb	B	EC	39 h		Sn-d-n; Sn-p-n; spall Sb; daughter ^{119}Te

TABLE I.4—*Continued*

Isotopes	Class	Type of Decay	Half-life	Energy of Radiation	Method of Production and Genetic Relationships
^{120}Sb	D	EC	6.0 d		Sb-d-$p2n$; ^{120}Sn-d-$2n$; spall-fission Bi; not found: Sn-p, Sb-γ, Sb-x rays
^{120}Sb	A	β^+, EC	16.4 m	1.70 spect.	Sn-d-n; Sn-p-n; ^{120}Sn-d-$2n$; Sb-n-$2n$; Sb-γ-n; Sb-d-t; Sb-p-pn
^{121}Sb: % abundance = 57.25					
^{122m}Sb	A	IT	3.5 m		Sb-n-γ; ^{121}Sb-n-γ
^{122}Sb	A	β^-	2.80 d	β_2 1.46 (coinc with γ) β-γ coinc spect.	Sn-d-$2n$; Sn-p-n; Sb-d-p; Sb-γ-n; Sb-n-γ; spall Sb, I(T); spall-fission Bi
^{123}Sb: % abundance = 42.75					
^{124m_2}Sb	A	IT, β^-	21 m		Sb-n-γ; ^{123}Sb-n-γ
^{124m_1}Sb	A	IT, β^-	1.3 m	3.2 abs	Sb-n-γ; ^{123}Sb-n-γ
^{124}Sb	A	β^-	60 d	β_1 2.291 (21%), β_2 1.69 (7%), β_3 0.95 (7%), β_4 0.68 (26%), β_5 0.50 (39%) spect.	Sn-p-n; Sn-d-$2n$; Sb-d-p; Sb-n-γ; spall Sb; Te-d-α; I-n-α; spall-fission Bi
^{125}Sb	A	β^-	~2.7 y	0.616 (18%), 0.299 (49%) 0.128 (33%) spect.	Sn-d-n; Sn-n-γ, β^- decay; spall-fission Th; fission ^{233}U; parent ^{125m}Te; daughter ^{125}Sn; not daughter ^{125}Sn
^{126}Sb	B	β^-	9 h	~1 abs	fission ^{235}U; daughter ^{126}Sn
Sb	E	β^-	10 m		fission ^{235}U
~^{126}Sb	D	β^-	28 d	1.9	fission U, ^{235}U
^{127}Sb	A	β^-	93 h	1.2 abs	fission ^{233}U, ^{235}U, U, Pu; parent ^{127}Te; parent (84%) ^{127}Te; parent (16%) ^{127m}Te; daughter ^{127}Sn
^{129}Sb	A	β^-	4.2 h		fission U, Pu; parent ^{129}Te

TABLE I.4—*Continued*

Isotopes	Class	Type of Decay	Half-life	Energy of Radiation	Method of Production and Genetic Relationships
^{130}Sb	D	β^-	40 m		fission ^{235}U
^{130}Sb	D	β^-	12 m		fission U
^{131}Sb	A	β^-	23.1 m		fission U, parent ^{131}Te; parent ^{131m}Te
^{132}Sb	B	β^-	2 m		fission U; parent ^{132}Te
^{133}Sb	B	β^-	4.4 m		fission U, parent ^{133m}Te
$^{134, 135}$Sb	D	β^-	$\sim$50 s		fission U
$<^{195}_{83}$Bi	E	α	1.7 m	6.2 ion ch	spall Pb
^{198}Bi	B	EC 99+%; α 5$\times$10^{-2} %	7 m	5.83 ion ch	spall Pb; parent Pb
^{199}Bi	B	EC 99+%; α 10^{-2} %	$\sim$25 m	5.47 ion ch abs mica	spall Pb; parent ^{199}Pb
^{200}Bi	B	EC	35 m		spall Pb; parent ^{200}Pb
^{201}Bi	B	EC 99+% α 3$\times$10^{-3}	62 m	5.15 ion ch	spall Pb; parent ^{201}Pb
^{201}Bi	B	EC	$\sim$2 h		spall Pb; parent ^{201}Pb
^{202}Bi	B	EC	95 m		daughter ^{202}Po
^{203}Bi	B	EC	12 h	α: 4.85 range emuls	spall Pb, parent ^{203}Pb; daughter ^{203}Po
^{204}Bi	B	EC, no β^+	12 h	conv: $\sim$0.2, $\sim$0.8 (weak), abs, spect.	^{204}Pb-d-2n; Pb-d-2n; daughter ^{204}Po; Tl-α-3n, parent ^{204m2}Pb; parent ^{204m1}Pb
^{205}Bi	B	EC	14.5 d		daughter ^{205}Po daughter ^{209}At
^{206}Bi	B	EC	6.4 d		Tl-α-3n; Pb-d-2n; ^{207}Pb-d-3n; ^{206}Pb-d-2n; daughter ^{206}Po daughter ^{210}At
^{207}Bi	B	EC	$\sim$50 y		Pb-d-3n; daughter ^{211}At; parent ^{207m}Pb
^{208}Bi	F	EC	long		Pb-d-2n

Table I.4—*Continued**

Isotopes	Class	Type of Decay	Half-life	Energy of Radiation	Method of Production and Genetic Relationships
^{209}Bi: % abundance = 100					
^{209}Bi	G	α	$\gg 10^{17}$ y sp act	$\sim$3.15 range emulsion	
^{210}Bi (RaE)	A	β^- 99+%; α 5×10^{-5}%	5.02 d	β^-; 1.17 spect.	natural source, daughter ^{210}Pb; parent ^{210}Po; parent ^{206}Tl; Pb-d-γ; Pb-α-pn; Bi-d-p; Bi-n-γ
^{210}Bi	A	α, β^- or IT ($\sim$0.3%)	$\sim$10^6 y yield	4.93 ion ch	Bi-n-γ; parent ^{206}Tl; parent ^{210}Po
^{211}Bi	A	α 99.68%; β^- 0.32%	2.16 m	α: 6.18 (84%), 6.272 (16%) spect.	natural source, daughter ^{211}Pb (AcB); parent ^{211}Po (AcC'), parent ^{207}Tl (AcC'')
^{212}Bi	A	β^- 66.3%; α 33.7%	60.5 m	α: 6.086 (27.2%); 6.047 (69.9%); 5.765 (1.7%); 5.622 (0.15%); 5.603 (1.1%); 5.481 (0.016%) spect.	natural source, daughter ^{212}Pb (ThB), parent ^{212}Po (ThC'), parent ^{208}Tl (ThC'')
^{213}Bi	A	β^- 98%; α 2%	47 m	β^-; 1.39 (68%), 0.959 (32%) spect.	daughter ^{217}At, parent ^{213}Po, parent ^{209}Tl
^{214}Bi	A	β^- 99+%; α 0.04%	19.7 m	α: 5.505 (45%); 5.444 (55%) spect.	natural source, daughter ^{214}Pb (RaB), daughter ^{218}At, parent ^{214}Po (RaC'), parent ^{210}Tl (RaC''); descendant ^{222}Fr
^{215}Bi	A	β^-	8 m		natural source, daughter ^{219}At, parent ^{215}Po

* Table taken from J. M. Hollander, *et. al.*, *Revs. Mod. Phys.* **25** (2) (1953).

CHAPTER 1

NITROGEN AND ITS COMPOUNDS

Nuclear Chemistry. Nitrogen as it occurs in nature consists of the two stable isotopes of mass numbers 14 and 15 in the ratio of 99.635:0.365. In addition to these stable isotopes four unstable radioactive isotopes ^{12}N, ^{13}N, ^{16}N, and ^{17}N have been prepared. The first two are positron emitters and have the half-lives 0.0125 sec and 9.93 min respectively. ^{16}N and ^{17}N are electron emitters with half-lives of 7.35 sec and 4.14 sec, respectively. It has been possible by fractionation procedures to obtain ^{15}N at greater concentrations than those found in nature. This "heavy" nitrogen concentrate has been used to prepare nitrogen compounds for use in various organic and biochemical studies, the heavy nitrogen serving as a tracer. Table I.4 includes the isotopes of nitrogen as well as other members of Group VA.

Molecular Nitrogen. The gas density of ordinary nitrogen at standard temperature and pressure is 1.25046 g/l. This value corresponds to the molecular formula N_2. Magnetic measurements in molecular nitrogen indicate that the material is diamagnetic with a specific susceptibility of -0.430×10^{-6} at 25°C. The nitrogen molecule in its ground state, therefore, has no resultant electronic angular momentum, either orbital or spin, and contains no unpaired electrons. Its electronic formula is commonly written :N:::N:. The molecular orbital electronic configuration for the N_2 molecule is $KK\sigma^2{}_{2s}\sigma^{*2}{}_{2s}\sigma^2{}_{2p_x}\pi^4{}_{2p_x 2p_y}$. The internuclear distance in the nitrogen molecule is 1.095 A, and studies of the vibrational and rotational spectra of molecular nitrogen indicate that there are two types of nitrogen molecules, *viz.* those with symmetrical nuclear spins and those with antisymmetrical nuclear spins. At ordinary temperatures these two forms occur in the ratio 2:1.

Because of the symmetry of the nitrogen molecule and the stability of its electronic states, intermolecular forces are exceedingly small. The equilibrium temperatures and ΔH values for the phase changes exhibited by molecular nitrogen at one atmosphere pressure are listed in the following scheme:

$$\underset{\text{cubic}}{N_2(\text{solid } \alpha)} \xrightleftharpoons{-237.49\,°C} \underset{\text{hexagonal}}{N_2(\text{solid } \beta)} \xrightleftharpoons{-209.96\,°C} N_2(\text{liquid}) \xrightleftharpoons{-195.78\,°C\ (1\ \text{atm})} N_2(\text{gas})$$

$$\Delta H_{\text{trans}} = 54.71 \text{ cal/mole}; \quad \Delta H_{\text{fusion}} = 172.3 \text{ cal/mole};$$
$$\Delta H_{\text{vap}} = 1332.9 \text{ cal/mole}.$$

11

The critical temperature is $126.26 \pm 0.04°K$ and the critical pressure is 33.54 ± 0.02 atm.[1] The densities of solid nitrogen in its stable form at each of the following temperatures are: $-252.5°C$ (solid α), 1.0265 g/ml; $-210°C$ (solid β), 0.8792 g/ml (see also Table I.3). The density of the liquid is given by the function $(1.1607 - 0.00455T)$ g/ml in which T is the absolute temperature. Nitrogen gas is only very slightly soluble in water and shows no tendency whatsoever to react with that substance.[2]

The nitrogen molecule is an exceedingly stable one; the energy of its dissociation into nitrogen atoms has been measured spectroscopically and has the value of 170,275 cal/mole at $0°K$ (see also Table I.3). It is this high degree of stability of the nitrogen molecule which accounts for the inertness of elementary nitrogen rather than any lack of chemical activity on the part of the nitrogen atom.

Chemical Reactions. At ordinary temperatures, elementary nitrogen is inert towards most chemical reagents. At high temperatures it reacts with oxygen to form nitrogen(II) oxide and at high temperatures and pressures in the presence of a catalyst it reacts with hydrogen to form ammonia. It also reacts at elevated temperatures with lithium (but not with Na, K, Rb, or Cs), calcium, strontium, barium, magnesium, beryllium, boron, aluminum, titanium, silicon, and chromium to form nitrides. At extremely high temperatures, 1800–1900°C, a mixture of carbon, hydrogen, and nitrogen slowly react to form hydrogen cyanide.

"Active" Nitrogen. When pure molecular nitrogen is subjected to a silent electrical discharge, it is partly changed to an unstable activated condition; on standing it returns to the unactivated state, giving a golden yellow afterglow.[3] The time of persistence of the glow depends chiefly on the size of the containing vessel. It can be shown by the fact that this glow is not affected by an electric field that it is not due to gaseous ions. "Active" nitrogen is more reactive with some substances than is ordinary nitrogen, *e.g.*

$$P_{4(white)} \xrightarrow{N_2^*} P_4 \text{ (red)} + \text{some phosphorus nitride}$$

$$6Na + N_2^* \xrightarrow{150°} 2Na_3N$$

$$HC\equiv CH + N_2^* \to 2HCN$$

$$2NO \xrightarrow{N_2^*} 2N_2 + O_2$$

[1] D. White *et al.*, *J. Am. Chem. Soc.* **73**, 5713 (1951).

[2] O. T. Bloomer and K. N. Rao, *Inst. Gas Technol. Res. Bull.* No. 18, 28 pp. (1952).

[3] E. Maxted, *Modern Advances in Inorganic Chemistry*, Oxford Univ. Press (1947), pp. 208–13.

It is believed that the activity of "active" nitrogen results from the presence of atomic nitrogen as well as metastable activated N_2 molecules.

Occurrence, Preparation, and Commercial Applications. Nitrogen occurs in the elementary form as the major constituent (about 79% by volume) of the atmosphere. The amount of nitrogen in the atmosphere is kept relatively constant by the balance between the removal of nitrogen from the air through bacterial, chemical, and electrical action and the addition of nitrogen to the air as a result of the decomposition of nitrogenous organic matter by bacterial action and by combustion. In the combined state nitrogen is widely distributed; it is a component of many important compounds, *e.g.* ammonia, proteins, and other organic materials. Its chief mineral source is the sodium nitrate found in deposits in northern Chile.

Nitrogen is chiefly prepared by two types of procedures: (1) separation from the atmosphere, and (2) decomposition of nitrogen compounds. The most economical large scale method for preparing nitrogen is by the fractional distillation of liquid air. Nitrogen, contaminated with the inert gases, may be obtained also by removing the oxygen, carbon dioxide, and water vapor from the air by appropriate chemical reagents. Methods for preparing nitrogen from its compounds include the following:

(1) *The reaction of ammonium ion and nitrite ion.* In practice a saturated solution of sodium nitrite is slowly added to a hot, saturated solution of ammonium chloride. The reaction proceeds according to the equation:

$$NH_4^+ + NO_2^- \rightarrow N_2 + 2H_2O$$

though the kinetics are complex.[4]

(2) *The reaction of ammonia with bromine.* Ammonia gas is bubbled through bromine water and the resulting gaseous mixture passed through various liquid reagents which absorb water vapor, unreacted bromine, and ammonia:

$$2NH_3 + 3Br_2 \rightarrow N_2 + 6H^+ + 6Br^-$$

Other active oxidizing agents as $Cr_2O_7^=$, O_3, F_2, MnO_2 liberate N_2 from NH_4^+ salts.

(3) *The decomposition of sodium or barium azide at 300°C.* If the salt is perfectly dry, spectroscopically pure nitrogen is obtained:

$$2NaN_3 \rightarrow 2Na + 3N_2$$

[4] E. Abel, *Monatsh.* **81**, 539 (1950).

(4) *The reaction of ammonia and heavy metal oxides.* Ammonia passed over copper(II) oxide reduces the oxide and liberates nitrogen as illustrated by the equation

$$3CuO + 2NH_3 \rightarrow 3Cu + 3H_2O + N_2$$

(5) *The reaction of sulfamic acid and/or urea on nitrites.* Sulfamic acid reacts instantaneously and quantitatively with NO_2^- at even very low concentrations to give N_2. At high nitrite concentration the N_2 is contaminated with N_2O_3.[5]

(6) *Catalytic, thermal decomposition of ammonia.* Ammonia may serve as a commercial source of pure nitrogen by its thermal decomposition in presence of platinum catalyst.

Elementary nitrogen is used in the manufacture of ammonia, calcium cyanamide, and other compounds. It is used in one method for case hardening steel, and also for filling the bulbs of incandescent lamps. Nitrogen may be used in most cases where a nonoxidizing, nonreducing, inert atmosphere is desired.

TABLE 1.1. OXIDATION STATES OF NITROGEN

+5	N_2O_5, HNO_3, nitrates, NO_2X
+4	$NO_2(N_2O_4)$
+3	N_2O_3, HNO_2, nitrites, NOX, NX_3
+2	NO, Na_2NO_2, nitrohydroxylamates
+1	N_2O, $H_2N_2O_2$, hyponitrites
0	N_2
$-\frac{1}{3}$	HN_3, azides
-1	NH_2OH, hydroxylammonium salts
-2	H_2NNH_2, hydrazinium salts
-3	NH_3, ammonium salts, amides, imides, nitrides.

Nitrogen stands apart from other members of its family not only because it is the most electronegative of the group but also for three other important reasons: (1) its valence shell (the L shell) is limited to four orbitals (one s and three p or hybrids of these) and, hence, nitrogen has a maximum covalence of four; (2) nitrogen, like carbon and oxygen, is capable of forming π bonds employing p orbitals on its atoms and the atoms of the element with which it combines; and (3) the small size of the nitrogen atom limits its coordination number because of steric factors. For these reasons, nitrogen forms many compounds (*e.g.* HN_3) for which there are no analogues in the chemistry of phosphorus, arsenic, and other members of the family. Likewise, nitrogen fails to form some compounds

[5] R. C. Brasted, *Anal. Chem.* **24**, 1111 (1952); **25**, 221 (1953); *J. Chem. Educ.* **28**, 582 (1951).

(*e.g.* the pentahalides, and the ortho "-ic" acids) which have analogues among the compounds of phosphorus and arsenic.

Though there is an element of arbitrariness about the assignment of oxidation states, it is convenient to organize the discussion of nitrogen compounds in terms of the oxidation states exhibited by the element. These are listed in the Table 1.1.

Ammonia and its Derivatives

Molecular Structure and Physical Properties of Ammonia. The simplest example of a molecule in which nitrogen attains a stable electronic configuration through the formation of three electron pair bonds is the ammonia molecule, NH_3. Spectroscopic studies indicate that the ammonia molecule has the pyramidal structure indicated in Fig. 1.1.

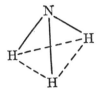

Fig. 1.1.   Structure of ammonia molecule.

The interbond angle is 107° which is close to the tetrahedral angle.   There is some evidence, therefore, that the nitrogen atom is tetrahedral, with the unshared pair of electrons occupying one of the four tetrahedral (sp^3) orbitals.   (Of course, there is a possibility that the bond orbitals area of the p type, spread apart beyond their usual 90° angle by the repulsive forces between the protons.)   Substituted ammonias such as $(CH_3)_3N$ have a similar pyramidal configuration.   It might be expected that a substituted ammonia of the type N*abc* would exhibit optical activity. No such molecule has ever been resolved, however, and it has been shown that this failure results from a very low energy barrier between the *d*- and *l*-forms (Fig. 1.2).   Under these circumstances racemization occurs so rapidly at room temperature as to preclude resolution.

Like water and hydrogen fluoride, ammonia has physical properties which are abnormal with respect to those of the hydrogen compounds of other members of the family.   This statement is particularly true with respect to its abnormally high boiling point, freezing point, heats of fusion and vaporization, heat capacity, and dielectric constant.   These abnormalities are attributed to the existence of hydrogen bonds in the liquid and solid states to an extent which varies with the temperature.

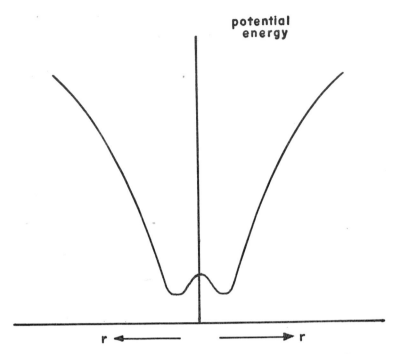

Fig. 1.2.   Energy barrier of d and l $Nabc$ type molecules.

TABLE 1.2.   PHYSICAL PROPERTIES OF NH₃

Melting point..................... ....−77.74°C
Boiling point.................................−33.42°C
ΔH (fusion) (at mp).. ....1352 cal/mole
ΔH (vaporization) (at bp)... . ...5581 cal/mole
Critical temperature.... . ...132.9°C
Critical pressure............................112.3 atm
Dielectric constant
   (liquid at − 60 ± 10°C)......................26.7
Density (liquid at −70°C)....................0.7253 g/ml
Density (liquid at −30°C)....................0.6777 g/ml
ΔH^0 (formation), 25°C...........................−11.04 kcal/mole
ΔF^0, 25°C...............................−3.976 kcal/mole
Equil. constant of formation, log K...............2.9144
Entropy, S^0..............................46.01 cal/deg mole
Heat capacity, $C_p{}^0$........ . ...8.523 cal/deg mole
Viscosity (liquid at 25°C).......................0.001350 poise
Vapor pressure (liquid at −20°C)................1426.8 mm Hg
Vapor pressure (liquid at 0°C)...................3221.0 mm Hg
Vapor pressure (liquid at 20°C).................6428.5 mm Hg
Entropy, $S^0{}_{298.1°K}$ (experimental) ....45.94 cal/deg/mole

The breaking of considerable numbers of hydrogen bonds when solid ammonia melts and when liquid ammonia boils causes the melting and boiling points, as well as the heats of fusion and vaporization, to be high. The breaking of these bonds as the temperature is increased increases the heat capacity. The important physical constants for ammonia are listed in Table 1.2. Ammonia is highly mobile in the liquid state, and as the above densities indicate, the liquid expands sharply with rise in temperature. Ammonia is colorless in the solid, liquid, and gaseous states.

Liquid Ammonia as a Solvent. The physical and chemical properties of liquid ammonia are such as to cause it to be a good solvent for a great many chemical substances. (See also Part I, Chap. 3, this volume.)

TABLE 1.3. SOLUBILITIES OF VARIOUS SALTS IN LIQUID AMMONIA

Substance	Soly. at 25°C (g/100 g NH₃)
AgCl	0.83
AgBr	5.92
AgI	206.84
AgNO₃	86.04
NH₄Cl	102.5
NH₄Br	237.9
NH₄I	368.5
NH₄NO₃	390.0
NH₄ClO₄	137.93
NaF	0.35
NaCl	3.02
NaBr	137.95
NaI	161.90
NaNO₃	97.6
Na₂SO₄	0.00
NaCNS	205.5
NaNH₂	0.004
Li₂SO₄	0.00
LiNO₃	243.66
KNH₂	3.6
KNO₃	10.4
KBr	13.50
KI	182.0
Ca(NO₃)₂	80.22
Ba(NO₃)₂	97.22

The solvent properties of ammonia are, in a rough way, intermediate between those of water and of ethyl alcohol. Liquid ammonia has a high dielectric constant, and dissolves a great many ionic substances; it is inferior to water in this respect, however. On the other hand, liquid ammonia is a better solvent for organic substances than is water. Among the unusual solvent properties of liquid ammonia is its ability to dissolve the alkali metals and calcium, strontium, and barium to yield dark blue solutions which have been said to contain metal ions and solvated electrons:

$$Na \xrightarrow{\text{liq. NH}_3} Na^+ + e \cdot xNH_3^-$$

According to the theory of Ogg [6] the ammoniated electron is not acceptable from a thermodynamic point of view and it is suggested that the electrons are quantized in cavities which they produce in the solvent. On evaporation of the alkali metal solutions the original alkali metal is obtained unchanged. Calcium, barium, and strontium solutions, however, leave residues of the metal ammonia complexes, $Ca(NH_3)_6$, $Sr(NH_3)_6$, and $Ba(NH_3)_6$ when they are evaporated. Very concentrated solutions of these active metals in liquid ammonia have a metallic, copper-like appearance rather than the blue color. The solutions of active metals in liquid ammonia are reducing agents of great power, and, for oxidants which are soluble in ammonia, make possible the carrying out of homogeneous reductions. Such reducing agents have been found to be very useful and convenient for a number of chemical processes. Examples of such reactions include:

Elementary Reductions: $\quad A^n + nM \rightarrow M_nA^n$ (A^n = an element of valence n)

Bond Reductions: $\quad R_3Sn\!-\!SnR_3 + 2Na \rightarrow 2R_3SnNa$

$$R_2Ge\!=\!GeR_2 + 2Na \rightarrow \underset{\underset{\displaystyle Na \quad Na}{|\quad\;\; |}}{R_2Ge\!-\!GeR_2} \xrightarrow{2Na} 2R_2GeNa_2$$

$$\underset{/}{\overset{\backslash}{}}C\!=\!C\underset{\backslash}{\overset{/}{}} + 2Na \rightarrow \underset{\underset{|\quad\;\; |}{}}{NaC\!-\!CNa}$$

Salt Reductions: $\quad 2KBr + Ca \rightarrow CaBr_2 + 2K$

$\qquad\qquad\qquad 3KNH_2 + Al \rightarrow Al(NH_2)_3 + 3K$

Reduction of
Covalent Compounds: $\quad A\!-\!H + M \rightarrow AM + \frac{1}{2}H_2$
(A = an element or radical)

$\qquad\qquad A\!-\!X + M \rightarrow MX + A$
(A = an element or radical)
(X = a halogen)

$$A + M \rightarrow MA$$

[6] R. A. Ogg, Jr., *Phys. Rev.* **69**, 668 (1946); *J. Chem. Phys.* **14**, 295, 399 (1946).

The chemical properties of ammonia, like the physical properties, are analogous in many respects to those of water, *e.g.*, liquid ammonia undergoes auto-ionization according to the equation

$$2NH_3 \rightleftarrows NH_4^+ + NH_2^-$$

which is analogous to

$$2H_2O \rightleftarrows H_3O^+ + OH^-$$

However, the extremely low electrical conductivity of liquid ammonia shows that its degree of ionization is even less than that of water:

$$(NH_4^+)(NH_2^-) = 1.9 \times 10^{-33} \text{ at } -50°C$$

The special character of the chemistry of liquid ammonia solutions derives, not from the similarities between the solvents ammonia and water, but rather from their differences.[7]   Principal among the differences are: (1) the greater proton affinity (or electron donor tendency) of ammonia than water, (2) the lesser tendency of ammonia to release protons than water.   The first of these is important for it means that since the acidity of all strong acids in liquid ammonia is leveled to that of NH_4^+ ion, and since NH_4^+ ion is a weaker acid than H_3O^+, liquid ammonia solutions do not afford acids as strong as those which are available in aqueous systems. On the other hand, the lesser proton donor tendency of ammonia as compared with water makes it possible to use bases (*e.g.* KNH_2 or KOC_2H_5) in liquid ammonia solutions which are considerably more basic than OH^- ion, the strongest base which is afforded by aqueous solutions. Because of the relatively high reactivity of the hydrogen atoms of the water molecule, salts of very weak acids are largely, if not completely, hydrolyzed, and the stronger reducing agents react with water to displace hydrogen.   This behavior is less true of liquid ammonia, however. Liquid ammonia chemistry, therefore, is characterized by the availability of stronger reducing agents, stronger bases, but weaker acids than is the chemistry of aqueous solutions.   Further, because of the easier susceptibility of the ammonia molecule than water to oxidation, and the lower acidity available in the solvent, chemistry in liquid ammonia solutions affords only relatively weak oxidizing agents.   A number of very useful synthetic reagents may be used in liquid ammonia.

Chemical Properties of Ammonia.   The tremendous number of chemical reactions which ammonia undergoes may be grouped into three chief classes: (1) addition reactions, usually called *ammoniation* (analo-

[7] C. A. Kraus, *Chem. Rev.* **26**, 95–104 (1940).

gous to hydration); (2) substitution reactions, commonly called *ammonolysis* (analogous to hydrolysis); and (3) oxidation-reduction reactions.

The first of these classes includes those reactions in which the ammonia adds to other molecules or ions either by the formation of covalent bonds through the unshared electron pair on the ammonia molecule or through electrostatic interactions. Ammonia forms complexes with a great many metal ions; examples of these complexes include $[Ag(NH_3)_2]^+$, $[Cu(NH_3)_4]^{++}$, $[Cr(NH_3)_6]^{+3}$, and $[Pt(NH_3)_4]^{++}$. The formation of such complex ions accounts for the solubility of many water-insoluble metal compounds in aqueous ammonia. Zinc hydroxide, for example, is readily soluble in a slight excess of aqueous ammonia:

$$Zn(OH)_2 + 4NH_3 \rightarrow [Zn(NH_3)_4]^{++} + 2OH^-$$

Ammonia molecules readily form addition compounds with molecules which have a vacant bonding orbital in the valence shell of one of their atoms. The reactions with sulfur trioxide, sulfur dioxide, and boron trifluoride are examples, of which the last may be formulated:

$$\ddot{:}\ddot{F}\ddot{:} \quad\quad H \quad\quad\quad :\ddot{F}:H$$
$$:\ddot{F}\ddot{:}B + :N:H \rightarrow :\ddot{F}:B:N:H$$
$$:\ddot{F}\ddot{:} \quad\quad H \quad\quad\quad :\ddot{F}:H$$

An outstanding property of ammonia is its very high solubility in water (700 volumes of ammonia gas in one volume of water at 20°C and one atmosphere pressure). This high solubility is the result of the tendency of the two substances to react with each other through hydrogen bond formation. The extent to which this association occurs in ordinary solutions is not known. Conductivity measurements on ammonia solutions show the presence of appreciable concentrations of ions in such solutions. It is best to consider such solutions to involve the following equilibria:

$$NH_3 + H_2O \rightleftarrows NH_4OH \rightleftarrows NH_4^+ + OH^-$$

The relatively weakly basic character of "ammonium hydroxide" solutions as compared with solutions of alkali hydroxides is variously interpreted as being due to the low degree of ionization of "ammonium hydroxide", or more recently, as resulting simply from the fact that the ammonia molecule is a weaker base than hydroxide ion. Solutions of ammonia react with acids, taking up protons to form ammonium ions:

$$
\begin{matrix} & H \\ H:\!\!&\overset{\displaystyle\cdot\!\cdot}{\underset{\displaystyle\cdot\!\cdot}{N}}\!\!&: \\ & H \end{matrix}
+ H:X \rightarrow
\left[
\begin{matrix} & H \\ H:\!\!&\overset{\displaystyle\cdot\!\cdot}{\underset{\displaystyle\cdot\!\cdot}{N}}\!\!&:H \\ & H \end{matrix}
\right]^{+} + X^{-}
$$

The ionization constant for ammonia in aqueous solution is 1.65×10^{-5} at 25°C.

Ammonia forms two solid hydrates, $NH_3 \cdot H_2O$ and $2NH_3 \cdot H_2O$, corresponding to ammonium hydroxide and ammonium oxide, but these substances melt at about the freezing point of liquid ammonia (Fig. 1.3).[8]

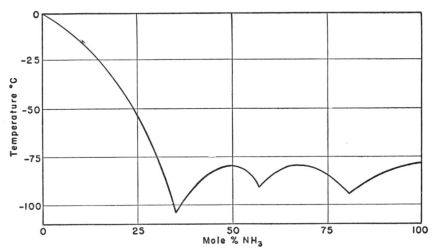

FIG. 1.3. The system H_2O—NH_3.

Studies of the heat capacities and thermodynamic properties of $NH_3 \cdot H_2O$ and $2NH_3 \cdot H_2O$ [9] demonstrate that they are well-defined, stoichiometric compounds. Infrared spectra indicate the absence of NH_4^+ ions in crystals of these substances.[10] Crystals of $NH_3 \cdot H_2O$ have been examined by Debye-Scherrer technique at -95 ± 10°C and found to be hexagonal with $a = 11.21 \pm 0.05$ and $c = 4.53 \pm 0.02$ A. Debye, Scherrer and Weissenberg photographs at the same temperature show the molecule $2NH_3 \cdot H_2O$ to be orthorhombic with a space group *Pbnm*. The unit cell contains four molecules and has dimensions $a = b = 8.41 \pm 0.03$, $c = 5.33 \pm 0.02$ A.[11]

[8] Louis D. Elliott, *J. Phys. Chem.* **28**, 887 (1924).
[9] D. L. Hildenbrand and W. F. Giauque, *J. Am. Chem. Soc.* **75**, 2811 (1953).
[10] R. Waldron and D. Hornig, *J. Am. Chem. Soc.* **75**, 6079 (1953).
[11] W. J. Siemons and D. H. Templeton, *Acta Cryst.* **7**, 194 (1954).

The second group of reactions which ammonia undergoes (ammonolyses) are those in which an atom or group of atoms or a substance is replaced by an amide group (—NH₂), an imide group (=NH), or a nitride group (≡N). Thus, phosgene, $COCl_2$, reacts with ammonia to yield urea:

$$COCl_2 + 4NH_3 \rightarrow CO(NH_2)_2 + 2NH_4Cl$$

Other examples include:

$$SO_2Cl_2 + 4NH_3 \rightarrow SO_2(NH_2)_2 + 2NH_4Cl$$
$$HgCl_2 + 2NH_3 \rightarrow HgNH_2Cl + NH_4Cl$$
$$FSO_3H + 3NH_3 \rightarrow NH_2SO_3NH_4 + NH_4F$$
$$CH_3COOC_2H_5 + NH_3 \rightarrow CH_3CONH_2 + C_2H_5OH$$

A great many such ammonolytic reactions have been studied and many of them are of considerable industrial importance.

The oxidation-reduction reactions which ammonia undergoes may be subdivided into those which involve a change in oxidation state of the nitrogen and those in which one or more of the hydrogen atoms on the ammonia molecule are displaced. Most important of the former group are the reactions of ammonia with oxygen. Ammonia burns readily in pure oxygen according to the following equation:

$$4NH_3 + 3O_2 \rightarrow 2N_2 + 6H_2O$$

It reacts much less readily in air. If, however, a mixture of 7.5 volumes of air to one of ammonia gas is passed over a hot platinum gauze catalyst, oxidation takes place in accordance with the following equation, to yield nitrogen(II) oxide [12]

$$4NH_3 + 5O_2 \rightarrow 4NO + 6H_2O$$

An optimum of 11 per cent NH_3 in air has been found. Above 830°C, Co_3O_4 is an active catalyst. The reaction between Na and NH_3 in presence of P results in the formation of $Na_2H_2P_2$ as well as $NaNH_2$. These compounds [13] react further with NH_4Br to give a P analog, $NaNH_2$, $NaPH_2$,

$$Na_2H_2P_2 + 2NaNH_2 + 4NH_4Br + 2Na \rightarrow 2NaPH_2 + 6NH_3 + 4NaBr$$

If reactants are supplied in the proper proportions and at a suitable rate, sufficient heat is liberated by the reaction to keep the catalyst hot; this

[12] K. Sasaki, *Rept. Govt. Chem. Ind. Res. Inst., Tokyo* **45**, 172 (1950).
[13] P. Royen and W. Zschaage, *Z. Naturforsch.* **86**, 777 (1953).

reaction is the first step in an important method for manufacturing nitric acid.

At elevated temperatures a number of metal oxides are reduced by ammonia to free metals:

$$3CuO + 2NH_3 \rightarrow 3Cu + 3H_2O + N_2$$

While, as has already been stated, the N—H bond is more inert than the O—H bond, the hydrogen atoms on the ammonia molecule may be displaced by the more active metals. Thus, though the alkali metals dissolve in liquid ammonia to give solutions from which the metal may be recovered unchanged by evaporation of the ammonia, on long standing these metals liberate hydrogen and yield metal amides:

$$2Na + 2NH_3 \rightarrow 2NaNH_2 + H_2$$

These reactions take place rapidly at high temperatures or in the presence of a catalyst such as platinum or iron. Another example of such a reaction is that of ammonia with hot magnesium to give magnesium nitride:

$$3Mg + 2NH_3 \rightarrow Mg_3N_2 + 3H_2$$

The reaction between chlorine or hypochlorous acid and ammonia is dependent upon the pH of the reaction media. At a pH less than 3 the chief product is NCl_3, at pH 3–5 the product is $NHCl_2$, and at pH above 8 NH_2Cl. In a strongly alkaline solution the monochloramine is hydrolyzed to hypochlorite. Solutions of trichloramine may be stabilized by small amounts of acid and those of $NClH_2$ by small amounts of alkali. Anhydrous solutions of both NCl_3 and NH_2Cl in organic solvents are fairly stable in the absence of light.[14]

The Nitrogen System of Compounds. The ordinary oxygen-containing compounds may be considered to be derivatives of water, or may be said to have water as a *parent solvent*, and to constitute the oxygen system of compounds. There is a large series of nitrogen compounds which may, in an analogous way, be considered as derivatives of ammonia, or to be based upon liquid ammonia as a parent solvent, and to constitute a *nitrogen system of compounds*.[15] This concept has proved to be an extremely valuable one, for it has been found that corresponding members of the two systems have analogous properties, particularly when studied in their respective parent solvents. Compounds belonging to the oxygen

[14] R. E. Corbett *et al., J. Chem. Soc.* **1953**, 1927; see also *Chem. Abst.* **48**, 5705 (1954).
[15] E. C. Franklin, *The Nitrogen System of Compounds*, Reinhold Publishing Co., New York (1935).

TABLE 1.4. ANALOGOUS COMPOUNDS AND REACTIONS OF H_2O AND NH_3

Compounds

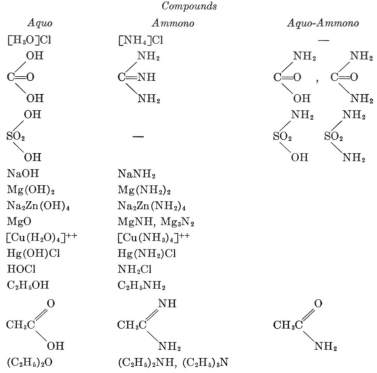

Aquo	*Ammono*	*Aquo-Ammono*
$[H_3O]Cl$	$[NH_4]Cl$	—

$$\underset{OH}{\overset{OH}{C}}{=}O \qquad \underset{NH_2}{\overset{NH_2}{C}}{=}NH \qquad \underset{OH}{\overset{NH_2}{C}}{=}O \ , \ \underset{NH_2}{\overset{NH_2}{C}}{=}O$$

$$\underset{OH}{\overset{OH}{S}O_2} \qquad\qquad — \qquad\qquad \underset{OH}{\overset{NH_2}{S}O_2} \ \ \underset{NH_2}{\overset{NH_2}{S}O_2}$$

Aquo	*Ammono*
NaOH	$NaNH_2$
$Mg(OH)_2$	$Mg(NH_2)_2$
$Na_2Zn(OH)_4$	$Na_2Zn(NH_2)_4$
MgO	$MgNH$, Mg_3N_2
$[Cu(H_2O)_4]^{++}$	$[Cu(NH_3)_4]^{++}$
$Hg(OH)Cl$	$Hg(NH_2)Cl$
HOCl	NH_2Cl
C_2H_5OH	$C_2H_5NH_2$

$$CH_3C\underset{OH}{\overset{O}{\diagup}} \qquad CH_3C\underset{NH_2}{\overset{NH}{\diagup}} \qquad CH_3C\underset{NH_2}{\overset{O}{\diagup}}$$

$(C_2H_5)_2O$ $(C_2H_5)_2NH$, $(C_2H_5)_3N$

Reactions

Aquo

$NaOH + [H_3O]Cl \rightarrow 2H_2O + NaCl$

$Zn + 2H_3O^+ \rightarrow Zn^{++} + H_2 + 2H_2O$

$$CH_3C\underset{OC_2H_5}{\overset{O}{\diagup}} + H_2O \xrightarrow{\ H_3O^+\ } CH_3C\underset{OH}{\overset{O}{\diagup}} + C_2H_5OH$$

$Al_2Cl_6 + 12H_2O \rightarrow 2[Al(H_2O)_6]^{+3} + 6Cl^-$

$$\underset{OH}{\overset{OH}{C}}{=}O \ + 2OH^- \rightarrow \underset{O-}{\overset{O-}{C}}{=}O \ + 2H_2O$$

$Mg^{++} + 2OH^- \rightarrow Mg(OH)_2$

$Zn(OH)_2 + 2OH^- \rightarrow [Zn(OH)_4]^{--}$

$PCl_5 + 3H_2O \rightarrow POCl_3 + 2H_3O^+ + 2Cl^-$

Table 1.4.—*Continued*

Ammono

$$NaNH_2 + NH_4Cl \rightarrow 2NH_3 + NaCl$$

$$Zn + 2NH_4^+ \rightarrow Zn^{++} + H_2 + 2NH_3$$

$$CH_3C\genfrac{}{}{0pt}{}{\nearrow NH}{\searrow NHC_2H_5} + NH_3 \xrightarrow{\ NH_4^+\ } CH_3C\genfrac{}{}{0pt}{}{\nearrow NH}{\searrow NH_2} + C_2H_5NH_2$$

$$AgCl + 2NH_3 \rightarrow [Ag(NH_3)_2]^+ + Cl^-$$

$$\genfrac{}{}{0pt}{}{NH_2}{\diagdown}C{=}NH\genfrac{}{}{0pt}{}{}{\diagup NH_2} + 2NH_2^- \rightarrow \genfrac{}{}{0pt}{}{NH-}{\diagdown}C{=}NH\genfrac{}{}{0pt}{}{}{\diagup NH-} + 2NH_3$$

$$Mg^{++} + 2NH_2^- \rightarrow Mg(NH_2)_2$$

$$Zn(NH_2)_2 + 2NH_2^- \rightarrow [Zn(NH_2)_4]^{--}$$

$$PCl_5 + 4NH_3 = PNCl_2 + 3NH_4^+ + 3Cl^-$$

system are called *aquo* compounds, those belonging to the nitrogen system, *ammono* compounds, and some which contain both nitrogen and oxygen and which may be considered to be derived jointly from water and ammonia, *aquo-ammono* compounds. A few analogous compounds and reactions in the two systems are listed in Table 1.4. The concept of the nitrogen system of compounds has been of great assistance in the study and interpretation of the chemistry of nitrogen compounds.

Preparation of Ammonia. The most convenient laboratory method for the preparation of ammonia consists in the reaction of ammonium salts, either in the dry or dissolved state with a strong base such as sodium, potassium, or calcium hydroxide. The large excess of the strong base, hydroxide ion, particularly at elevated temperatures, displaces the weaker base ammonia from the ammonium ion:

$$NH_4^+ + OH^- \rightarrow NH_3 + H_2O$$

Ammonia solutions always liberate ammonia gas when they are heated but the liberation is more nearly complete if an excess of hydroxide ion is present. Ammonia may also be obtained in the laboratory by the action of water on such metal nitrides as Mg_3N_2:

$$Mg_3N_2 + 6H_2O \rightarrow 3Mg(OH)_2 + 2NH_3$$

A unique process possessing commercial potentialities for the production of ammonia involves the ultimate hydrolysis of manganese nitride, Mn_3N_2. Methane and oxygen are passed over MnO resulting in the formation of an active form of manganese. The latter is converted to Mn_3N_2 by nitrogen of the air at 1800°F and under 400 lb/sq in. pressure. The Mn_3N_2 is hydrolyzed at 800°F to MnO and NH_3. The MnO is recycled.[16]

$$4CH_4 + 1\tfrac{1}{2}O_2 + MnO \rightarrow 4CO + 8H_2 + Mn$$
$$3Mn + N_2 \rightarrow Mn_3N_2$$
$$Mn_3N_2 + 3H_2O \rightarrow 2NH_3 + 3MnO$$

There are three important commercial sources of ammonia. The most important of these is the Haber process which involves the direct combination of nitrogen and hydrogen.[17]

$$N_{2(g)} + 3H_{2(g)} \rightarrow 2NH_{3(g)} + 24,400 \text{ cal}$$

In accordance with the principle of Le Châtelier the formation of ammonia in this reaction is favored by high pressures and low temperatures. However, if the temperature falls below about 1000°C, the rate of the reaction is too low. At this temperature, however, the equilibrium pressure of ammonia is too low for satisfactory yields. This problem is solved by the use of a catalyst Among the variety of catalytic materials tried for this purpose, finely divided iron containing one or more "promoters" has been found to be most effective. The catalyst is usually prepared by reducing a mixture of iron (1%), iron(II) and iron(III) oxides (ratio 0.57), aluminum oxide (1.3%), and K_2O (0.2%) with a 3:1 mixture of hydrogen and nitrogen at high temperatures. The Haber Process is usually operated at from 450–600°C and at pressures up to 1000 atmospheres. This process is the chief method of nitrogen fixation.

The next most important industrial source of ammonia is as a by-product in the production of coke by the destructive distillation of coal. The nitrogen content of bituminous coal is about one per cent, and when such coal is heated in the absence of air, the nitrogen is discharged in the form ammonia, free nitrogen, and other nitrogeneous substances. The ammonia is separated by absorption in water, from whence it may be liberated by treatment with calcium hydroxide or steam. This ammonia is either converted to ammonium sulfate for use in fertilizers or is redissolved in water to form "ammonium hydroxide" solution.

The third important industrial source of ammonia is the cyanamide process. Limestone is heated with an excess of coke in an electric furnace; calcium carbide is the chief product:

$$CaCO_3 + 4C \rightarrow CaC_2 + 3CO$$

[16] P. L. Paul, U. S. **2,706,147**, Apr. 12, 1955.
[17] *Chem. Eng.* **61** (5), 332 (1954).

The calcium carbide is then heated in a stream of nitrogen gas at about 1000°C, and calcium cyanamide is obtained:

$$CaC_2 + N_2 \rightarrow CaCN_2 + C$$

The calcium cyanamide is hydrolyzed with steam under pressure in accordance with the equation:

$$CaCN_2 + 3H_2O \rightarrow CaCO_3 + 2NH_3$$

Calcium cyanamide is useful as a fertilizer and as an intermediate in the production of other nitrogen compounds as well as a source of ammonia.

Uses of Ammonia. Because of its wide use as an industrial chemical and in agriculture, ammonia is produced in enormous quantiites. Its chief uses include the production of other compounds of nitrogen, particularly nitric acid and ammonium salts; among the latter, the sulfate, nitrate, chloride, and carbonate are especially important. Ammonia is used also in the production of a variety of organic chemicals, including various dyes, drugs, and plastics. The mild alkalinity of aqueous ammonia causes it to be used as a household cleansing agent. Because of its high heat of vaporization and the ease with which ammonia gas is liquefied under pressure, ammonia is widely used as a refrigerant.

Ammonium Salts. Ammonia forms a large series of ammonium salts by reaction with the various acids. Ammonium ion undergoes slight hydrolysis in accordance with the equation:

$$NH_4^+ + H_2O \rightleftharpoons NH_3 + H_3O^+$$

Ammonium salts of strong acids are stable in the solid state at ordinary temperatures, but readily decompose when heated; ammonia is usually, though not always, a product of such decompositions:

$$NH_4Cl \rightarrow NH_3 + HCl$$
$$(NH_4)_2SO_4 \rightarrow NH_3 + NH_4HSO_4$$

Ammonium nitrite and ammonium nitrate yield nitrogen and nitrogen(I) oxide, respectively:

$$NH_4NO_2 \rightarrow N_2 + 2H_2O$$
$$NH_4NO_3 \rightarrow N_2O + 2H_2O$$

Ammonium salts of weak acids undergo partial decomposition even at room temperature. Ammonium salts of extremely weak acids are not formed except at very low temperatures.

Ammonium salts, except for their tendency to undergo hydrolysis and to undergo thermal decomposition, are very similar to the corresponding salts of the alkali metals, particularly with respect to their high solubility in water and their crystal form.   The electronic structure of the ammonium ion is illustrated in Fig. 1.4; it may be seen from this diagram that this electronic configuration is the same as that of the sodium ion.   However, in the sodium ion, all the protons are concentrated

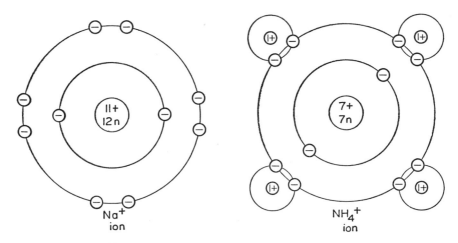

Fɪɢ. 1.4.   Electronic structure of NH_4^+ ion.

in a single nucleus, whereas in the ammonium ion the positively charged particles are distributed among the nitrogen nucleus and the four hydrogen nuclei.   The ammonium ion has, therefore, a more diffuse structure than the sodium ion, and corresponds in ionic radius more closely to the potassium ion.   Consequently many pairs of corresponding potassium and ammonium salts are isomorphous, and have very similar solubilities.

Various attempts to produce free "ammonium" by the reduction of ammonium salts have been unsuccessful.   If, however, a solution of ammonium chloride is electrolyzed with a mercury cathode or is treated with sodium or potassium amalgam a product is obtained which is undoubtedly ammonium amalgam:

$$NH_4^+ + NaHg_x \rightarrow (NH_4)Hg_x + Na^+$$

At $-85°C$ this amalgam is a hard, stable substance, but at room temperature it is a pasty mass which, on standing, rapidly changes into mercury, ammonia, and hydrogen:

$$2(NH_4)Hg_x \rightarrow 2NH_3 + H_2 + 2xHg$$

Ammonium amalgam is a strong reducing agent.

Among the more important ammonium salts, ammonium chloride is used in soldering, in galvanizing iron to remove oxides from the metal surface, and in the construction of dry cells. The bromide and iodide are used in preparing photographic materials. Ammonium sulfate and the primary and secondary phosphates are used as fertilizers. Ammonium nitrate, though difficult to detonate, is a high explosive and is a component of several explosive mixtures.

Amides, Imides, and Nitrides. As is indicated in Table 1.4, the metal amides and imides are the bases of the nitrogen system.[18] The metal amides may be divided into two groups: (a) the active metal amides and (b) the heavy metal amides. The active metal amides may be obtained by a variety of reactions including—

(a) the reaction of the metal with liquid or gaseous ammonia:

$$M + NH_3 \rightarrow MNH_2 + \tfrac{1}{2}H_2$$

(b) the reaction of the metal hydride with ammonia:

$$LiH + NH_3 \rightarrow LiNH_2 + H_2$$

(c) the ammonolysis of the metal nitride:

$$Li_3N + 2NH_3 \rightarrow 3LiNH_2$$

(d) metathesis reactions involving another amide:

$$KNH_2 + NaI \xrightarrow[NH_3]{liq.} NaNH_{2(s)} + KI$$

(e) the action of an alkali metal on nitrogen(I) oxide in liquid ammonia:[19]

$$2Na + N_2O + NH_3 \rightarrow NaNH_2 + NaOH + N_2$$

The above reaction may be carried out at room temperature in glass.

[18] For review articles concerning amides and organo-alkali amides see: F. W. Bergstrom and W. C. Fernelius, *Chem. Revs.* **12**, 43–179 (1933); **20**, 413–81 (1937); R. Levine and W. C. Fernelius, *ibid.* **54**, 449 (1954).

[19] S. Abe *et al.*, *Summ. Repts. Res. Inst. Tohoku Univ. Ser.* **A, 4,** 105 (1952).

A secondary process resulting in the formation of a metal azide, as NaN_3, may take place, represented by

$$2NaNH_2 + N_2O \rightarrow NaN_3 + NaOH + NH_3$$

Potassium amide is a white, crystalline, highly hygroscopic compound, which is a good conductor of electricity in the fused state and in liquid ammonia solution. It melts at 338°C, and is energetically hydrolyzed in the presence of water. Sodium amide is similar in properties but melts at 210°C. The amides of potassium, cesium, and rubidium are very soluble in liquid ammonia; sodium amide dissolves to the extent of only 1.5 g/l at 20°C, while lithium amide, the alkaline earth metal amides, and the heavy metal amides and imides are virtually insoluble in liquid ammonia. Potassium amide is rapidly oxidized on exposure to the atmosphere:

$$2KNH_2 + 3O_2 \rightarrow 2KNO_2 + 2H_2O$$

Heavy metal amides and imides may be prepared by metathetical reactions in liquid ammonia, of which the following are examples:

$$Cd(SCN)_2 + 2KNH_2 \xrightarrow[NH_3]{liq.} Cd(NH_2)_{2(s)} + 2KSCN$$

$$PbI_2 + 2KNH_2 \xrightarrow[NH_3]{liq.} PbNH_{(s)} + NH_3 + 2KI$$

Lithium imide, Li_2NH, may be prepared by the action of Li on NH_3 at 400°C forming first $LiNH_2$ and thence Li_2NH. The crystals are cubic with 4 molecules per cell. It is antimorphous with CaF_2 and isomorphous with Li_2O. Lithium amide, $LiNH_2$, is tetragonal with eight molecules per cell. The structure is approximately cubic close packing of NH_2^- with Li^+ ions occupying half the tetrahedral holes in each layer.[20] In some cases, neither the amide nor imide is stable and the nitride is precipitated from the ammonia solution (*cf.* action of NaOH on $AgNO_3$ in water):

$$3HgBr_2 + 6KNH_2 \xrightarrow[NH_3]{liq.} Hg_3N_{2(s)} + 6KBr + 4NH_3$$

Some of the heavy metal amides, imides, and nitrides prepared in this way are explosive and must be handled with extreme care.

[20] R. Juza and K. Opp, *Z. anorg. u. allgem. Chem.* **266**, 313 (1951).

Besides these explosive nitrides, there is another large class of nitrides which are often very stable. There are three chief ways in which these stable nitrides are prepared: (a) the direct reaction of the metal with nitrogen or with ammonia at high temperatures—some of the metals (such as magnesium and aluminum) have such an affinity for nitrogen at these temperatures that they react with it even in the presence of some oxygen—and (b) the deammoniation of the metal amide by heating it:

$$3Ba(NH_2)_2 \rightarrow Ba_3N_2 + 4NH_3$$

The nitrides are slowly converted to oxides when roasted in air, and generally undergo hydrolysis in the presence of water. Like the oxides, many of the nitrides have high fusion and sublimation temperatures; many of them have a high degree of thermal stability. The nitrides of phosphorus, boron, and silicon, *viz.* P_3N_5, BN, Si_3N_4, are closely connected in behavior with those of the metals. They are probably highly polymerized products. Many of the transition metals form nitrides belonging to the class of interstitial compounds. These compounds are exceedingly hard and have many characteristically metallic properties. Their formulas do not necessarily correspond to the normal oxidation states of the metals.

The rate of proton transfer between the NH_3 molecule and the amide ion, NH_2^-, has been reported.[21] The value 4.6×10^{11} cm^3/mole sec is given with an activation energy which cannot exceed more than a few kilocalories.

HYDRAZINE AND HYDROXYLAMINE

Molecular Structure, Physical and Chemical Properties of Hydrazine. Hydrazine is the nitrogen analogue of hydrogen peroxide in which the two OH groups have been replaced by NH_2 groups, thus:

$$H:\overset{..}{\underset{..}{O}}:$$
$$:\overset{..}{\underset{..}{O}}:H$$

hydrogen peroxide

$$\overset{H}{\underset{..}{H:\overset{..}{N}:}}$$
$$:\overset{..}{\underset{..}{N}}:H$$
$$H$$

hydrazine

Hydroxylamine is related to both these compounds in that only one of

---

[21] *Chem. Eng. News* **32**(18), 1775 (1954).

the OH groups has been replaced by NH_2:

$$\begin{array}{c} H \\ H \!:\! \overset{\displaystyle ..}{\underset{\displaystyle ..}{N}} : \\ :\overset{..}{\underset{..}{O}}:H \end{array}$$

hydroxylamine

Pure hydrazine is a colorless, highly hygroscopic liquid which freezes at 1.8°C. Its normal boiling point is 113.5°C and at 15°C it has a density of 1.0144 g/ml. Its critical temperature is 380°C. The heat of formation of liquid hydrazine is 12,050 cal/mole at 25°C. The heat of vaporization is 10 kcal/mole at 113.5°C and the entropy is 25.9 cal/deg mole at 113.9°C. Anhydrous hydrazine has an unusually high dielectric constant, 53, and this value would suggest that the liquid is a good ionizing solvent. Many salts have been shown to be readily soluble in liquid hydrazine, and the resulting solutions are good conductors of electricity. Hydrazine is completely miscible with water and with the lower molecular weight alcohols. Its solubility in most organic solvents, however, is limited. Hydrazine is not associated in the gaseous state.[22]

One of the chief chemical characteristics of hydrazine is its strong reducing properties. It undergoes auto oxidation in both dilute and concentrated aqueous solutions with the intermediate formation of H_2O_2, then to N_2 and H_2O. Copper catalyzes the reaction.[23] It burns vigorously in air, and is violently oxidized by the halogens, nitric acid, and other such oxidants. It is, therefore, of great interest as a possible rocket fuel.[24] Silver nitrate and other metallic salts are reduced by hydrazine. The hydrazine molecule has two unshared pairs of electrons and each constitutes a basic center on the molecule. Hydrazine reacts with acids, therefore, to produce two series of salts, containing the $N_2H_5^+$ and the $N_2H_6^{++}$ ions respectively. The internal vibrational spectrum of $N_2H_6^{++}$ has been determined [25] and found to be complicated by H bonds with Cl^- ions. Hydrazine is a weaker base than ammonia even with respect to accepting the first proton. The equilibria which presumably exist in aqueous solutions of hydrazine and its salts and the two ionization

[22] G. Briegleb *et al.*, *Z. physik. Chem.* **199**, 15 (1952).

[23] L. F. Audrieth and P. H. Mohr, *Ind. Eng. Chem.* **43**, 1774 (1951).

[24] See L. F. Audrieth and B. A. Ogg, *The Chemistry of Hydrazine*, John Wiley & Sons, 1951, New York.

[25] L. Couture-Mathieu and J. P. Mathieu, *Ann. phys.* **9**, 255 (1954).

constants are:

$$N_2H_4 + H_2O \rightleftarrows N_2H_4 \cdot H_2O \rightleftarrows N_2H_5^+ + OH^-$$

$$\frac{[N_2H_5^+][OH^-]}{[N_2H_5OH]} = 8.5 \times 10^{-7} \text{ at } 25°C$$

$$N_2H_5^+ + H_2O \rightleftarrows N_2H_6OH^+ \rightleftarrows N_2H_6^{++} + OH^-$$

$$\frac{[N_2H_6^{++}][OH^-]}{[N_2H_6OH^+]} = 8.9 \times 10^{-16} \text{ at } 25°C$$

"Dibasic" salts undergo thermal dissociation to the "monobasic" salts on moderate heating, and their aqueous solutions are acidic:

$$[N_2H_6]Cl_2 \xrightarrow[\text{dry}]{140°C} [N_2H_5]Cl + HCl$$

Most hydrazinium salts are very soluble in water; some of them deliquesce. The properties of hydrazine recall those of liquid water and liquid ammonia and hydrazine would be expected to be the parent solvent for a system of compounds analogous to those concerned in water and ammonia chemistry. Thus $N_2H_5^+$ is analogous to NH_4^+ and H_3O^+, and $N_2H_3^-$ is analogous to NH_2^- and OH^-. Hydrazinolysis would be analogous to ammonolysis and hydrolysis. However, such reactions have been little investigated. It has been shown that the hydrazine solutions of $N_2H_5^+$ ion dissolve some metals which are not affected by hydrazine alone. Like water and ammonia, hydrazine forms complexes with various metal salts, as $[Pt(N_2H_4)_4]X_2$ and $[Pt(N_2H_4)_2(NH_3)_2]X_2$.

Hydrazine reacts vigorously with $SOCl_2$ to yield a white solid of the formula $SO(NHNH_2)_2$, and with sulfur dioxide to give the compound
$NH(SO_2H)$
$|$. Sulfur trioxide vapors react with hydrazine to give
$NH(SO_2H)$
H_2NNHSO_3H. Sodium metal dissolves in liquid hydrazine to give a blue solution. On standing the blue color disappears and sodium hydrazide, $NaNHNH_2$, is formed with the evolution of hydrogen. Sodium hydrazide is soluble in hydrazine; the solid sometimes explodes with great violence on contact with a trace of moisture.

One of the most interesting compounds which hydrazine forms is the hydrate of the formula $N_2H_4 \cdot H_2O$. This substance is a colorless liquid which fumes in moist air. It has a density of 1.0305 g/ml at 21°C; it freezes at $-40°C$ and boils at 118.5°C under one atmosphere pressure. Vapor density-temperature measurements indicate that the vapor and perhaps the liquid are partially dissociated into N_2H_4 and H_2O molecules. Such measurements indicate also that the dissociation is complete at 138°C and 744.1 mm pressure.   The nature of the bond between N_2H_4 and H_2O is not known and insufficient data are available for the calculation of thermodynamic quantities.   It may be supposed, however, that the compound has the structure,

$$\begin{array}{cc} \text{H H} & \\ \text{H:}\overset{..}{\text{N}}\text{:}\overset{..}{\text{N}}\text{:---H:}\overset{..}{\text{O}}\text{:,} & \\ \overset{..}{\text{H}} \quad\quad \overset{..}{\text{H}} & \end{array}$$

analogous to that usually written for $NH_3 \cdot H_2O$, involving union through a hydrogen bridge.   Presumably this substance is present in all alkaline solutions of hydrazine salts or aqueous solutions of hydrazine.   The heat of formation of liquid hydrazine hydrate at 25°C is 10,300 cal/mole. Hydrazine hydrate attacks rubber, cork, and, though slowly, glass.   Like the anhydrous product, it is readily susceptible to atmospheric oxidation. It has been reported to undergo slow, spontaneous decomposition into nitrogen, hydrogen, and ammonia.

Preparation of Hydrazine.   Hydrazinium salts are obtained by a variety of different reactions, none of which are entirely satisfactory. The oldest among the methods now used is the Raschig method,[26] which depends upon the oxidation of ammonia by the hypochlorite ion in alkaline, aqueous solution.   The reaction proceeds in two steps, the first being the formation of chloramine:

$$NH_3 + ClO^- \rightarrow NH_2Cl + OH^-$$

Chloramine may be considered ammonohypochlorous acid.   The second step involves the ammonolysis of chloramine:

$$NH_2Cl + 2NH_3 \rightarrow NH_2NH_2 + NH_4^+ + Cl^-$$

The difficulty with this process is that the chloramine is also converted into nitrogen, ammonia, and hydrogen chloride.   In order to obtain appreciable yields of hydrazine it is necessary that the reaction mixture contain glue or gelatin, or some similar substance.   The function of these substances is to tie up certain impurities such as copper(II) ion which tend to catalyze the interfering reaction.   It has been found that an increase in the yield of hydrazine is favored by the presence of a large excess of ammonia and an excess of NaOH.   The presence of ammonium salts

[26] F. Raschig, *Ber.* **40**, 4588 (1907).

greatly decreases the yield. The reaction mixture is ordinarily heated to 80–90°C for from thirty to sixty minutes. After being allowed to cool, the reaction mixture is neutralized with sulfuric acid; this treatment brings about the crystallization of the slightly soluble salt, $N_2H_6SO_4$. There is some question as to whether NH_2Cl is actually an intermediate in the Raschig synthesis.[27] Proof for its nonexistence is offered in the absence of reaction between NH_2Cl and NH_3 in dry ether.

The sulfate may be converted to hydrazine hydrate by distilling it together with potassium hydroxide and water (in the weight ratio 2:2:5) in a silver still. Hydrazine hydrate may also be obtained from hydrazinium bromide, N_2H_5Br, by reaction with potassium hydroxide solution and ethyl alcohol; potassium bromide precipitates, and the alcohol is then removed by distillation.

Several methods for the preparation of anhydrous hydrazine have been published. The first of these involves the dehydration of the hydrate with crushed barium oxide by heating them in an atmosphere of nitrogen or hydrogen. The resulting liquid is fractionally distilled at reduced pressures (2–30 mm) in an atmosphere of hydrogen to obtain pure hydrazine. In a second method advantage is taken of the insolubility of ammonium sulfate in liquid ammonia and of the fact that the following reaction therefore goes to completion in that solvent:

$$N_2H_5SO_4 + 2NH_{3(l)} \rightarrow (NH_4)_2SO_{4(s)} + N_2H_4$$

The ammonium sulfate is filtered off, and the hydrazine is separated from the liquid ammonia by allowing the ammonia to evaporate. A third procedure involves the treatment of hydrazine hydrate with sodium hydroxide [28] which causes the separation of the system into two liquid phases, one of which contains the hydrazine in a highly concentrated form. Still a fourth method involves an azeotropic distillation of hydrazine hydrate with certain organic solvents.

More recently a promising method of hydrazine synthesis in a nonaqueous system has been developed.[29] This process involves the gas phase reaction of chlorine with an excess of ammonia to yield (almost quantitatively) chloramine:

$$Cl_2 + 2NH_3 \rightarrow ClNH_2 + NH_4Cl$$

[27] E. Wiberg and M. Schmidt, *Z. Naturforsch.* **6B**, 336 (1951).

[28] E. L. Bulgozdry and E. L. Wagner, *J. Am. Chem. Soc.* **73**, 5866 (1951).

[29] H. H. Sisler *et al.*, *J. Am. Chem. Soc.* **73**, 1619 (1951); **76**, 3906 (1954); **76**, 3909 (1954); **76**, 3912 (1954); **76**, 3914 (1954).

The chloramine is then passed into liquid ammonia where it reacts to form hydrazine:

$$ClNH_2 + 2NH_3 \rightarrow N_2H_4 + NH_4Cl$$

This reaction is not quantitative for nitrogen is formed as a byproduct (from the reaction of chloramine with hydrazine). It has been found that the hydrazine yield is increased by keeping the chloramine concentration in the liquid ammonia low and by raising the temperature of the liquid phase reaction. Yields as high as 80 per cent of theoretical have been obtained. A variety of chemical as well as physical methods have been developed for obtaining pure hydrazine from the solution of hydrazine and ammonium chloride in liquid ammonia obtained by the above reactions.

Among the other chemical reactions which yield hydrazine or its salts are the following: (a) the reduction of potassium nitrososulfite ($K_2[(NO)_2SO_3]$) with sodium amalgam,

$$(NO)_2SO_3^= + 6Na + 5H_2O \rightarrow N_2H_4 + SO_4^= + 6Na^+ + 6OH^-$$

(b) the reduction of substituted nitramides (cf.) such as nitroguanidine

$(H_2NC\overset{\displaystyle NH}{=}NHNO_2)$ with sodium amalgam, (c) the reduction of hyponitrites (cf.), (d) the hydrolysis of various aliphatic hydrazo compounds, or the reduction and hydrolysis of aliphatic diazo compounds:

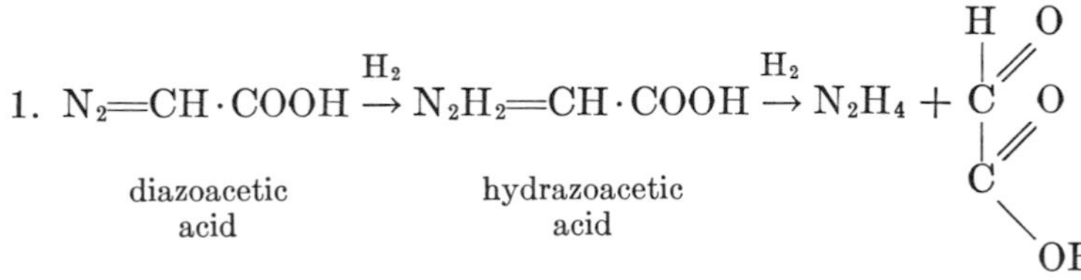

1. $N_2{=}CH \cdot COOH \xrightarrow{H_2} N_2H_2{=}CH \cdot COOH \xrightarrow{H_2} N_2H_4 + \begin{matrix} H & O \\ | & \| \\ C & O \\ | & \| \\ C \\ \quad\searrow \\ \qquad OH \end{matrix}$

       diazoacetic   hydrazoacetic
          acid   acid

2. $H_2N{-}CH(SO_3H)_2 \xrightarrow{HONO} N_2{=}C(SO_3H)_2 \xrightarrow[\text{with}]{\text{Reduction}} N_2H_4 + CO_2 + H_2SO_4 + 2H_2SO_3$

      Obtained from   sulfite
      KCN and KHSO_3   and then
                             hydrolysis

(e) The direct action of oxygen on ammonia in a ratio of 1 part of the atter to five of the former at 100–400°C, 100 kg/sq in. in the presence of an Ag_2O catalyst and a BaO_2 promoter. It is claimed that there is a

20% reaction per pass.[30]   (f) The action of molten urea on a carbonyl-forming metal as iron or nickel at a temperature of 132–150°C at atmospheric pressure.   The hydrazine is formed as a gas and passes out of the granular metal mass along with oxides of carbon.   By cooling the vapor mixture to 100°C the hydrazine is recovered from the oxides of carbon.   Semicarbazid is formed as byproduct when iron is used as the carbonyl forming metal.[31]

Physical and Chemical Properties of Hydroxylamine.   It has already been shown that hydroxylamine, NH_2OH, is analogous in formula to hydrazine on the one hand and to hydrogen peroxide on the other. These analogies are reflected in the chemical properties of the substance. In some respects the NH_2OH molecule may be thought of as being $[\frac{1}{2}N_2H_4 \cdot \frac{1}{2}H_2O_2]$.   In the pure state hydroxylamine is a white solid which melts at 33°C to give a liquid having a density of 1.204 g/ml.

A number of structures have been postulated for hydroxylamine involving N—O linkages all of which must be discounted in view of infrared and diffraction data.[32]   No data are available for the spectrum of liquid hydroxylamine due to its instability.   The solid has been examined by infrared (in Nujol).   The stretching vibrations suggest two forms of hydroxylamine, a *cis* and a *trans*,

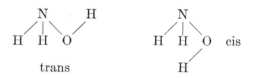

The O—H stretching is almost the same as that found in water.   The value is shifted to lower values in the solid due to hydrogen bonding. Molecular parameters for NH_2OH are: N—O = 1.46 A; O—H = 0.96 A; N—H = 1.01 A; H—O—N angle = 103°; H—N—O angle = 105°; and H—N—H angle = 107°.

Thermodynamic functions for the ideal gaseous state (25°C) at 1 atm are: $-(F^0 - H_0^0/T) = 4735$ cal/deg mole; $(H^0 - H_0^0/T) = 8.98$ cal/deg mole; $S^0 = 56.33$ cal/deg mole; $C_p^0 = 11.17$ and $H^0 - H_0^0 = 2677$ cal/mole.

The pure compound is not very stable and the liquid decomposes with increasing rapidity into N_2, N_2O, and other products as the temperature is raised.   Under reduced pressure, 22 mm, liquid hydroxylamine boils

[30] W. H. Marshall, Jr., **U. S. 2,583,584**, Jan. 29, 1952.
[31] H. J. Passino, **U. S. 2,675,301**, Apr. 13, 1954.
[32] P. A. Giguere and I. D. Liu, *Can. Jour. of Chem.* **30**, 948 (1952).

at a temperature of 58°C, but even under these conditions there is some decomposition. Rapid heating of hydroxylamine sometimes leads to explosions. Hydroxylamine is completely miscible with water and the lower alcohols, but has a relatively low solubility in most of the other common organic solvents; it is very hygroscopic. Aqueous solutions of hydroxylamine up to 60% NH_2OH are reasonably stable.

It has been pointed out [33] that liquid hydroxylamine has properties analogous to those of water and that it may be considered as the parent solvent for a system of acids, bases, and salts. Many salts dissolve in liquid hydroxylamine just as they do in liquid ammonia and water. Examples of these salts are KI, KCN, KBr, $NaNO_3$, $Ba(NO_3)_2$, NaCl, KCl, NaOH, $Ba(OH)_2$, NH_3, and K_2SO_4. Likewise, the solubility of hydroxylamine in other solvents is similar to that of water. Hydroxylamine combines with many substances to form solvates analogous to the hydrates formed by water, the ammonates formed by ammonia, and the hydrazinates formed by hydrazine, as $[Co(NH_2OH)_6]Cl_3$ and $[Zn(NH_2OH)_2]Cl$. Hydroxylamine likewise enters into solvolysis reactions analogous to ammonolysis and hydrolysis.

Like water, ammonia, and hydrazine, hydroxylamine can act either as a base or an acid by gaining or losing protons, respectively. Solutions of hydroxylamine in water are weakly basic and the following equilibria are presumed to exist in the solution:

$$NH_2OH + H_2O \rightleftarrows NH_2OH \cdot HOH \rightleftarrows NH_3OH^+ + OH^-$$

$$\frac{[NH_3OH^+][OH^-]}{[NH_2OH]} = 6.6 \times 10^{-9}$$

The size of the equilibrium constant indicates that hydroxylamine is less basic than either ammonia or hydrazine. Aqueous solutions of hydroxylammonium salts such as $[NH_3OH]Cl$ undergo considerable hydrolysis to yield definitely acidic solutions. Hydroxylammonium chloride, $[NH_3OH]Cl$, hydroxylammonium nitrate, $[NH_3OH]NO_3$, and hydroxylammonium sulfate, $[NH_3OH]_2SO_4$, are familiar, stable salts of hydroxylamine. They are white, crystalline compounds. The chloride and nitrate are highly soluble in water, and the sulfate somewhat less soluble. The nitrate decomposes into nitrogen(II) oxide, water, and other products when heated.

Anhydrous hydroxylamine exhibits acidic properties in that one of its protons may be replaced by active metals to yield compounds such as $NaONH_2$. These metal hydroxylamates are said to be considerably less explosive than the corresponding hydrazinates.

[33] L. F. Audrieth, *Trans. Ill. State Acad. Sci.* 22, 385 (1930).

Hydroxylamine, like hydrogen peroxide, can act either as an oxidizing or reducing agent, and, as in the case of that substance, the behavior is largely dependent upon whether the solution is acidic or basic. In acidic solution, hydroxylamine reduces Ag^+, Au^{+3}, Hg^{++}, MnO_4^-, Br_2, and other oxidizing agents with the liberation of nitrogen and oxides of nitrogen. Alkaline solutions of hydroxylamine oxidize iron(II) to iron(III) hydroxide, but reduce copper(II) hydroxide to copper(I) oxide. Titanium(III) and chromium(II) salts in acid solution reduce the hydroxylammonium ion to the ammonium ion.

Hydroxylamine hydrochloride and sodium nitrite react in the presence of iodine or a mixture of KI and nitric acid according to the following steps:

$$[NH_3OH]^+ + HNO_2 \rightarrow HNO + HNO + H_3O^+$$
$$HNO + HNO \rightarrow H_2O + N_2O$$
$$HNO + HNO \rightarrow H_2N_2O_2 \text{ (to the extent of about 1 per cent)}$$

Iodine has an accelerating effect while $NaNO_2$ has a decelerating effect. The action of iodine is explained by the following:

$$2[NH_3OH]^+ + 2I_2 \rightarrow 6H^+ + 4I^- + N_2O + H_2O$$

Hydrogen ion catalyzes the reaction by favoring the formation of iodine through the $NO_2^- + I^-$ reaction.[34]

Hydroxylamine reacts quantitatively with nitrosodisulfonate salts, as $(KSO_3)_2NO$, to give a colorless $(KSO_3)_2NOH$ according to the equation:

$$2NH_2OH + 4(KSO_3)_2NO \rightarrow N_2O + 4(KSO_3)_2NOH + H_2O$$

The reaction is reversible in the sense that the hydroxy compound may be hydrolyzed to hydroxylamine. There is no evidence for the formation of nitroxyl as an intermediate. Since the nitroso salt is violet and the hyroxy salt is colorless, a titrimetric analysis is feasible.[35]

Hydroxylamine undergoes condensation reactions with a variety of organic molecules containing C=O groups:

$$\underset{H_3C}{\overset{H_3C}{\diagdown}} C{=}O + H_2NOH \longrightarrow \underset{H_3C}{\overset{H_3C}{\diagdown}} C{=}NOH + H_2O$$

[34] H. Holzapfel, *Wiss. Z. Univ. Leipzig, Math.-Naturw. Reihe*, No. 2, 1951/52, No. 4, 30–8.
[35] H. Gehlen and G. Dase, *Z. anorg. u. allgem. Chem.* **275**, 327 (1954).

Preparation of Hydroxylamine. The best and cheapest commercial method for the production of hydroxylammonium salts depends upon the hydrolysis of nitroparaffins in sulfuric acid solution, specifically the reaction with nitromethane:

$$CH_3NO_2 + H_3O^+ + H_2O \xrightarrow{H_2SO_4} HC\underset{OH}{\overset{O}{\diagup}} + NH_3OH^+$$

$$\xrightarrow{H_2SO_4} CO \uparrow + 2H_2O$$

Another method by which hydroxylammonium salts may be prepared is by the electrolytic reduction of solutions of sodium nitrate or nitric acid in aqueous hydrochloric or sulfuric acid. The best yields (65%) are obtained when 50% sulfuric acid is used with amalgamated lead electrodes; the yield varies sharply with change in electrode material. After the reduction is complete, the solution is neutralized, the sulfate removed by treatment with barium chloride, the resulting filtrate evaporated to dryness, and $[NH_3OH]Cl$ extracted from the residue with ethyl alcohol.

A third method for the preparation of hydroxylammonium salts is the reduction of sodium nitrite by zinc dust in the presence of acetone to yield acetoxime. The acetoxime is hydrolyzed to yield hydroxylammonium chloride by heating the oxime with concentrated aqueous hydrochloric acid solution. Calcium nitrite has been successfully converted to $NH_2OH \cdot 0.5H_2O$ by reduction with SO_2. Calcium sulfate is also formed which is removed by filtration.[36]

Numerous other reactions yield some hydroxylamine or its salts, such as the reduction of nitrogen(II) oxide with tin and hydrochloric acid and the reduction of nitrites and nitrates with sodium amalgam, hydrogen sulfide, hydrosulfurous acid, *etc.* in alkaline solution. Nitrogen(II) oxide may be reduced directly by hydrogen to NH_2OH using a platinum-charcoal catalyst.[37] In these reactions other reduction products than hydroxylamine are also obtained.

A very useful laboratory method depends upon the hydrolysis of alkali hydroxylaminodisulfate, $HON(SO_3M)_2$, one of the products of the nitrite-hydrogensulfite reaction.[38] This substance is usually prepared by

[36] British 660,413, Nov. 7, 1951.
[37] British 667,870, Mar. 12, 1952.
[38] *Organic Syntheses*, Collective Volume I, p. 318 (1941).

the reaction of nearly neutral alkali nitrite solution with sulfur dioxide or a hydrogensulfite at 0 to $-5°C$. These reactions are discussed in a later section. The hydroxylaminodisulfate ion undergoes hydrolysis when heated in acid solution in accordance with the equation:

$$HON(SO_3)_2^= + 2H_2O + H^+ \rightarrow NH_3OH^+ + 2HSO_4^-$$

The hydroxylammonium salt is commonly isolated by conversion to acetoxime,

$$(CH_3)_2C{=}O + NH_2OH \rightarrow (CH_3)_2C{=}NOH + H_2O$$

which is then removed by steam distillation; the oxime is hydrolyzed with concentrated hydrochloric acid, the acetone distilled off, and the hydroxylammonium chloride crystallized by evaporation:

$$(CH_3)_2C{=}NOH + H^+ + Cl^- + H_2O \rightarrow (CH_3)_2C{=}O + \underbrace{NH_3OH^+ + Cl^-}_{}$$
$$\downarrow \text{evap.}$$
$$[NH_3OH]Cl$$

Free, anhydrous hydroxylamine is obtained by treating hydroxylammonium chloride with sodium salts of the lower alcohols. Thus, sodium butoxide is added to a mixture of the chloride and butyl alcohol. Precipitation of sodium chloride occurs in accordance with the following equation:

$$[NH_3OH]Cl + Na[OC_4H_9] \rightarrow NaCl_{(s)} + NH_2OH + C_4H_9OH$$

Hydroxylamine, in the form of white flakes, separates from the butyl alcohol solution when the mixture is cooled to $-10°C$.

Free hydroxylamine may also be obtained by heating solid anhydrous hydroxylamine salts or complexes; tertiary hydroxylammonium phosphate yields hydroxylamine when heated at moderate temperatures. Zinc oxide dissolves in aqueous solutions of hydroxylammonium chloride to form the complex salt, $[Zn(NH_2OH)_2]Cl_2$. When this substance is heated *in vacuo*, hydroxylamine distills off.

Because of its tendency to undergo decomposition, free hydroxylamine is usually stored at $0°C$.

Hydrazoic Acid and the Azides

Although of much less industrial importance than some other nitrogen compounds such as ammonia and nitric acid, hydrogen azide is none the less one of the most interesting of nitrogen compounds. Its formula,

HN_3, clearly demonstrates the inadequacy of the simple definitions of valence. Hydrogen azide is over 97% nitrogen and thus has a higher nitrogen content than any other substance except elementary nitrogen. It may be considered the nitric acid analogue of the ammonia system (the three oxygen atoms of HNO_3 replaced by two nitrogen atoms to give HNN_2) of acids, bases, and salts. It and many of its derivatives are highly explosive. The azide ion, $:N_3^-$, and the azide radical, $\cdot N_3$, are similar in certain respects to halide ions and atoms respectively and are thus "halogenoid" in character. [See Vol. III of this Series.] The chemistry of hydrazoic acid and its derivatives is, therefore, both complex and very interesting.[39]

Chemical and Physical Properties of Hydrogen Azide. Pure hydrogen azide is a colorless liquid which freezes at about $-80°C$ and boils at $37°C$. Its density in the temperature range 0 to $21°C$ is given by the equation, $d^t_{4°} = \dfrac{1.126}{1 + 0.0013t}$. Both the liquid and the vapor are treacherously and violently explosive and must be handled with extreme care. The vapor density of hydrogen azide corresponds with the monomeric formula, HN_3. On being heated, or under the action of ultraviolet light, gaseous hydrogen azide decomposes to give N_2, H_2, and NH_3. The thermal decomposition takes place at a measurable rate at temperatures above $290°C$. As the gas cools, ammonium azide, NH_4N_3, is deposited on the container walls. The standard free energy of formation of gaseous hydrogen azide at $25°C$ is 78.525 cal/mole [40] and the entropy of the ideal vapor at 1 atmosphere and $25°C$ is 56.74 cal/deg/mole.

The dielectric constant of liquid hydrogen azide has not been measured, but the fact that it dissolves a number of salts (as NH_4Br, NH_4I, $CoCl_2$, $MgCl_2$, KCl, KBr, KI, KN_3, $NaBr$, NaI, and $Ni(NO_3)_2$) to yield electrically conducting solutions indicates that the dielectric constant is fairly large. Iodine dissolves in liquid hydrogen azide to give an electrically conducting solution.

Hydrogen azide is soluble in water, ether, and ethyl alcohol. The aqueous solutions are weakly acidic, similar in strength to acetic acid solutions of the same concentration:

$$\frac{[H^+][N_3^-]}{[HN_3]} = 1.8 \times 10^{-5}$$

The heat of formation of aqueous hydrogen azide has been calculated [41]

[39] L. F. Audrieth, *Chem. Rev.* **15**, 169 (1934).
[40] E. H. Eyster and R. H. Gilette, *J. Chem. Phys.* **8**, 369 (1940).
[41] W. A. Roth and Fr. Mueller, *Ber.* **62**, 1188 (1929).

to be 53,400 cal/mole.   The heat of solution of HN_3 was found to be 7080 cal/mole.

Preparation of Hydrazoic Acid and Azides.   A large variety of reactions result in the formation of hydrogen azide or its salts.   Among the better processes are the following:

(1) *The reaction of nitrous oxide with molten sodium amide at 190 $\pm$ 4°C in a nickel crucible:*

$$2NaNH_{2(l)} + N_2O_{(g)} \rightarrow NaN_{3(s)} + NaOH_{(s)} + NH_{3(g)}$$

This reaction is used commercially and gives yields as high as 90%. The sodium azide is separated from the sodium hydroxide by dissolving the mixture in water and recrystallizing the azide.

(2) *The interaction of hydrazinium ion and nitrous acid.*   The yield depends largely upon the acidity of the solution.   Up to 60% yield was obtained by the addition of aqueous sodium nitrite solutions to solutions of hydrazinium chloride in 16 to 25% phosphoric acid:

$$N_2H_5^+ + HNO_2 \rightarrow HN_3 + H^+ + 2H_2O$$

(3) *The reaction of sodium nitrate with molten sodium amide.*   Yields above 60%, based on the nitrate, are obtained when powdered sodium nitrate is added little by little to molten sodium amide at 175°C:

$$3NaNH_{2(l)} + NaNO_3 \rightarrow NaN_3 + 3NaOH + NH_3$$

A similar reaction is obtained when solutions of a metal amide and a metal nitrate in liquid ammonia are heated to 120–140°C.   In the case of the potassium salts in liquid ammonia yields as high as 75% are obtained; the yields with sodium salts are much lower.

(4) *The oxidation of hydrazinium salts.*   The effects of a variety of oxidizing agents on hydrazinium sulfate have been studied.[42]   Best yields were obtained with hydrogen peroxide, ammonium vanadate, potassium chlorate, potassium perchlorate, and potassium peroxydisulfate, all in sulfuric acid solution.

(5) *The reaction of an alkaline solution of hydrazine hydrate with a benzene solution of nitrogen trichloride:*

$$N_2H_5OH + NCl_3 + 4OH^- \rightarrow N_3^- + 3Cl^- + 5H_2O$$

Free hydrogen azide may be obtained by distillation from solutions of azides in sparingly volatile acids such as sulfuric; or, more conveniently,

[42] A. W. Browne and F. F. Shetterley, *J. Am. Chem. Soc.* **31**, 221 (1909), *et ante.*

by allowing concentrated sulfuric acid to drop slowly on solid sodium or potassium azide. Traces of moisture may be removed from the gaseous hydrogen azide by anhydrous calcium chloride.

Reactions of Hydrazoic Acid (Aqueous Hydrogen Azide). As already stated, HN_3 is a weak acid. Its aqueous solutions react with metal hydroxides, oxides, and carbonates, therefore, to yield metal salts, azides. Because of the weakness of the acid, however, azides of weak bases are highly hydrolyzed in aqueous solution.

Pure aqueous solutions of hydrazoic acid may be kept indefinitely, but, in the presence of catalysts such as platinum black, platinum sponge, and platinum foil, decomposition into ammonia and nitrogen takes place, presumably through the following mechanism:

$$3HN_3 \rightarrow 3HN^= + 3N_2$$
$$3HN^= \rightarrow N_2 + NH_3$$
$$\overline{3HN_3 \rightarrow 4N_2 + NH_3}$$

The similarity of azides to the corresponding halides is shown by the fact that precipitates of silver, lead, and mercury (I) azides are obtained when solutions of hydrazoic acid are mixed with soluble silver, lead, and mercury (I) salts. The azide radical apparently falls between chlorine and bromine in the activity series. Many attempts have been made to discharge the N_3 group as $(N_3)_2$. These trials have failed, but the evidence is that the N_3 radical is the primary anodic product in the electrolysis of azides or hydrazoic acid in aqueous and nonaqueous solutions. Its existence is only transient, however, as it quickly breaks down to give molecular nitrogen.

Mixtures of hydrochloric and hydrazoic acid react slowly in accordance with the following equation:

$$3HN_3 + HCl \rightarrow NH_4Cl + 4N_2$$

When a mixture of the two acids is boiled, some chlorine is also obtained (compare with HNO_3 and HCl, *aqua regia*). Hydrazoic acid and hydrogen chloride react rapidly in the dry state to give ammonium chloride. Like mixtures of nitric and hydrochloric acids, mixtures of hydrazoic acid and hydrochloric acid dissolve platinum, gold, and other such noble metals. There is, therefore, some superficial, experimental basis for considering hydrazoic acid as *ammononitric* acid. Hydrazoic acid oxidizes hydriodic acid to free iodine with the formation of nitrogen and ammonium ion; with hydrogen bromide free bromine is obtained.

Hydrazoic acid reacts with nitrous acid in accordance with the following equation:

$$HN_3 + HNO_2 \rightarrow N_2 + H_2O + N_2O$$

The reactions of hydrazoic acid with sulfuric acid are of considerable interest. Hydrogen azide reacts with 100% sulfuric acid to give hydrazinium hydrogen sulfate, $[N_2H_6](HSO_4)_2$; with concentrated sulfuric acid, the normal sulfate, $[N_2H_6]SO_4$, is obtained. When the two acids are heated together in moderately concentrated solution, considerable amounts of hydroxylammonium ion and some ammonium ion are obtained, but no hydrazinium ion. If, however, sulfuric acid reacts with a benzene solution of hydrogen azide, large amounts of hydrazinium sulfate, and some hydroxylammonium and anilinium sulfate are formed along with a considerable evolution of nitrogen gas. At 60°C, the chief product is the aniline salt. These reactions have been explained as resulting from the primary formation of the imide or imine radical (HN):[43]

$$HN_3 \rightarrow N_2 + (HN<)$$

Additional information on the decomposition of HN_3 has been offered in a study of the low pressure decomposition at about 1000°C in a quartz tube. One of the products condenses on the surface of the quartz (cooled to liquid nitrogen temperature) forming a blue paramagnetic solid. On warming to -125°C the blue solid changes to NH_4N_3. It is presumed that the NH (imine) radicals condenses to give the blue paramagnetic solid. The solid may, however, be the diimide, HN:NH, or a mixture of the monomer and dimer, or of higher polymers of NH. The half life of the imine radical is estimated to be 9×10^{-4} sec when the pressure of hydrazoic acid is 0.07 mm and the rate of flow 10 m/sec through a 1.7 cm quartz tube heated to 1060°C.[44]

The NH radical may combine with water to form hydroxylamine,

$$(HN<) + HOH \rightarrow NH_2OH$$

with benzene to form aniline,

$$(HN<) + C_6H_6 \rightarrow C_6H_5NH_2$$

or with itself to form diimide which, being unstable, breaks down to form hydrazine and nitrogen:

$$4(HN<) \rightarrow [2N_2H_2] \rightarrow N_2H_4 + N_2$$

[43] K. F. Schmidt, *Ber.* **57**, 704 (1924).
[44] F. O. Rice and M. Freamo, *J. Am. Chem. Soc.* **73**, 5529 (1951).

In addition to those reactions already stated, hydrazoic acid enters into a variety of oxidation-reduction reactions. Consideration is first given to those in which the azide acts as a reducing agent. In the presence of thiosulfates, sulfides, and other substances which act as catalysts, iodine oxidizes the azide ion to elementary nitrogen:

$$2N_3^- + I_2 \rightarrow 3N_2 + 2I^-$$

Cerium(IV) salts oxidize azides completely to nitrogen:

$$2Ce(SO_4)_2 + 2HN_3 \rightarrow Ce_2(SO_4)_3 + H_2SO_4 + 3N_2$$

The reactions with hypochlorous acid lead to the formation of chlorazide:

$$HN_3 + HOCl \rightarrow H_2O + ClN_3$$

The action of ozone on azides in alkaline solutions gives a deep orange colored substance which has not been isolated and whose structure has not been established. On standing, or upon acidification, this color disappears. Attention was called to the fact that hydrazoic acid may be considered an *ammononitric* acid. The behavior of hydrazoic acid as an oxidizing agent is in accordance with this analogy. Examples of parallel reactions in which hydrazoic acid and nitric acid act as strong oxidizing agents include the following:

$$Mg + 3HN_3 \rightarrow Mg(N_3)_2 + N_2 + NH_3$$
$$H_2S + HN_3 \rightarrow S + N_2 + NH_3$$
$$Pt + 2HN_3 + 4HCl \rightarrow PtCl_4 + 2N_2 + 2NH_3$$
$$3Mg + 8HNO_3 \rightarrow 3Mg(NO_3)_2 + 2NO + 4H_2O$$
$$3H_2S + 2HNO_3 \rightarrow 3S + 2NO + 4H_2O$$
$$3Pt + 4HNO_3 + 12HCl \rightarrow 3PtCl_4 + 4NO + 8H_2O$$

Other such reactions include the oxidation of iron(II) ion to iron(III) ion, the oxidation of ammonostannites to ammonostannates, and the oxidation of sulfur to sulfuric acid by hot hydrazoic acid solution. Methylamine is oxidized to guanidine (ammonocarbonic acid) by a solution of ammonium azide in liquid ammonia:

$$CH_3NH_2 \xrightarrow[\text{liq. } NH_3]{NH_4N_3} C{=}NH \begin{smallmatrix} NH_2 \\ \\ NH_2 \end{smallmatrix}$$

| an ammono- alcohol | ammonium ammono- nitrate | ammono- carbonic acid |

Azides.　The common metallic azides, except the copper, silver, lead, mercury (I), and thallium (I) salts are readily soluble in water and may be prepared by the standard methods for preparing soluble metal salts: (1) by the action of hydrazoic acid on the metals, oxides, hydroxides, or carbonates, (2) by the action of the soluble metal perchlorate on potassium azide, and (3) by the reaction of barium azide with a soluble metal sulfate.　Double and complex azides such as $NH_4N_3 \cdot Ni(N_3)_2$, $3NaN_3 \cdot Cr(N_3)_3$, $[Co(NH_3)_6](N_3)_3$, and $[Co(NH_3)_5Cl](N_3)_2$ have been prepared by the usual methods.　Complex compounds in which the azide ion is one of the coordinating groups have been made, *e.g.* $[Co(NH_3)_4(N_3)_2]N_3$, $[Co en_2(N_3)_2]N_3$, $Li[B(N_3)_4]$, and $Na_2[Sn(N_3)_6]$.

All azides are characterized by thermal instability, and, at elevated temperatures, all of them decompose to give nitrogen, the free metal, and varying quantities of metal nitride.　The azides of the heavy metals tend to undergo explosive decomposition over a range of temperatures, depending upon crystal size, purity, and rate of heating.　Many of the metal azides, particularly, the lead, silver, copper (I), cadmium, and mercury compounds, may be exploded by impact or friction.　Lead azide has been subjected to extensive investigation as a detonator and was so used by the Germans in World War I.　Numerous patents concerning the use of mixed azides as detonators have been issued.

The thermal decomposition of various metal azides has been used as a method for preparing pure nitrogen and for preparing various metals in a high state of purity.　Hydrides of the alkali and alkaline earth metals may be obtained by decomposing the corresponding azides in an atmosphere of hydrogen.　Sodium and barium hydrides have been prepared in this manner.

In addition, a variety of alkyl and aryl azides such as CH_3N_3 and $C_6H_5N_3$, and a number of very interesting nonmetal, inorganic azides have been prepared.　As already noted, the reaction of hypochlorites with azides in acid solution yields chlorine azide, ClN_3:

$$OCl^- + 2CH_3COOH + N_3^- \rightarrow ClN_3 + H_2O + 2CH_3COO^-$$

Chlorine azide [see also Vol. III of this Series] is a colorless gas which is tremendously explosive.　The analogous compounds of bromine and iodine, BrN_3 and IN_3, have been prepared.　*Bromine azide* is a volatile, orange-red liquid which freezes at $-45°C$.　It hydrolyzes rapidly to give hypobromous and hydrazoic acids which then react to yield nitrogen gas. *Iodine azide* is a light yellow solid, stable only at sub-zero temperatures. The fact that the azide radical is more electronegative than iodine is suggested by the fact that the reaction of iodine azide with an insufficient quantity of sodium metal results in the formation of sodium azide and free iodine.   Fluorine reacts with hydrazoic acid, in a stream of nitrogen, to yield *fluorine azide*, FN_3, according to the reaction:

$$4HN_3 + 2F_2 \rightarrow NH_4F + N_2 + 3FN_3$$

This greenish-yellow, explosive gas decomposes, slowly at room temperature, more rapidly at higher temperatures, to give the colorless, stable gas, *difluorodiazine*, N_2F_2:

$$2FN_3 \rightarrow 2N_2 + N_2F_2$$

Dicyandiazide, $(CNN_3)_2$, is obtained by the action of cyanogen bromide on sodium azide.   It melts at 40.3°C, begins to decompose at 70°C and decomposes violently at temperatures above 170°C.

Cyanuric triazide, $(CN)_3(N_3)_3$, is obtained by the reaction of cyanuric chloride with sodium azide or by the diazotization of cyanuric hydrazide. Cyanuric triazide is a crystalline solid having a melting point of 94°C. It may be detonated by heat or impact and has been suggested as a detonating agent.

Sulfuryl azide, $SO_2(N_3)_2$, is obtained as a colorless liquid by the reaction of sulfuryl chloride with sodium azide; it explodes violently when heated and sometimes spontaneously at ordinary temperatures.

Carbonyl azide, $CO(N_3)_2$, an extremely explosive, easily volatile, crystalline solid, is obtained by the diazotization of the corresponding hydrazide:

$$CO(NHNH_2)_2 + 2HNO_2 \rightarrow CO(N_3)_2 + 4H_2O$$

Azidosulfuric acid, N_3SO_3H, the analogue of halosulfuric acid, exists only in aqueous solution and then only transiently, but several of its salts have been prepared.   The potassium salt is obtained by the reaction of powdered hydrazinosulfuric acid with concentrated solutions of potassium nitrite:

$$H_2NHNSO_3H + K^+ + NO_2^- \rightarrow N_3SO_3^- + K^+ + 2H_2O$$

It crystallizes in large flat, extremely explosive prisms.   Ammonium, sodium, and barium salts have also been prepared.   The acid hydrolysis of azidosulfates results in the formation of hydrazoic acid and sulfuric acid.

Azidodithiocarbonic Acid and Azidocarbondisulfide. Either hydrazoic acid or its salts react with carbon disulfide to produce azidodithiocarbonic acid or a metal azidodithiocarbonate:

$$HN_3 + CS_2 \rightarrow HSCSN_3$$
$$MN_3 + CS_2 \rightarrow MSCSN_3$$

Azidodithiocarbonic acid is a white, crystalline solid, moderately soluble in water, and has an acid strength comparable with that of sulfuric acid. As one might expect, the dry solid is exceedingly sensitive to shock and heat, and slowly decomposes at room temperatures. Its aqueous solution possesses considerable stability, however. The heavy metal salts of this acid are violently explosive. The potassium, cesium, ammonium, and substituted ammonium salts are characterized by a tendency to undergo changes in color when exposed to sunlight. The cesium salt becomes deep purple when exposed to strong sunlight.

The oxidation of azidodithiocarbonic acid or one of its salts leads to the formation of the halogenoid, azidocarbondisulfide, $(SCSN_3)_2$:

$$2NaSCSN_3 + I_2 \rightarrow 2NaI + (SCSN_3)_2$$

Azidocarbondisulfide is obtained as a white, microcrystalline, explosive solid. It decomposes violently at higher temperatures, and rapidly at room temperature to give polymeric thiocyanogen, sulfur, and nitrogen:

$$(SCSN_3)_2 \rightarrow (SCN)_2 + 2S + 2N_2$$
$$X(SCN)_2 \rightarrow (SCN)_{2x}$$

It reacts with solutions of potassium hydroxide according to the equation:

$$(SCSN_3)_2 + 2KOH \rightarrow KSCSN_3 + KOSCSN_3 + H_2O$$
$$\text{gradually}$$
$$\text{decomposes}$$

This reaction is analogous to

$$Cl_2 + 2KOH \rightarrow KCl + KOCl + H_2O$$

The unstable halogen derivatives, $ClSCSN_3$, $BrSCSN_3$, and Br_3SCSN_3 have been prepared, as has the compound of the formula $CNSCSN_3$. All of these reactions are in accordance with the characterization of the compound as a halogenoid.

Structure of the Azides.   Electron diffraction studies on the ionic azides, NaN_3 and KN_3, show that the azide ion is linear and symmetrical. The electronic charges on the $(N—N—N)^-$ atoms are -0.83, 0.66, and 0.83 respectively,[45] the nitrogen atoms being evenly spaced at $1.15 \pm .02$ A apart:

$$\overset{\text{1.15A}}{N \longrightarrow} \overset{\text{1.15A}}{N \longrightarrow} N^-$$

This arrangement corresponds to resonance among the structures,

$$(1) \quad -:\overset{..}{N}{=}\overset{+}{N}{=}\overset{..}{N}:^-$$

$$(2) \quad {=}:\overset{..}{N}{-}\overset{+}{N}{\equiv}N:$$

$$(3) \quad :N{\equiv}\overset{+}{N}{-}\overset{..}{N}:^{=}$$

whereas structure (1) alone requires an internitrogen distance 1.22 A. Electron diffraction investigations on the covalent molecule of methylazide, however, indicate the following configuration:

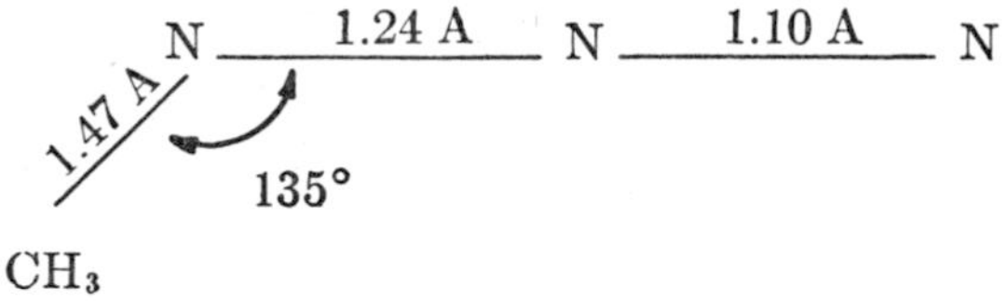

$$N \underline{\quad 1.24 \text{ A} \quad} N \underline{\quad 1.10 \text{ A} \quad} N$$

1.47 A   135°

CH₃

The charges on each of the three nitrogen atoms are -0.37, 0.52, and -0.15.[45a]   Studies of the infrared adsorption spectrum of HN_3 reveal the structure

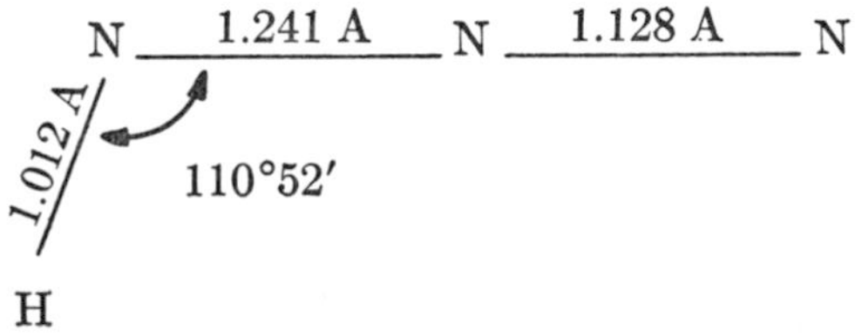

$$N \underline{\quad 1.241 \text{ A} \quad} N \underline{\quad 1.128 \text{ A} \quad} N$$

1.012 A   110°52′

H

---

[45] A. Bonnemay and R. Daudel, *Compt. rend.* **230**, 2300 (1950).
[45a] Bonnemay and Daudel, *loc. cit.*

A similar configuration was found for the covalent azide group in cyanuric triazide:

These values are not compatible with resonance of covalent azides among the three structures:

$$(1) \quad R-\overset{..}{N}=\overset{+}{N}=\overset{..}{N}:^-$$

$$(2) \quad R-{}^-\overset{..}{N}-\overset{+}{N}\equiv N:$$

$$(3) \quad R-\overset{+}{N}=\overset{+}{N}-\overset{..}{N}:^=$$

but are compatible with resonance between structure (1) and (2), the calculated values for the two internitrogen distances being 1.24 A and 1.12 A. Structure (3) in the covalent azides is relatively less stable than (2) and (1) because of the existence of formal charges of the same sign on adjacent atoms. The fact that ionic azides have three important resonance forms (resonance energy about 45,000 cal/mole) whereas covalent azides have only two important resonance forms (resonance energy about 25,000 cal/mole), accounts for the large difference in stability of covalent and ionic azides, and for the fact that the covalent compounds are so much more explosive than the ionic azides.[46]

HYPONITROUS ACID, NITROGEN(I) OXIDE, AND THE HYPONITRITES

The chief compounds of nitrogen in which that element is formally assigned an oxidation state of $+1$ are nitrogen(I) oxide, N_2O, hyponitrous acid, $H_2N_2O_2$, and the hyponitrites, $M_2N_2O_2$ and MHN_2O_2. It has been stated that nitrogen(I) oxide may not properly be considered the anhydride of hyponitrous acid because the system represented by

$$N_2O + H_2O \rightarrow H_2N_2O_2$$

has such a high free energy change ($\Delta F^0{}_{298°} = 42,760$ cal) that the reaction is not attainable in practice. However, there are other anhydrides which are not readily hydrated, particularly among the metal oxides, and in view of the fact that hyponitrous acid undergoes spontaneous decomposition to give nitrogen(I) oxide and water, it seems quite proper to consider N_2O as the acid anhydride of the compound $H_2N_2O_2$. The kinetics of the decomposition of the hyponitrite ion in aqueous solution have been thoroughly investigated [47] and the mechanism of the process appears to be:

$$N_2O_2^= + H_2O \rightarrow HN_2O_2^- + OH^- \quad (1)$$
$$HN_2O_2^- + H_2O \rightarrow H_2N_2O_2 + OH^- \quad (2)$$
$$H_2N_2O_2 \rightarrow N_2O + H_2O \quad (3)$$

with reaction (3) being the rate-determining step. The rate equation based on this mechanism and established experimentally is

$$\frac{d[N_2O]}{dt} = \frac{k[N_2O_2^=]_s}{[OH^-][1 + B(OH^-)]}$$

where k and B are constants which vary with temperature and $[N_2O_2^=]$, represents the total hyponitrite concentration.

Some additional information on the kinetics of the decomposition of hyponitrites (forming N_2O) has been obtained in the study of the thermal decomposition of calcium hyponitrite, $CaN_2O_2 \cdot 4H_2O$.[48] The decomposition at 125–140°C appears to proceed according to the sequence of

[46] L. Pauling, *The Nature of the Chemical Bond*, pp. 199, 210, Cornell University Press (1940).

[47] E. Abel and J. Proisl, *Monatshefte* **72**, 1 (1938).

[48] T. M. Oza and V. T. Oza, *J. Chem. Soc.* **1953**, 909; *J. Indian Chem. Soc.* **27**, 409 (1950).

reactions described by

$$CaN_2O_2 \cdot 4H_2O \rightarrow CaO + H_2N_2O_2 + 3H_2O$$
$$H_2N_2O_2 \rightarrow H_2O + N_2O$$
$$3H_2N_2O_2 \rightarrow 2H_2O + 2N_2 + 2HNO_2$$
$$2HNO_2 \rightarrow \tfrac{2}{3}H_2O + \tfrac{2}{3}HNO_3 + \tfrac{4}{3}NO$$

Although anhydrous CaN_2O_2 has never been prepared it is postulated that the decomposition would follow the path represented by

$$3CaN_2O_2 \rightarrow 2CaO + Ca(NO_2)_2 + 2N_2$$
$$3Ca(NO_2)_2 \rightarrow 2CaO + Ca(NO_3)_2 + 4NO$$

Preparation of Nitrogen(I) Oxide. Many of the chemical processes which lead to the formation of nitrogen(I) oxide may be grouped into two general classes: (a) the reduction or oxidation of compounds containing nitrogen in higher or lower oxidation states respectively and (b) the elimination of water from one of the several compounds of the formula $N_2O \cdot xH_2O$.

In the first class is the reduction of nitrites and nitrates by means of a variety of reducing agents such as hydrogen sulfide, active metals plus acids, sulfurous acid, sodium amalgam, and tin(II) chloride, the last named being particularly well suited for this purpose. Usually these methods yield a mixture of nitrogen(I) oxide and nitrogen(II) oxide; the latter may be removed by washing the gas with iron(II) sulfate solution or better, with a solution of dichromate in sulfuric acid. The air oxidation of NH_3 using a lead catalyst leads to N_2O formation if the gas flow rate is slow and low temperatures are used.[49]

The second class of reactions may all be represented by the general equation:

$$N_2O \cdot xH_2O \rightarrow N_2O + xH_2O$$

Examples of such reactions include:

$$N_2O \cdot 6H_2O \xrightarrow{\text{below } 0°} N_2O + 6H_2O$$

hydrated nitrogen(I) oxide

$$NH_2NO_2 \longrightarrow N_2O + H_2O$$

nitramide

$$[NH_3OH]NO_2 \longrightarrow N_2O + 2H_2O$$

hydroxylammonium nitrite

$$NH_4NO_3 \longrightarrow N_2O + 2H_2O$$

ammonium nitrate

[49] K. Tuszynski, *Roczniki Chem.* **23**, 397 (1949).

The first of these reactions, *viz.* the decomposition of the hydrate of nitrogen(I) oxide is of value for obtaining the gas in a very pure state. The hydrate is stable only at low temperatures, decomposing below 0°C. The most suitable of the reactions in this class is the thermal decomposition of solid ammonium nitrate (or a mixture of sodium or potassium nitrate and ammonium sulfate). The salt, NH_4NO_3, melts at 169.6°C and, if heated to 170–260°C, yields nitrogen(I) oxide at a conveniently rapid rate. The gas contains only a little nitrogen(II) oxide as an impurity.

The reaction of hydroxylammonium ion and a nitrite proceeds in the cold when solutions containing these ions are mixed.

Other reactions resulting in the formation of nitrogen(I) oxide include the decomposition of hydrazinium nitrite:

$$[N_2H_5]NO_2 \rightarrow N_2O + NH_3 + H_2O$$

and the reaction of hydrazoic acid with nitrous acid:

$$HN_3 + HNO_2 \rightarrow N_2 + N_2O + H_2O$$

Nitrogen(I) oxide is likewise obtained by the action of dilute acids on the compound of the formula $K_2SO_4 \cdot N_2O$. This compound is obtained by the reaction of nitrogen(II) oxide with sulfite solutions.[50]

It has also been shown that nitrogen(I) oxide may be obtained by the reaction of ammonia and oxygen in the presence of a manganese oxide-bismuth oxide catalyst.[51] A maximum yield of 71% was obtained at 200°C with a space velocity of 5 ml gas mixture per ml of catalyst per minute.

Nitrogen(I) oxide is evolved from the action of warm 72% HNO_3 on sulfamic acid:

$$NH_2SO_3H + HNO_3 \rightarrow N_2O + H_2SO_4 + H_2O$$

Because of its endothermic nature (see below) nitrogen(I) oxide should increase in stability with rise in temperature, and it might be expected that the reaction $2N_2 + O_2 \rightarrow 2N_2O$ should reverse itself at elevated temperatures. However, thermodynamic calculations show that even at temperatures above 1000°C only exceedingly small yields of the oxide are obtainable at equilibrium.

[50] H. Gehlen, *Ber.* 64B, 1267 (1931); 65B, 1130 (1932).
[51] K. Kobe and P. Hosman, Am. Chem. Soc. Meeting, September, 1947.

Physical Properties and Molecular Structure of Nitrogen(I) Oxide.
Because of the great theoretical and practical interest in the oxides of
nitrogen, the physical constants of these compounds have been carefully
determined.[52] The more important values for N_2O are listed in the
following table:

TABLE 1.5. PHYSICAL CONSTANTS OF NITROGEN(I) OXIDE

Melting point.............................. $-90.84\,°C$
Boiling point.............................. $-88.51\,°C$
Critical temperature......................... $36.5\,°C$
Critical pressure.......................... 71.7 atm
Heat of fusion............................. 1563 cal/mole
Heat of vaporization....................... 3958 cal/mole
Heat of formation, $\Delta H^0{}_{298°}$.................... $19,650$ cal/mole
Free energy of formation $\Delta F^0{}_{298°}$................ $24,930$ cal/mole (calcd. from H^0 and S^0 values)
Standard entropy of gas $S^0{}_{298°}$.................. $\begin{cases} 52.58 \text{ cal/deg (from spectroscopic} \\ \text{measurements)} \\ 51.44 \text{ cal/deg (from heat capacity} \\ \text{measurements)} \end{cases}$

Vapor pressure equations:

Solid: $\log_{10} p_{cm} = \dfrac{-1286}{T} + 9.13061 - 0.0014038T$

Liquid: $\log_{10} p_{cm} = \dfrac{-893.56}{T} + 6.72158\,(-90.84\,°C \text{ to } -87.25\,°C)$

The value for $\Delta F^0{}_{298°}$ was calculated from ΔH^0 and from values of ΔS^0
obtained by application of the third law. The very small temperature
range $-98.84\,°C$ to $-88.51\,°C$ in which liquid nitrogen(I) oxide is the
stable phase at atmospheric pressure is worth noting.

Electron diffraction experiments on the oxides of nitrogen do not lead
to conclusive results since the scattering powers of nitrogen and oxygen
atoms are approximately equal. The results of such experiments do
indicate a linear molecule, however. Also, the interpretation of the
infrared adsorption spectrum requires a linear model of the molecule.
This information combined with the fact that the molecule has zero dipole
moment leads to the conclusion that the ground state of the nitrogen(I)
oxide molecule is a state of resonance between the two structures:

$$\overset{..}{-}\overset{+}{\underset{}{:N::N::O:}} \quad\text{and}\quad \overset{+}{:N:::N:\underset{..}{O}{:}^{-}}$$

Resonance between these two structures leads to calculated values of
1.12 A and 1.19 A for the N—N and N—O bond distances respectively.

[52] W. F. Giauque *et al.*, *J. Am. Chem. Soc.* **57**, 991 (1935).

The sum of these two, 2.31 A, is equal to the value obtained from the spectroscopically determined value for the moment of inertia.

It is interesting to note that there is a difference of 1.14 units in the standard entropy of nitrogen(I) oxide as determined from heat-capacity measurements and as obtained from spectroscopic data. This anomaly is explained in terms of the assumption that there is randomness of orientation of the N_2O molecules at low temperatures, *i.e.*, that the molecule does not differentiate between the orientations NNO and ONN. It is believed that this randomness is not complete, however. The magneto-rotatory power of N_2O has been determined at $\lambda = 578$ mμ. The value of $\Lambda_0^{760} = 7.75 \times 10^{-6}$ min. The value of $\Lambda_n = 5.02 \times 10^{-5}$ radians. The rotativity does not vary with change of state.[53]

Nitrogen(I) oxide is colorless, almost odorless, and has a sweetish taste. It is soluble in water to the extent of one volume per volume of water at 0°C and one-half volume at 25°C. Alcohol dissolves four times its volume of nitrogen(I) oxide at 0°C.

Chemical Properties of Nitrogen(I) Oxide and its Industrial Applications. The positive free energy of formation of nitrogen(I) oxide expresses itself in the powerful oxidizing action of the compound. The compound, however, is not as strong an oxidizing agent as is pure oxygen, though it is more vigorous in this respect than is oxygen in the concentration found in the air at normal pressure. Oxidation reactions of nitrogen(I) oxide must be initiated by high temperature or a catalyst (presumably to catalyze the decomposition $N_2O \rightarrow N_2 + O$). Once started, many such reactions proceed vigorously. Mixtures of hydrogen and nitrogen(I) oxide must be heated to a fairly high temperature before they explode, but in the presence of platinum sponge the reaction takes place at room temperature, and the sponge becomes incandescent. Phosphorus may be vaporized in nitrogen(I) oxide without reaction, but once ignited it burns more vigorously than in air. Metals, particularly those whose oxides have high heats of formation, ignite readily in nitrogen(I) oxide when they are heated. Weakly burning sulfur is extinguished by the gas, but brightly burning sulfur evolves sufficient energy to start the reaction and proceeds to burn even more vigorously than in air. Likewise, glowing charcoal, or feebly glowing wood, becomes inflamed in nitrogen(I) oxide. These facts may be summarized by saying that reactions in which nitrogen(I) oxide acts as an oxidizing agent (or oxygen carrier) involve large decreases in free energy but have higher energies of activation than those involving molecular oxygen. Nitrogen(I) oxide shows no tendency to react with oxygen to form nitrogen(II) oxide or other oxides of nitrogen.

[53] R. de Mallemann and F. Suhner, *Compt. rend.* **233**, 122 (1951).

Nitrogen (I) oxide is used as an anesthetic. Inhaled in small amounts, it produces a state of hysterical excitement, often accompanied by boisterous laughter. Because of these symptoms the gas is commonly called "laughing gas". Dentists and surgeons use nitrogen (I) oxide as an anesthetic because it is pleasant, quick in its action, and without harmful aftereffects.

Nitrogen (I) oxide is highly soluble in cream under pressure. If a closed container of sweetened cream is charged with nitrogen (I) oxide, and the cream discharged through a valve to the atmosphere, a product very similar to whipped cream produced in the conventional manner is obtained. This process is widely used in restaurants and soda fountains.

A process for the "quick-freezing" of foods by dipping them in liquid nitrogen (I) oxide has been reported.

Preparation and Properties of Hyponitrous Acid and its Salts. The relationship between hyponitrous acid, hyponitrites, and nitrogen (I) oxide has been discussed in an earlier paragraph. A variety of methods are known for the production of hyponitrites, most of which involve the reduction of nitrites or nitrogen (II) oxide or the oxidation of hydroxyl-amine. It is presumed that hyponitrites are formed whenever the radical $>$NOH (the nitroxyl radical) is formed in alkaline solution. The radical dimerizes to produce hyponitrous acid, HON$=$NOH, which in alkaline solution yields $HN_2O_2^-$ or $N_2O_2^=$ ions. Methods reported for the preparation of hyponitrous acid or its salts include:

(1) *The reduction of aqueous solutions of sodium nitrite with sodium amalgam.*[54] The equation is

$$2NO_2^- + 4Na(Hg)_x + 2H_2O \rightarrow N_2O_2^= + 4Na^+ + 4OH^- + 4xHg$$

In sufficiently concentrated solution $Na_2N_2O_2 \cdot 8H_2O$ crystallizes. Trituration with alcohol serves to remove sodium hydroxide and the salt may then be further purified by recrystallization from its concentrated aqueous solutions.

(2) *The electrolytic reduction of sodium nitrite.* This process is merely a modification of (1) in which sodium amalgam produced by the electrolysis of sodium hydroxide solution using a mercury cathode is caused to circulate into a vessel where it comes in contact with an alkaline solution of sodium nitrite.[55]

[54] J. R. Partington and C. C. Shah, *J. Chem. Soc.* 2071 (1931).
[55] E. Abel and J. Proisl, *Monatshefte* **72**, 1 (1938).

(3) *The reduction of sodium nitrite by tin(II) chloride,*[56] *or by other reducing agents such as stannites or iron(II) hydroxide.*

(4) *The reduction of nitrogen(II) oxide by the addition compound of sodium with pyridine:*[57]

$$2Na(Py)_2 + 2NO \rightarrow Na_2N_2O_2 + 4Py$$

(5) *The reduction of nitrogen(II) oxide by atomic hydrogen at liquid air temperature, yielding a mixture of hyponitrous acid and nitramide.*

(6) *The reduction of alkyl nitrites by hydroxylammonium salts and alkali alkylates in alcohol solution:*[58]

$$[NH_3OH]Cl + Na[OC_2H_5] \rightarrow NH_2OH + NaCl_{(s)} + C_2H_5OH$$
$$NH_2OH + C_2H_5NO_2 + 2Na[OC_2H_5] \rightarrow Na_2N_2O_{2(s)} + 3C_2H_5OH$$

(7) *The oxidation of hydroxylamine by oxides of the noble metals:*

$$2HONH_2 + 2HgO \rightarrow H_2N_2O_2 + 2H_2O + 2Hg$$

(8) *The hydrolysis of sodium hydroxylamine monosulfonate, HONH-SO_3Na, in concentrated caustic alkali solution:*

$$2HONHSO_3^- + 4OH^- \rightarrow N_2O_2^= + 2SO_3^= + 4H_2O$$

The silver salt is sometimes used as the starting point for the preparation of other hyponitrites. This salt is relatively insoluble in water and is obtained as a bright yellow precipitate when silver nitrate is added to alkaline solutions of soluble hyponitrites. Silver hyponitrite is photosensitive and darkens on standing in the light. It may be heated to above 100°C without decomposition but explodes at higher temperatures; the lead salt behaves similarly.

Free hyponitrous acid is even less stable than its salts. It can be prepared by treating silver hyponitrite with a solution of hydrogen chloride in ether:

$$Ag_2N_2O_{2(s)} + 2HCl_{(ether)} \rightarrow 2AgCl_{(s)} + H_2N_2O_{2(ether)}$$

Evaporation of the ethereal solution yields white crystals of $H_2N_2O_2$.[59] These crystals decompose on standing (or much more rapidly on heating) yielding nitrogen, oxides of nitrogen, and water. Heating crystals of hyponitrous acid sometimes leads to an explosion.

[56] von F. Raschig, *Z. anorg. Chem.* **155**, 225 (1926).
[57] E. Weitz and W. Vollmer, *Ber.* **57**, 1016 (1924).
[58] L. W. Jones and A. W. Scott, *J. Am. Chem. Soc.* **46**, 2172 (1924).
[59] A. Hantzsch and L. Kaufmann, *Ann.* **292**, 323 (1896).

Hyponitrous acid is a weak, diprotic acid. Solutions of alkali hyponitrites, therefore, are alkaline to litmus. Values for the ionization constants of the acid at 25°C [60] are:

$$\frac{[H^+][HN_2O_2^-]}{[H_2N_2O_2]} = 9 \times 10^{-8}$$

$$\frac{[H^+][N_2O_2^=]}{[HN_2O_2^-]} = 1.0 \times 10^{-11}$$

The kinetics of the decomposition of hyponitrites to yield nitrogen(I) oxide have already been discussed. The free acid undergoes a similar reaction when its aqueous solution is treated with sulfuric acid:

$$H_2N_2O_2 \rightarrow N_2O + H_2O$$

Hyponitrous acid is not a strong oxidizing agent; even hydrogen iodide is not affected by the pure acid. It is converted to nitrous or nitric acid by strong oxidants and is reduced with difficulty to hydrazine by active hydrogen.

Nitramide. Nitramide, a compound which is isomeric with hyponitrous acid, is obtained by the hydrolysis of potassium nitrocarbonate, $NO_2NKCOOK$, with concentrated sulfuric acid: [61]

$$NO_2NKCOOK + 2H_2SO_4 \rightarrow NO_2NH_2 + CO_2 + 2KHSO_4$$

The resulting mixture is saturated with ammonium sulfate, extracted with ether, the ether extract evaporated, the residue dissolved in absolute alcohol, and petroleum ether added, bringing about the precipitation of white crystals of NH_2NO_2 which melt at 72–75°C. Nitramide is an aquo-ammono analogue of nitric acid. It is weakly acidic in aqueous solution in accordance with the following equilibrium constant:

$$\frac{[H^+][NHNO_2^-]}{[NH_2NO_2]} = 2.55 \times 10^{-7} \text{ at } 15°C$$

Aqueous solutions of nitramide decompose slowly in accordance with the equation:

$$NH_2NO_2 \rightarrow N_2O + H_2O$$

Though nitramide is not explosive under ordinary conditions, the solid should be prepared only as needed and should be stored over phosphorus(V) oxide in a refrigerator. Nitramide differs in properties from

[60] W. M. Latimer and H. W. Zimmerman, *J. Am. Chem. Soc.* **61**, 1550 (1939).
[61] *Inorganic Syntheses* **I**, 68–72 (1939).

hyponitrous acid, its isomer, in that it decomposes less rapidly in solution than does the latter compound. Hyponitrite ion, $N_2O_2^=$, however, is much more stable than nitramide ion, $NHNO_2^-$. In fact it appears that $NHNO_2^-$ is less stable than NH_2NO_2,[62] thus accounting for the fact that nitramide decomposes much more rapidly in alkaline than in acid solutions.

NITROGEN (II) OXIDE AND THE NITROSYL COMPOUNDS

The chief compound in which nitrogen exhibits an oxidation state of $+2$ is nitrogen (II) oxide, NO. This oxide does not correspond in oxidation state to any of the common acids of nitrogen, but there is some basis for considering it to be the anhydride of nitrohydroxylamic acid (*cf.*).

Preparation of Nitrogen (II) Oxide. Three chief industrial methods for the production of nitrogen (II) oxide have been developed. The first of these involves the direct union of nitrogen and oxygen. The free energy of the reaction,

$$\tfrac{1}{2}O_2 + \tfrac{1}{2}N_2 \rightarrow NO,$$

is highly positive ($\Delta F^0_{298^\circ} = 20{,}650$ cal) and it is, therefore, necessary to go to high temperatures before equilibrium conditions are such as to bring about any appreciable yield of the oxide. In the arc process, air is passed through an electric arc (temperature about 3500°C) and then is cooled rapidly to a temperature at which the rate of decomposition of nitrogen (II) oxide is slow (under 1500°C). By this means a yield of 2 to 3% NO is obtained.

F. Daniels has recently developed a process in which the reaction of nitrogen and oxygen is brought about by the high temperature developed when fuel gas is burned in air. The nitrogen (II) oxide is rapidly chilled by passing it through a bed of gravel and is permitted to react with more oxygen to form nitrogen dioxide which is collected by adsorption on silica gel and is eventually converted to nitric acid.[63]

The third and more important industrial method is the catalytic oxidation of ammonia at a platinum catalyst. This step is the first one in the commercial production of nitric acid by the Ostwald process and has already been discussed.

Nitrogen (II) oxide is formed in a number of laboratory reactions, particularly reductions of nitric acid, but in most cases it is produced in conjunction with other gases. Two convenient laboratory methods by

[62] C. A. Marlies and V. K. LaMer, *J. Am. Chem. Soc.* **57**, 1812 (1935).
[63] *Chem. Eng. News* **33**, 2373 (1955).

which nitrogen(II) oxide may be prepared in a relatively pure state follow.

(1) *The reaction of iron(II) ion with nitrite ion in acid solution.* The reaction is carried out by introducing a solution of iron(II) sulfate in dilute sulfuric acid into a solution of sodium nitrite:

$$Fe^{++} + NO_2^- + 2H^+ \rightarrow Fe^{+3} + NO(g) + H_2O$$

Small amounts of higher oxides of nitrogen and carbon dioxide are removed by passing the gas over sodium hydroxide pellets.[64]

(2) *The reaction of iodide ion with nitrite ion in sulfuric acid solution.* Fifty per cent sulfuric acid is added slowly to a solution that is four molar in potassium nitrite and one molar in potassium iodide:

$$2NO_2^- + 2I^- + 4H^+ \rightarrow 2NO + I_2 + 2H_2O$$

The gas evolved is passed through 90% sulfuric acid, 50% potassium hydroxide, a trap cooled to $-75°C$, phosphorus(V) oxide, and liquid nitrogen(II) oxide. This process yields a product of exceedingly high purity.[65]

Physical and Chemical Properties of Nitrogen(II) Oxide. Nitrogen(II) oxide is a colorless gas. Its principal physical constants are listed in the following table:

TABLE 1.6. PHYSICAL CONSTANTS OF NITROGEN(II) OXIDE

Melting point.............................$-163.51°C$
$\Delta H_{-163.51°}$ (fusion).........................549.5 cal/mole
$\Delta H^0{}_{298°}$ (formation)........................21,500 cal/mole
Boiling point..............................$-151.74°C$
$\Delta H_{-151.74°}$ (vaporization)....................3292.6 cal/mole
$\Delta F^0{}_{298°}$ (formation).........................20,650 cal/mole

Vapor pressure equations:

Solid: $\log_{10} p_{cm} = -867/T + 0.00076T + 9.05125$ (T = abs temp).
Liquid: $\log_{10} p_{cm} = -776/T - 0.002364T + 8.562128$ (T = abs temp).

Values for $K = \dfrac{p_{NO}}{p_{N_2}{}^{\frac{1}{2}} p_{O_2}{}^{\frac{1}{2}}}$

25°C	7.25×10^{-16} (calc)	2402°C	5.8×10^{-2} (obs)
727°C	8.86×10^{-5} (calc)	3227°C	2.09×10^{-1} (calc)
1538°C	1.14×10^{-2} (calc)	4727°C	5.26×10^{-1} (calc)

$S^0{}_{298°}$ of gas....................... $\begin{cases} 50.35 \text{ cal/deg/mole (calc)} \\ 49.60 \text{ cal/deg/mole (abs)} \end{cases}$

Critical temperature.......................$-94°C$
Critical pressure..........................65 atm
Density (liquid) at bp.....................1.269 g/ml.

[64] *Inorganic Synthesis* 2, 126 (1946).
[65] H. L. Johnston and W. F. Giauque, *J. Am. Chem. Soc.* 51, 3194 (1929).

Nitrogen (II) oxide has a molecular weight in the gaseous state which corresponds to the molecular formula, NO. The molecule, therefore, contains an odd number of electrons. As would be expected from this fact, nitrogen (II) oxide is paramagnetic. The molecule has a magnetic moment of 1.837 Bohr magnetons at 22.9°C which is equal to the value calculated from the theory (one unpaired electron per molecule).

It is interesting to note that the values of the entropy obtained from thermal measurements (abs.) and those calculated from spectral data differ by 0.75 cal/deg/mole. This difference has been explained by assuming that the nitrogen (II) oxide in the solid state consists of double molecules, N_2O_2, and that there is limited randomness in the orientation of these molecules in the crystal. Further evidence for the dimeric form of solid nitrogen (II) oxide is provided by the fact that the solid is diamagnetic.

At very low temperatures crystals of N_2O_2 may be formed and the nature of these crystals have been characterized at −175°C.[66] Precession photographs indicate the monoclinic system with space group $P2_1/a$, with two N_2O_2 molecules in the unit cell of dimensions $a = 6.68$, $b = 3.96$, $c = 6.55$ A, $\beta = 127.9°$. Each of the two dimers in the unit cell have two possible orientations. This orientation is expected on the basis of the residual entropy of 1.5 eu per mole of dimer. The statistically averaged dimer is a rectangular planar molecule with a short edge of 1.12 A and a long edge of 2.4 A. The x-ray evidence cannot distinguish between parallel and antiparallel orientations of NO groups within the dimer. The actual shape of a dimer molecule must be fairly close to rectangular, since the x-ray data do not permit the two long edges to differ by more than 0.5 A. Infrared and Raman spectra of liquid and solid NO are reported.[67] In the liquid there are 4 strong and 2 weaker Raman lines as well as 2 strong infrared bonds. It is claimed that these spectra are due to the N_2O_2 molecule, existing as a bent O—NN—O structure.

Nitrogen (II) oxide does not support combustion unless activated, as *e.g.* by high temperature. The gas reduces acid permanganate; this reaction is used as the basis for a volumetric method for the determination of NO. Nitrogen (II) oxide reacts rapidly with oxygen to produce the dioxide, NO_2.

Nitrogen (II) oxide undergoes a great variety of addition reactions, which, for their reasonable understanding, require a consideration of the electronic structure of the molecule. The NO molecule contains an odd

[66] W. J. Dulmage *et al.*, *Acta Cryst.* **6**, 760 (1953).
[67] A. L. Smith *et al.*, *J. Chem. Phys.* **19**, 189 (1951).

number of electrons, but its lack of color, its slight tendency to dimerize at room temperature, and its low reactivity toward many materials under ordinary circumstances suggest an inherently greater stability than is characteristic of many odd molecules. L. Pauling [68] has postulated resonance between the following structures:

$$:\overset{\cdot}{N}::\overset{\cdot\cdot}{O}: \qquad :\overset{\cdot\cdot}{N}::\overset{\cdot+}{O}:$$

$$\text{I} \qquad\qquad \text{II}$$

This resonating structure is commonly represented by

$$:N{\equiv}\!\!\equiv O:$$

and the nitrogen and oxygen are said to be connected by two electron-pair bonds and one three-electron bond. In terms of molecular orbital theory this molecule is represented by the formulation

$$KK\sigma^2_{2s}\sigma^{*2}_{2s}\sigma^2_{2p_x}\pi^4_{2p_z2p_y}\pi^{*1}_{2p_z2p_y}$$

The N—O distance, 1.14 A (between the double and triple bond distances), as well as other characteristics of the substance, is in accord with this structure.

One might expect a molecule with this structure to be capable of entering into chemical combination in any one of the following ways: (a) By losing the odd electron to form a positive ion of the structure $:N{\equiv}O:^+$; in actual compounds electron loss is seldom complete, the usual situation being the formation of a highly polar covalent link with the NO radical forming the positive end of the bond; (b) by gaining an electron to form the negative ion NO^-, presumably of the structure $:\overset{\cdot\cdot}{N}{=}\overset{\cdot\cdot}{O}:^-$; (c) by sharing a pair of electrons to form a coordinate link. Either the molecule, the NO^+ ion, or the NO^- ion could act as a donor in this manner. This variety of ways in which nitrogen(II) oxide can combine accounts for the multiplicity of nitrosyl compounds.

Nitrosyl Compounds. An excellent summary of inorganic nitrosyl compounds has been published [69] in which these compounds are classified according to the three modes of reaction of the NO molecule listed above.

(1) *Compounds containing positive nitrosyl radicals.* The compounds, NOF, NOCl, and NOBr (but not NOI), can be obtained by a variety of reactions including the direct combination of NO with the halogen:

$$2NO + X_2 \rightarrow 2NOX$$

[68] *The Nature of the Chemical Bond*, pp. 266–70, Cornell University Press (1940).
[69] T. Moeller, *J. Chem. Educ.* **23**, 441–4, 542–8 (1946); see also F. Seel and R. Schwarfel, *Z. anorg. u. allgem. Chem.* **274**, 169 (1953).

Some information on the kinetics of the $NO-Cl_2$ system is derivable from studies made on the reaction between hydrogen and chlorine in the presence of NO and NOCl.[70]   A sequence of non-branching chain reactions are suggested:

$$(1) \quad NO + Cl_2 \rightarrow NOCl + Cl$$
$$(2) \quad NOCl \rightarrow NO + Cl$$
$$(3) \quad Cl_2 \rightarrow Cl + Cl$$
$$(4) \quad Cl + H_2 \rightarrow HCl + H$$
$$(5) \quad H + Cl_2 \rightarrow HCl + Cl$$
$$(6) \quad Cl + NOCl \rightarrow NO + Cl_2$$
$$(7) \quad H + NOCl \rightarrow NO + HCl$$

Reaction (1) is the fastest initiation step.   Chlorine has been found to have an accelerating effect on the rate of decomposition of NOCl.   Reaction (1) followed by reaction (6) would explain this acceleration.   The bimolecular decomposition of NOCl represented by $2NOCl \rightarrow 2NO + Cl_2$ at elevated temperatures is not as important in the over all decomposition as the combined system represented by reactions (1) and (6).

The oxidation of NOCl by ozone in the presence of N_2O_5 results in the formation of NO_2Cl and oxygen: $NOCl + O_3 \rightarrow NO_2Cl + O_2$. With large excess of O_3 the reaction (in the presence of N_2O_5) is half order with respect to NOCl.   The reaction may be represented by $NO_2 + O_3 \rightarrow NO_3 + O_2$ followed by $NOCl + NO_3 \rightarrow NO_2Cl + NO_2$. The energy of activation of the latter system is about 6 kcal/mole.[71]

Characteristic physical constants for the nitrosyl halides are listed in the following table: (see also Vol. III, this series)

TABLE 1.7.   PHYSICAL PROPERTIES OF THE NITROSYL HALIDES

Property	NOF	NOCl	NOBr
Molecular weight	49.008	65.465	109.924
Melting point (°C)	−132.5	−64.5	−55.5
Boiling point (°C)	−59.9	−6.4	ca. 0
Color in gas phase	colorless	orange-yellow	red
Dipole moment (D)	—	1.83	1.87

The physical constants of the nitrosyl halides are those of covalent compounds, but they are also those of polar materials.   Measurements

[70] P. G. Ashmore and J. Chanmugam, *Trans. Faraday Soc.* **49**, 254 (1953).
[71] H. S. Johnston and L. Leighton, Jr., *J. Am. Chem. Soc.* **75**, 3612 (1953).

on the N–X distance in NOCl and NOBr show that the N–X distance in each case is considerably larger than the sum of the single bond covalent radii of nitrogen and the halogen. Furthermore the nitrogen to oxygen bond distance in both molecules is between that of a double and that of a triple bond between these two atoms. It is therefore assumed [72] that the structure of these molecules involves resonance between the two structures,

$$:\overset{..}{O}::\overset{..}{N} \qquad \text{and} \qquad :O:::N:^+$$
$$\overset{.}{:}\overset{.}{X}\overset{.}{:} :\overset{..}{X}:^-$$

with about 50% ionic character in NOCl and NOBr and considerably more, of course, in NOF. Some variations are found in the literature with regard to the physical properties of the nitrosyl halides. The values $-59.6 \pm 0.3°C$ [73] and $-61.5°C$ [74] for the melting point of NOCl are listed. The heats of sublimation, fusion, and vaporization of NOCl are given as 7590 ± 0.025, 1430 ± 180, and 6160 ± 27 cal/mole respectively.[75] The vapor pressure of the solid and liquid NOCl are represented respectively by $\log P_{mm} = -((1660 \pm 32)/T) + 9.37 \pm 0.20$ and $\log P_{mm} = -((1347 \pm 6)/T) + 7.922 \pm 0.025$.

The negative nature of the Cl^- of NOCl has been elucidated in exchange studies involving NOCl and Me_4NCl. The exchange is complete in 6 min or less at $-10°C$. The exchange is thought to occur by ionization of NOCl to NO^+ and Cl^- rather than through a nitrosonium ion mechanism since NOCl and Cl^- are both electron pair donors. Interaction between two such donors would be expected to be small.[76]

The bond angles are $106° \pm 2°$ and $117° \pm 3°$ respectively for NOCl and NOBr. The structural considerations are supported by the values of the observed dipole moments, and by the fact that nitrosyl chloride apparently forms nitrosyl salts with certain covalent chlorides, as $[NO^+][SbCl_6]^-$, $[NO^+]_2[SnCl_6]^=$, and $[NO^+]_2[PtCl_6]^=$.[77] Nitrosyl chloride also forms loose addition compounds with zinc, aluminum, and mercury(II) chlorides and compounds containing coordinated NO radicals with copper(I) and manganese(II) chlorides. Further evidence for the positive NO radical is found in the existence of compounds having the formulas $NOClO_4$ and $NOBF_4$, which are similar in properties and

[72] J. A. A. Ketelaar and K. J. Palmer, *J. Am. Chem. Soc.* **59**, 2629 (1937).

[73] W. G. Burns and F. S. Dainton, *Trans. Faraday Soc.* **48**, 21 (1952).

[74] Nat. Bureau Stand., Circular **500**.

[75] Burns and Dainton, *loc. cit.*

[76] J. Lewis and R. G. Wilkins, *Chemistry and Industry*, **1954**, 634.

[77] R. W. Asmussen, *Z. anorg. u. allgem. Chem.* **243**, 127 (1939).

crystal structure to the compounds NH_4ClO_4 and NH_4BF_4 as well as H_3OClO_4 and H_3OBF_4, respectively. Furthermore, $NOClO_4$ has been shown to be a binary electrolyte in nitromethane solution. It may, therefore, reasonably be assumed that these compounds are ionic and have the structure $NO^+ClO_4^-$ and $NO^+BF_4^-$. Nitrosyl perchlorate may be prepared by injecting a gaseous mixture of NO and NO_2 into an aqueous solution of $NaClO_4$ and H_2SO_4. The co-formed $NaHSO_4$ is removed and the $NOClO_4$ is crystallized out. The density of the compound is reported as 2.169 at 18°C. When heated below 100°C the $NOClO_4$ decomposes without melting:

$$2NOClO_4 \rightarrow N_2O_4 + Cl_2 + 3O_2$$

Above 100°C the decomposition proceeds as

$$2NOClO_4 \rightarrow N_2O_4 + Cl_2 + 3O_2$$

The heat of formation of $NOClO_4$ is -41.79 ± 0.08 kcal/mole.[78]

Another compound of this type is nitrosyl hydrogensulfate (the so-called "chamber crystals" obtained in the lead chamber process for making sulfuric acid), which has the formula $NOSO_4H$ and which has been shown to dissociate in sulfuric acid solution into NO^+ and HSO_4^- ions.[79] All these salts are decomposed by water but, when dry, are quite stable at moderate temperatures. The hydrolysis of nitrosyl hydrogen sulfate is rapid and complete:

$$NO[SO_4H] + H_2O \rightarrow H_2SO_4 + HNO_2$$

Nitrosyl chloride may act as an ionizing solvent for a number of nitrosyl compounds.[80] The compound $NOFeCl_4$ ionizes in NOCl with a $K = 0.00373$ at $-10°C$. The monosolvate, $NOFeCl_4 \cdot NOCl$, also forms and has a dissociation pressure of $\times 224$ mm at 0°C. In the electrolysis of $NOFeCl_4$ in NOCl solvent the transference ratio of NO^+ to $FeCl_4^-$ is about 7 : 1 suggesting a solvo-chain mechanism of transporting NO^+. The solubility of the highly conducting $NOAlCl_4$ is 61.2 g per 100 g of solvent. The monosolvate, $NOAlCl_4 \cdot NOCl$, also forms and has a dissociation pressure of 180 mm at 0°C. The compound $NOAlCl_4$ has properties intermediate between those pure heteropolar and molecular compounds. Sublimation is possible at low pressures without decomposi-

[78] K. Crase et al., *Z. anorg. Chem.* **259**, 154 (1949); **260**, 295 (1949).
[79] A. Hantzsch, *Z. physik. Chem.* **65**, 41 (1909); A. Hantzsch and K. Berger, *Z. anorg. allgem. Chem.* **190**, 321 (1930).
[80] A. Burg and D. F. McKenzie, *J. Am. Chem. Soc.* **74**, 3143 (1952).

tion.[81] The two compounds $NOBF_4$ and $(NO)_2SnCl_6$ are nearly insoluble and non-solvated. The NO^+ group acts as a Lewis acid and NO as well as Cl^- as bases. Nitrosyl salts react with the slightly soluble methyl ammonium chloride in the sense of an acid-base reaction: $NO^+ + Cl^- \rightarrow NOCl$. Another neutralization reaction involving nitrosyl sulfuric acid, $NOHSO_4$, and the NO^+ radical has been reported as taking place.[82] The compound $N_2O_2HSO_4$ results when NO under pressure is passed into $NOHSO_4$. The same compound is formed when $NOHSO_4$ is reduced in concentrated sulfuric acid with SO_2, methanol, or formic acid. Other compounds containing this $N_2O_2^+$ radical are known. The salt $N_2O_2AlCl_4$ is prepared by the action of NO under pressure on $NOAlCl_4$ in liquid SO_2. Nitrosyl chloride will act in the same capacity in a sealed tube reaction with SO_2 and aluminum. The compound N_2O_2Cl has not been formed from the $NO + NOCl$ reaction up to 20 atm pressure. Solid $N_2O_2^+$ salts are unstable. The aluminum salt $N_2O_2AlCl_4$ is stable only at high NO pressures and at low temperatures. It is concluded that NO^+ and $N_2O_2^+$ salts closely resemble one another in chemical properties and solubilities.

Other compounds which presumably contain the positive nitrosyl radical but which have not been sufficiently studied for definite conclusions include $(NO)_2SeO_4$, $NOHSeO_4$, $(NO)_2S_2O_7$, $NOReO_4$, $NOSCN$, $NOPF_6$, $NOAsF_6$, $NOSbF_6$, $NO[Cr(NH_3)_2(SCN)_4]$, and $NOSO_3F$, $PdCl_2 \cdot 2NOCl$, $NOBCl_4$, $NOHgCl_3$, $(NO)_2TiCl_4$.[83]

(2) *Compounds containing the negative nitrosyl radical, NO^-.* When dry NO is passed into a solution of sodium in liquid ammonia a white precipitate having the empirical formula NaNO, and commonly known as sodium nitrosyl, is obtained.[83a] It is a white, rather unstable solid which differs distinctly in chemical properties and in x-ray diffraction pattern from sodium hyponitrite which has the same percentage composition. It is diamagnetic and is believed to contain the NO^- ion. In the absence of air hydroxylamine salts in alkaline solutions form NaNO to the extent of about 10%. The reaction is represented by the decomposition of hydroxylamine alone:

$$2NH_2OH \rightarrow H_2O + NH_3 + HNO$$

The pH is important with respect to the nature of the disproportionation. In the presences of strong alkali the HNO reacts further with NH_2OH

[81] H. Hautgraaf and A. M. de Roos, *Rec. trav. chim.* **72**, 963 (1953).

[82] F. Seel *et al.*, *Z. Naturforsch.* **8b**, 607 (1953).

[83] J. R. Partington and A. L. Whymers, *J. Chem. Soc.* 1949, 3135.

[83a] E. Zintl and A. Harder, *Ber.* **66A**, 760 (1933).

to yield nitrogen and as a side reaction the hyponitrite ion, $N_2O_2^=$.   The dimer, $H_2N_2O_2$, is favored in an acidic solution, decomposing to give N_2O and water [84] as represented by

$$H_2N_2O_2 \rightarrow N_2O + H_2O$$

(3) *Compounds containing coordinated nitrosyl radicals.*   As previously stated, the structure of the NO molecule is such that one might expect the NO group to be able to coordinate as a neutral molecule, as an NO^- ion after gaining an electron, or as an NO^+ ion after losing an electron.   It should be added that while there is the theoretical possibility of coordination taking place through either the nitrogen or oxygen atom, all the evidence indicates that the nitrogen always acts as the donor atom.

From the fact that volatile nitrosyl carbonyl compounds such as $Fe(NO)_2(CO)_2$ and $Co(NO)(CO)_3$ exist, one might be tempted to conclude that the NO group has coordinated as a neutral molecule.[85]   However, the fact that these substances are diamagnetic and hence do not contain unpaired electrons casts doubt on the validity of this conclusion.   Furthermore, neutral molecules reacting with nitrosyl carbonyls replace the CO groups rather than the NO groups.   These considerations indicate that coordination of NO groups as neutral molecules is very unusual if it occurs at all.

If the NO radical coordinates as a negative ion it would function somewhat like a halide ion.   There are a few complexes which do appear to contain the NO^- groups; *e.g.* the complex salts of the ion $[Co(NH_3)_5(NO)]^{++}$.   The properties of these salts, particularly their diamagnetic behavior, suggest the presence of trivalent cobalt, formed from the cobalt(II) ion by transfer of an electron to nitrogen(II) oxide.   Salts of $[Co(NH_3)_5NO]^{++}$ are comparable in character with those of $[Co(NH_3)_5Cl]^{++}$.   It is probable, also, that the ions $[Ru(NH_3)_4(H_2O)(NO)]^{+3}$ and $[Ru(NH_3)_4Cl(NO)]^{++}$ contain coordinated NO^- groups.[86]

It appears more likely, however, that in the great majority of its complexes, the NO group coordinates as the positive ion; this ion is isoelectronic and isosteric with the cyanide ion and the carbon monoxide molecule:

$$\overset{+}{:N:::O:} \qquad :C:::O: \qquad \overset{-}{:C:::N:}$$

[84] R. Nast and I. Föppl, *Z. anorg. u. allgem. Chem.* **263**, 310 (1950).

[85] W. Hieber *et al.*, *Chem. Ber.* **85**, 647 (1952).

[86] D. P. Mellor and D. P. Craig, *J. Proc. Roy. Soc. N.S. Wales* **78**, 25 (1944); W. Hieber *et al.*, *Chem. Ber.* **85**, 647 (1952).

Similarities among complexes containing these three radicals would be expected and are, indeed, found.[87]   However, the formation of the NO^+ ion from the NO molecule requires the release of an electron, and it is usually assumed that this electron is transferred to the acceptor metal atom or ion.   As a result the metal must undergo a reduction of one unit in oxidation state.   This change accounts for the fact that the nitroprussides M_2^I $[Fe(CN)_5NO]$ apparently contain Fe^{+2} rather than Fe^{+3} iron.   Experimental evidence for this belief is the larger stabilities of the nitroprussides than pentacyanoiron(III) complexes, $[Fe(CN)_5A]^=$ (A = H_2O, NH_3), and the diamagnetic behavior of nitroprussides.   Thus, complexes containing the ions $[Fe(CN)_5NO]^=$, $[Fe(CN)_5CO]^{+3}$, and $[Fe(CN)_6]^{+4}$ are very similar in properties.   Similar analogies are found in salts of the ions $[Mn(CN)_5NO]^{-3}$ and $[Mn(CN)_6]^{-5}$, in the ruthenium complexes $[Ru(CN)_5(NO)]^=$ and $[Ru(CN)_6]^{-4}$, as well as in the bivalent osmium derivatives $[OsCl_5(NO)]^=$ and $[OsCl_6]^{-4}$.   This concept of bonding, however, introduces the inconsistency of placing a negative formal charge on the metal atom or ion.   Thus, the structure

$$\overset{=}{M} \colon \overset{+}{N} \colon \colon \colon \overset{+}{O} \colon$$

would characterize each coordinated NO group.   Pauling avoids this difficulty (which also obtains in cyanide and carbonyl complexes) by assuming the presence of four bonding electrons, the second pair being contributed by the metal atom or ion.   Thus, he postulates that structures of the type

$$M \colon \colon \overset{+}{N} \colon \colon O \colon$$

make a major contribution to the normal state of the complex.[88]   No final decision can be made at present concerning the validity of this "double-bond" concept.   Such a decision requires data on M—N bond distances in a variety of nitrosyl complexes.

TABLE 1.8.   REPRESENTATIVE NITROSYL COMPLEXES

$Co(NO)(CO)_3$	$Ru(NO)_4$	$[Fe(NO)_2(S_2O_3)]^-$	$[Fe(NO)_2S_2O_3]^-$
$Fe(NO)_2(CO)_2$	$Fe(NO)_3NH_3$	$Co(NO)_2Br$	$[Ni(NO)(S_2O_3)_2]^{-3}$
$Pd(NO)_2Cl_2$	$[RuCl_5NO]^-$	$[Ru(NH_3)_4Cl(NO)]^+$	
$Fe(NO)_2(SCSOC_2H_5)_2$	$[Co(NH_3)_5(NO)]^{++}$	$[Pt(NO)Cl_3]^-$	
$Pt(NO)(C_5H_5N)Cl_2$	$[Ni(NH_3)_5NO]^+$	$[Co(NH_3)_5(NO)]_2^{+4}$	
$[Fe(CN)_5NO]^-$	$[Mn(CN)_5(NO)]^{-3}$		

[87] N. V. Sidgwick and R. W. Bailey, *Proc. Roy. Soc. London* **A144**, 521 (1934).

[88] L. Pauling, *The Nature of the Chemical Bond*, pp. 250–8, 269–70, Cornell University Press (1940).

Nitrosyl coordination complexes are much too numerous for a complete list to be given. Table 1.8 is, therefore, merely representative rather than exhaustive.

NITROXYLIC AND NITROHYDROXYLAMIC ACIDS

Salts of two acids having compositions which may be expressed by the formula $NO \cdot nH_2O$ have been prepared. The first of these, nitroxylic acid, H_2NO_2, sometimes called hydronitrous acid, is known only in the form of its sodium salt, Na_2NO_2. This substance is obtained either by the electrolytic reduction of solutions of sodium nitrite in liquid ammonia [89] or by the addition of sodium nitrate to solutions of sodium in liquid ammonia until the blue color disappears. Slightly soluble, brilliant, yellowish sodium nitroxylate precipitates from the liquid ammonia solution. On contact with water or moist air, sodium nitroxylate reacts explosively with the evolution of hydrogen. In the absence of water and oxygen, however, this substance is stable up to 100°C; at higher temperatures, it undergoes violent decomposition to form sodium monoxide, nitrite, nitrate, and molecular nitrogen. No other nitroxylates have been prepared.

Nitrohydroxylamic acid, $H_2N_2O_3$, is also unknown as the free acid. However, a number of metal nitrohydroxylamates have been prepared. When a concentrated solution of sodium ethylate in absolute alcohol is mixed with a saturated solution of hydroxylammonium chloride in alcohol, the precipitated sodium chloride filtered off, and ethyl nitrate added to the filtrate, a solution of sodium nitrohydroxylamate is obtained. When this solution is cooled, the solid $Na_2N_2O_3$ separates as a fine powder. The salt dissolves in water to give alkaline solutions, presumably because $HN_2O_3^-$ and $H_2N_2O_3$ are weak acids and the $N_2O_3^=$ ion undergoes hydrolysis. The addition of acids to solutions containing $N_2O_3^=$ ions causes immediate decomposition in accordance with the equation:

$$N_2O_3^= + 2H_3O^+ \rightleftarrows 2NO + 3H_2O$$

It has been stated that this reaction is reversible and that NO in aqueous solution on long standing reacts to yield nitrohydroxylamic acid which decomposes in accordance with the following equations:

$$H_2N_2O_3 \rightarrow >NOH + HNO_2$$
$$2 >NOH \rightarrow H_2N_2O_2 \rightarrow N_2O + H_2O$$

[89] E. B. Maxted, *J. Chem. Soc.* 111, 1016 (1917); E. Zintl and O. Kohn, *Ber.* 61, 189 (1928).

The same mechanism would account for the decomposition of sodium nitrohydroxylamate, when its aqueous solution is heated, to yield nitrogen(I) oxide and the nitrite ion. Slightly soluble alkaline earth metal salts of the type BaN_2O_3 may be precipitated from solutions of the sodium salt. Lead, cadmium, silver, and mercury nitrohydroxylamates may be similarly prepared but, in the case of the silver and mercury salts, decomposition slowly takes place because of reduction of the metal ion to the free metal by the nitrohydroxylamate ion. Solutions of nitrohydroxylamates are readily oxidized even by atmospheric oxygen. They may also be reduced by various reducing agents such as tin(II) chloride.

A compound which is probably identical to the nitroxylhydroxylamate is referred to in the literature as sodium α-oxyhyponitrite, $Na_2N_2O_3$. It has been prepared by the action of hydroxylamine and sodium ethoxide in alcoholic solution on ethylnitrate. An allotropic beta form of the same compound results from the oxidation of sodium hyponitrite by liquid N_2O_4. The hyponitrite and α-oxyhyponitrite may be distinguished by the differences in their ultraviolet absorption. The α-hyponitrite in neutral or dilute acid solutions yields on spontaneous decomposition $NaNO_2$, $NaOH$, and N_2O.[90] The α-form reacts with silver nitrate to give first a yellow and then a black silver deposit. The β-form reacts with silver nitrate to give only a stable yellow precipitate of $Ag_2N_2O_2$. The structure of the β-hyponitrite is suggested as being H–O–N:N–O–O–H in contrast to the structure of $H_2N_2O_2$ as $N:N(OH)_2 \rightarrow O$.

The hyponitrite may be estimated in the presence of nitrite by taking advantage of the activity of the latter with thiourea as contrasted to the inactivity of thiourea on the former.

Nitrous Acid, Its Salts, Anhydride, and Acid Halides

Nitrogen Sesquioxide. Nitrogen sesquioxide, N_2O_3, is the anhydride of nitrous acid. It is not very stable and decomposes extensively even at room temperature to give an equimolar mixture of nitrogen(II) oxide and nitrogen dioxide:

$$N_2O_3 \rightleftharpoons NO + NO_2$$

When an equimolar mixture of NO and NO_2 is condensed, a blue liquid which consists of N_2O_3 with undoubtedly some dissolved NO and NO_2 and which boils at 3.5°C is obtained. This liquid solidifies when the temperature is reduced to -103°C. These boiling point and freezing point values are approximate. The addition of N_2O_3 or an equimolar

[90] C. C. Addison *et al.*, *J. Chem. Soc.* **1952**, 338.

mixture of NO and NO_2 to an alkaline solution results in the production of nitrite ion:

$$N_2O_3(NO + NO_2) + 2OH^- \rightarrow 2NO_2^- + H_2O$$

The reaction of the sesquioxide with water yields nitrous acid along with nitric acid and other products. The reason for the complexity of this reaction lies in the various reactions which nitrous acid undergoes; this matter is discussed later. Liquid N_2O_3 and water are not miscible in all proportions at room temperature. For example, if equimolar amounts of the two substances are mixed at any temperature below 55°C two liquid layers are obtained. When the system is heated above that temperature (in a closed tube) the system becomes homogeneous.[91] The reaction of N_2O_3 (or NO + NO_2) with sulfuric acid results in the production of nitrosyl hydrogensulfate:

$$NO + NO_2 + 2H_2SO_4 \rightarrow 2NOHSO_4 + H_2O$$

This reaction takes place almost quantitatively. Equimolecular quantities of water have no effect on the NO^+ ion, but do convert NO_2^+ ion into molecular nitric acid. Any reaction involving solutions of such a concentration that NO_2^+ and water are formed or in which NO_2^+ is one of the reactants will necessarily result in the formation of nitric acid. Such is the case when either N_2O_4 or N_2O_5 react with sulfuric acid.[92]

The equilibrium system of NO_2—HNO_2—HNO_3 has been investigated in nitric acid as a solvent.[93] Three equilibria are suggested:

$$HNO_3 + HNO_2 \rightleftarrows N_2O_4 + H_2O \rightleftarrows 2NO_2 + H_2O$$

The investigations of the physical properties of N_2O_3 have been limited by the instability of the oxide. A study of the equilibrium has been made:[94]

$$N_2O_{3(g)} \rightleftarrows NO_{2(g)} + NO_{(g)}$$

It was found that $\Delta F^0_{298°}$ for the reaction equals -441 cal and that $\Delta H^0 = 10,300$ cal. The values of K_P depend upon the pressure since the gases in equilibrium are not perfect.

$\Delta F^0_{298°}$ for the reaction

$$N_2 + \tfrac{3}{2}O_2 \rightarrow N_2O_3$$

[91] T. M. Lowry and J. T. Lemon, J. Chem. Soc. 1936, 1.
[92] D. J. Millen, J. Chem. Soc. 1950, 2600.
[93] K. Vetter, Z. anorg. Chem. 260, 242 (1949).
[94] F. H. Verhoek and F. Daniels, J. Am. Chem. Soc. 53, 1250 (1931).

is equal to 33,805 cal. The structure of N_2O_3 molecules is discussed in a later section.

Nitrous Acid. Nitrogen sesquioxide reacts with water to yield solutions which contain nitrous acid (HNO_2) but which also contain nitric acid and the oxides NO and NO_2 (or N_2O_4). If the water is cold, and if the solution is dilute, the concentration of nitrous acid is considerably larger than that of nitric acid. The most convenient method for obtaining a solution of nitrous acid is by the treatment of a solution of a soluble nitrite with a strong acid. Particularly convenient is the reaction of barium nitrite with sulfuric acid:

$$Ba(NO_2)_2 + H_2SO_4 \rightarrow BaSO_{4(s)} + 2HNO_2$$

Nitrous acid in aqueous solution is unstable with respect to the following decomposition:

$$3HNO_2 \rightleftharpoons H_3O^+ + NO_3^- + 2NO$$

The kinetics of this reaction have been carefully studied.[95] It was found that the reaction is reversible and that the rates of both the forward and the reverse reactions are measurable. That the reaction is relatively easily reversible at lower temperatures but becomes less so as the temperature is raised is indicated by the following data in which values of the equilibrium constant at various temperatures are listed:

$$T \text{ (°C)} \ldots\ldots 12.5 \ldots\ldots 15 \ldots\ldots 24.9 \ldots\ldots 30$$
$$K \quad \ldots\ldots 13.3 \ldots\ldots 14.1 \ldots\ldots 28.7 \ldots\ldots 39.6$$
$$\Delta H^0 = 11,900 \text{ cal}$$

The attainment of equilibrium is comparatively slow in cold, dilute solutions, but in warm, concentrated solutions the quantity of nitrous acid which is present is very small. The nitrite to nitrate oxidation has been further elucidated and is described by the following:

$$(1) \qquad 2HNO_2 \rightarrow NO + NO_2 + H_2O$$
$$(2) \qquad 2NO + O_2 \rightarrow 2NO_2$$
$$(3) \qquad 2NO_2 \rightleftharpoons N_2O_4$$
$$(4) \quad N_2O_4 + H_2O \rightarrow HNO_2 + HNO_3$$

Step (2) is modified by the sequence:

$$NO + OH \rightarrow NO^+ + OH^- \rightarrow NO \cdot OH \rightleftharpoons HNO_2$$

The OH radical arises from the reaction $OH^- + H_2O \rightarrow OH + H_2O^-$.[96]

[95] E. Abel, *Z. phys. Chem.* **148**, 337 (1930).
[96] E. Abel, *Monatsh.* **80**, 771 (1949).

The kinetics of oxidation of formic acid by nitrous acid in both sulfuric acid and nitric acid media have been investigated.[97]   In the former media the rate determining step is a bimolecular reaction between the formic acid and the HNO_2 in dilute acid and between formic acid and NO^+ or $H_2NO_2^+$ in more acidic media.   The rate determining step in nitric acid media is a bimolecular reaction between the formic acid and HNO_2 in less than 2.5 M HNO_3 and between formic acid and NO^+ at higher concentrations of HNO_3.

The reaction between nitrous acid and hydrogen peroxide is suggested as resulting in the formation of a nitrosyl peroxide.[98]   The following sequence of reactions describe the process:

$$H_2O_2 + HNO_2 \rightarrow HO_2^-NO^+ + H_2O \quad \text{(nitrosyl peroxide formation)}$$
$$HO_2^-NO^+ + H^+ \rightarrow H_2O_2 + NO^+$$
$$NO^+ + H_2O_2 \rightarrow NO^+\cdot OH + OH \rightarrow NO^+(OH)_2 \rightarrow H_2O + NO_2^+$$
$$NO_2^+ + OH^- \rightleftarrows HNO_3 \rightleftarrows NO_3^- + H^+$$
$$H_2O \rightleftarrows H^+ + OH^-$$

It may be that this nitrosyl peroxide is identical to a previously described pernitrous acid [99] formed when nitrous acid and hydrogen peroxide react at low acidities.

Nitrous acid is a weak acid.   Its ionization constant has been measured conductimetrically at various temperatures: [100]

T (°C)	0	12.5	30
$K = \left(\dfrac{[H^+][NO_2^-]}{[HNO_2]} \right)$	3.2×10^{-4}	4.6×10^{-4}	6.0×10^{-4}

Because of its marked instability nitrous acid has never been prepared in the pure state.

Nitrous acid is a rapid oxidizing agent and a moderately strong one, as is indicated by the following electrode potentials:

$$NO + 2H_2O \rightarrow H_3O^+ + HNO_2 + e^- \quad E^0 = -0.99 \text{ volt}$$
$$9H_2O + NH_4^+ \rightarrow HNO_2 + 7H_3O^+ + e^- \quad E^0 = 0.86 \text{ volt}$$

[97] J. V. L. Longstaff and K. Singer, *J. Chem. Soc.* 1954, 2604, 2610.
[98] E. Abel, *Monatsh.* 83, 1111 (1952).
[99] E. Halfpenny and P. L. Robinson, *J. Chem. Soc.* 1952, 928.
[100] A. Klemenc and E. Hayek, *Monatsh.* 54, 407 (1929).

Thus it oxidizes such reducing agents as iodide, tin(II) ion, iron(II) ion, titanium(III) ion, hydrogen sulfide, thiosulfate ion, arsenous acid, and sulfur dioxide. Most of these reactions are complex and involve a number of steps. In most cases the mechanisms have not been worked out. An exception is the nitrite-hydrogensulfite reaction, discussed in a later section. One of the most valuable oxidation-reduction reactions of nitrous acid is its interaction with ammonia and ammonia derivatives. In the simplest case, it is

$$NH_3 + HNO_2(NH_4^+ + NO_2^-) \rightarrow N_2 + 2H_2O$$

Urea likewise reacts with nitrous acid to yield nitrogen:

$$CO(NH_2)_2 + 2HNO_2 \rightarrow CO_2 + 2N_2 + 3H_2O$$

but with aromatic amines such as aniline, the intermediate diazonium salt may be isolated in the cold:

$$C_6H_5NH_2 + HNO_2 + HCl \rightarrow [C_6H_5N_2]^+Cl^- + 2H_2O$$

These diazonium compounds are important intermediates in the synthesis of many valuable organic compounds.

Nitrous acid reacts quantitatively with the sulfamate [101] ion to yield nitrogen,

$$NH_2SO_3^- + HNO_2 \rightarrow N_2 + SO_4^= + H^+ + H_2O$$

and with secondary amines to produce nitroso compounds:

$$R_2NH + HNO_2 \rightarrow R_2N \cdot NO + H_2O$$

The $NO_2^- + HSO_3NH_2$ reaction yields some N_2O_3 depending upon the concentration of the NO_2^-.

Other oxidation reactions of nitrous acid or nitrites with sodium in liquid ammonia and with hydroxylamine [102] have already been discussed. The kinetics of HNO_2 as an oxidant indicate its existence as NO^+ and OH^-.[103] Nitrous acid reacts with hydrazoic acid in accordance with the following equation to produce nitrogen and nitrogen(I) oxide:

$$HN_3 + HNO_2 \rightarrow N_2O + N_2 + H_2O$$

[101] R. C. Brasted, *J. Chem. Educ.* **23**, 32 (1946); *ibid.* **28**, 442 (1951); *ibid.* **28**, 592 (1951); *Anal. Chem.* **24**, 1111 (1952); *ibid.* **25**, 221 (1953).

[102] A. A. Bothner-By and L. Friedman, *J. Chem. Phys.* **20**, 459 (1952).

[103] E. Abel, *Monatsh.* **80**, 379 (1949).

Nitrous acid may also function as a reducing agent, but only by reacting with a strong oxidizing agent, such as the permanganate ion:

$$HNO_2 + 4H_2O \rightarrow 3H_3O^+ + NO_3^- + 2e^-, \quad -0.94 \text{ volt}$$

Hydrogen peroxide likewise oxidizes nitrous acid to nitric acid at a measurable rate. The reaction with silver bromate is quantitative and is of analytical interest:

$$3H_2O + Ag^+ + BrO_3^- + 3HNO_2 \rightarrow 3H_3O^+ + 3NO_3^- + AgBr_{(s)}$$

Preparation and Properties of Nitrites. Nitrous acid forms a large series of salts which are, in general, much more stable than the free acid. Because of the weakness of nitrous acid, the nitrite ion undergoes a certain degree of hydrolysis to yield slightly alkaline solutions:

$$NO_2^- + H_2O \rightleftharpoons HNO_2 + OH^-$$

Nitrites are obtained by two general methods: (1) the reduction of nitrates, and (2) the reaction of mixtures of NO and NO_2 with metal hydroxides. The general equation for the first method can be written:

$$NaNO_3 + R \rightarrow NaNO_2 + RO$$

where R is the reducing agent. When the starting material is the sodium or potassium salt, the use of a reducing agent is not necessary, because fused sodium or potassium nitrate decomposes according to the equation:

$$2NaNO_3 \rightarrow 2NaNO_2 + O_2$$

Lead is commonly used as the reducing agent in the laboratory preparation of nitrites. Reducing agents used in larger scale operations include coke, iron, pyrite, iron(II) sulfide, iron(II) oxide, sulfur dioxide, sulfur, carbon monoxide, and a variety of other substances. The first two of these are to be preferred over the others from an industrial standpoint. In some cases the nitrate is mixed with the hydroxide or carbonate before fusion and reduction.

In the second method for the manufacture of nitrites, the mixture of NO and NO_2, corresponding to the composition N_2O_3, is allowed to react with aqueous solutions of alkali hydroxides (or carbonates) or with the solid hydroxides. The adsorbing solutions used include NaOH, KOH, Na_2CO_3, and $Ca(OH)_2$. A direct method of preparation of NH_4NO_2, is described by reacting N_2O_3 with 30% $NH_3 \cdot H_2O$.[104]

[104] K. Sasaki et al., **Japan** 5978 ('51), Oct. 8.

Alkali and alkaline-earth metal nitrites are characterized by high solubility in water and in liquid ammonia, and by a colorless or slightly yellowish appearance. Heavy metal nitrites, on the other hand, have only a slight solubility in water. The alkali and alkaline earth metal nitrites exhibit a fair degree of thermal stability and may be melted with little or no decomposition. The heavy metal nitrites are, however, much less stable. Silver nitrite, for example, in aqueous suspensions or in the is dry state decomposes reversibly in accordance with the equation:

$$2AgNO_2 \rightleftharpoons Ag^+ + NO_3^- + Ag_{(s)} + NO_{(g)}$$

Equilibrium is established only very slowly in this reaction at room temperature, but at 100°C equilibrium is established very rapidly.

The nitrites, in general, with the exception of the noble metal salts, do not readily form large crystals. Most of them, except the silver salt, are hygroscopic though they are usually low in water of crystallization; those of the alkali and noble metals generally crystallize as the anhydrous salts.

Like nitrous acid, the nitrite ion can act either as an oxidizing or reducing agent, and in alkaline solution the following electrode reaction occurs:

$$7OH^- + NH_3 \rightarrow NO_2^- + 5H_2O + 6e^-, \quad E^0 = 0.15 \text{ volt}$$

Nitrite ions can coordinate with various metal ions such as Co^{+3}, Fe^{++}, Cr^{+3}, Cu^{++}, and Pt^{++} to form complexes. Among these, the ion of the formula $[Co(NO_2)_6]^{-3}$ is one of the most important. It is interesting to note that the nitrite ion can coordinate either through the nitrogen atom or through one of the oxygen atoms. Attached in the former way the group is called a "nitro" group whereas when attached in the latter manner it is denoted as a "nitrito" group, thus:

$$M:NO_2 \qquad\qquad M:ONO$$
$$\text{nitro} \qquad\qquad\quad \text{nitrito}$$

an important phase of coordination compound isomerism involves this sort of metal-ligand attachment. Nitroso, [M(ONO)], complexes isomerize to nitrito, [M(NO_2)], complexes on standing.[105]

The structure of the nitrite ion has been investigated through the x-ray analysis of nitrite crystals and further through the study of the Raman spectrum of sodium nitrite in aqueous solution. The results of

[105] B. Adell, *Acta Chem. Scand.* **4**, 1 (1950).

these studies indicate the following triangular configuration:

$$120\text{--}130°$$

Values of 1.23 A and 116° have also been reported for the N—O distance and O—N—O angle respectively.[106] The N—O bond is intermediate in strength between the double and single bond, and the structure may be interpreted as resulting from resonance of the following type:

$$\left\{ \ddot{\text{N}}. \qquad .\ddot{\text{N}}. \quad \right\}^{-}$$
$$\left\{ -\!:\!\ddot{\text{O}}\!:\ :\!\ddot{\text{O}}\cdot, \ :\!\ddot{\text{O}}\cdot \quad .\ddot{\text{O}}\!:\!- \right\}$$

The Nitrite-hydrogensulfite Reaction. It has already been pointed out that the nitrite-hydrogensulfite reaction is one of the very few instances in which the various steps in the reduction of nitrite ion or nitrous acid have been determined. The amount and nature of the products of the nitrite-hydrogensulfite reaction are dependent upon the ratio of the reactants. A large excess of hydrogensulfite favors the formation of the corresponding nitridotrisulfate, such as slightly soluble $N(SO_3K)_3 \cdot 2H_2O$, and it has been observed that the best yields of this substance are obtained when the mole ratio of hydrogensulfite to the nitrite is 4:1 or more and when the hydrogensulfite and nitrite solutions are heated to boiling before mixing: [107]

$$NO_2^- + 4HSO_3^- \rightarrow N(SO_3)_3^{-3} + 2H_2O + SO_3^{=}$$

Free nitridotrisulfuric acid is not known, since nitridotrisulfates hydrolyze immediately in acid solution to give imidodisulfates:

$$N(SO_3)_3^{-3} + H_2O \xrightarrow{\ H_3O^+\ } HN(SO_3)_2^{=} + HSO_4^-$$

The imidodisulfates hydrolyze at a slower rate in acid solution to yield sulfamates:

$$HN(SO_3)_2^{=} + H_2O \xrightarrow{\ H_3O^+\ } H_2NSO_3^- + HSO_4^-$$

[106] G. B. Carpenter, *Acta Cryst.* **5**, 132 (1952).
[107] H. Sisler and L. F. Audrieth, *J. Am. Chem. Soc* **60**, 1947 (1938).

It is interesting to note that sulfamates, imidodisulfates, and nitrido-trisulfates may be considered to be aquo ammono sulfates.[108]

If the nitrite-hydrogensulfite reaction is allowed to occur at from -5 to $0°C$, with a much smaller excess of hydrogensulfite than that given above, and in a solution buffered with potassium acetate and acetic acid, the chief product is the hydroxylaminodisulfate ion: [109]

$$NO_2^- + 2HSO_3^- + H_3O^+ \rightarrow HON(SO_3)_2^= + 2H_2O$$

This ion hydrolyzes in steps in strong acid to yield hydroxylammonium ion:

$$HON(SO_3)_2^= + H_2O \xrightarrow{H^+} HONHSO_3^- + HSO_4^-$$
$$HONHSO_3^- + H_3O^+ \rightarrow HONH_3^+ + HSO_4^-$$

The various steps in the nitrite-hydrogensulfite reaction and the hydrolyses of the various intermediates are outlined in the diagram to follow. The reduction of nitrous acid in its simplest aspect is depicted horizontally, leading to ammonia as end product. Actual, as well as hypothetical, sulfation reactions are represented diagonally. Hydrolytic processes are represented vertically.

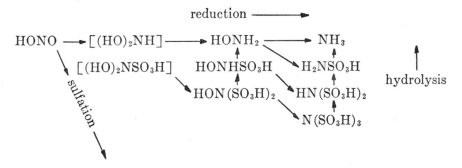

The principal credit for working out the various steps in this reaction belongs to the famous German chemist, Raschig.[110]

The Halogen Derivatives of $+3$ Nitrogen. There are two chief groups of inorganic halogen compounds of nitrogen in which that element has the oxidation state $+3$ and which can therefore be considered as derivatives of nitrous acid. The nitrosyl halides make up the first of

[108] L. F. Audrieth, M. Sveda, H. H. Sisler, and M. J. Butler, *Chem. Rev.* **26**, 49–94 (1940).

[109] G. K. Rollefson and C. F. Oldershaw, *J. Am. Chem. Soc.* **54**, 977 (1932).

[110] Schwefel- und Stickstoff Studien, *verlag Chemie. G.m.b.h.*, Leipzig-Berlin (1924).

these groups.   These compounds, already discussed in a previous section, are the acid halides of nitrous acid, as is indicated by such reactions as that of nitrosyl fluoride with water:

$$NOF + H_2O \rightarrow HNO_2 + HF$$

It is interesting to note that the nitrosyl compounds, as $NOBF_4$ and $NOClO_4$, the NO^+ group, may be considered as derived from nitrous acid acting as a base:

$$ONOH \rightleftharpoons ON^+ + OH^-$$

Of course, this ionization equation is only hypothetical, and if such ionization occurs, it is only to an exceedingly small extent.

In addition to the preparation of nitrosyl halides by the direct union of nitrogen(II) oxide with the corresponding molecular halogen, other preparative reactions are available:

$$NOCl_{(g)} + AgF_{(s)} \longrightarrow NOF_{(g)} + AgCl_{(s)}$$

$$NOBF_4 + NaF \xrightarrow{300°} NaBF_4 + NOF \; [111]$$

$$2NO_{2(g)} + KCl_{(s)} \xrightarrow{25°} KNO_{3(s)} + NOCl_{(g)} \; [112]$$

$$NOHSO_4 + HCl \rightarrow H_2SO_4 + NOCl$$

A convenient preparation of NOCl involves the action of $POCl_3$ on $NaNO_2$.   Yields up to 50% may be obtained.   The other reaction products have not been completely characterized but evidence for $NaPO_3$ and NaCl has been shown.[113]

The fluoride and chloride have a high degree of thermal stability but the bromide undergoes decomposition even at room temperature, and, of course, the iodide is not even formed.

The second group of halogen derivatives of +3 nitrogen are the trihalides, represented by the general formula NX_3.   There are three such compounds known, *viz.* NF_3, NCl_3, and NI_3, the corresponding bromine compound not having been prepared.   In addition to these substances, compounds of the formula $NI_3 \cdot nNH_3$ where $n = 1, 2, 3$, and 12 have been reported.

Nitrogen trifluoride is a colorless gas which condenses to a colorless liquid at $-119°C$ under one atmosphere pressure and solidifies at

[111] von G. Balz and E. Mailander, *Z. anorg. Chem.* **217**, 161 (1934).

[112] C. W. Whittaker, F. O. Lundstrum, and A. R. Merz, *Ind. Eng. Chem.* **23**, 1410 (1931).

[113] R. C. Brasted and C. R. Naeser, Abst. Boston Meeting, A.C.S. 1939.

−216.6°C. It differs from the chloride and iodide in that it is very stable and nonexplosive. It does not undergo hydrolysis even in solutions of alkali hydroxides, but if a mixture of NF_3 and water vapor is activated by an electric spark, reaction takes place with the evolution of a blue flame in accordance with the following reaction:

$$2NF_3 + 3H_2O \rightarrow NO + NO_2 + 6HF$$

Nitrogen trifluoride reacts explosively with hydrogen when a mixture of the two gases is activated by an electrical spark:

$$2NF_3 + 3H_2 \rightarrow N_2 + 6HF$$

Nitrogen trifluoride can be obtained by direct union of the two elements or by the reaction of fluorine with the trichloride:

$$N_2 + 3F_2 \rightarrow 2NF_3$$
$$2NCl_3 + 3F_2 \rightarrow 2NF_3 + 3Cl_2$$

The most convenient method, however, is by the electrolysis of anhydrous ammonium hydrogen fluoride. Small quantities of NHF_2 and NH_2F are formed simultaneously.

Nitrogen trichloride is a yellow, oily liquid with a strong, offensive odor which is particularly irritating to the eyes. It is an exceedingly and treacherously explosive substance. It explodes on contact with materials which it can chlorinate or on heating to 95°C. Nitrogen trichloride decomposes slowly in diffuse light with the evolution of nitrogen and chlorine. It may be kept for a time in benzene solution in the absence of light. It may be distilled if great care is exercised; it boils below 71°C and is not frozen at −40°C. It is formed almost quantitatively by the action of an excess of chlorine or hypochlorous acid with ammonium ion in an excess of strong acid:

$$4H_2O + NH_4{}^+ + 3Cl_2 \rightarrow NCl_3 + 4H_3O^+ + 3Cl^-$$

If the pH of the solution is greater than 4.4 but less than 5.0 it has been found that dichloramine, $NHCl_2$, is the chief product, and if it is greater than 8.5 only chloramine, NH_2Cl, is obtained.[114] Small amounts of NCl_3 can be conveniently prepared by the electrolysis of concentrated aqueous solutions of ammonium chloride.

When iodine is added to ammonia, usually in alcoholic or potassium iodide solution, a brown precipitate of the formula $NI_3 \cdot NH_3$ is obtained.

[114] R. M. Chapin, *J. Am. Chem. Soc.* 51, 2112 (1929).

This substance is the so-called "nitrogen tri-iodide" and, when dry, it explodes at the slightest touch. The compound of the formula NI_3 is best prepared by the action of dry ammonia on such dibromiodides as $KIBr_2$:[115]

$$3KIBr_2 + 4NH_3 \rightarrow 3KBr + 3NH_4Br + NI_3$$

Nitrogen tri-iodide, NI_3, is sometimes obtained in needle crystals which are red by transmitted light, but coppery black by reflected light. Like the trichloride, the tri-iodide is exceedingly explosive, and may be set off by the slightest touch when dry.

The contrast in stability between that of nitrogen trifluoride and the corresponding chlorine and iodine compounds is very striking, and calls for some explanation. In the first place, it should be pointed out that the endothermic character and resulting instability of NCl_3 and NI_3 as well as various other nitrogen compounds results not from any exceptional weakness of the N—Cl or N—I bond but rather from the exceedingly high stability of the multiple bond in the N_2 molecule. The energy of formation of N_2 molecules from free N atoms is so large that nitrogen compounds, unless they contain bonds of rather high energy, tend to have negative heats of formation, which is the case in nitrogen trichloride and tri-iodide. In the trifluoride, however, the bond energy of the N—F bond is large enough, because of the large amount of ionic resonance energy,[116] to give the NF_3 molecule a positive heat of formation, and, hence, to stabilize it.

NITROGEN DIOXIDE AND TETROXIDE

The two oxides, nitrogen dioxide, NO_2, and nitrogen tetroxide, N_2O_4, are always discussed together because of the rapidity and reversibility of the reaction

$$2NO_{2(g)} \rightleftharpoons N_2O_{4(g)}$$

and because, at ordinary temperatures and pressures, the equilibrium conditions are such that appreciable concentrations of both gases are present at equilibrium. In the liquid state (below 21.15°C) the nitrogen dioxide molecules are largely dimerized. At 135°C, however, the gas is 99% dissociated into NO_2 molecules.

Physical and Chemical Properties of NO_2 and N_2O_4. The important physical constants for these substances are listed in the following table.

[115] H. W. Cremer and D. R. Duncan, *J. Chem. Soc.* 2750 (1930).

[116] L. Pauling, *The Nature of the Chemical Bond*, p. 62, Cornell University Press (1940).

Those quantities listed in column A apply to the equilibrium mixture of the two oxides whereas those in columns B and C refer specifically to NO_2 and N_2O_4 respectively. The vapor pressures of the solid and liquid are represented by the following equations, respectively,

TABLE 1.9. PHYSICAL PROPERTIES OF NO_2 AND N_2O_4

	A $2NO_2 \rightleftarrows N_2O_4$	B NO_2	C N_2O_4
Melting point (°C)	−11.20	—	—
Boiling point (°C)	21.15	—	—
ΔH_f (cal/mole)	3502	—	—
ΔH_v (cal/mole)	9110	—	—
$\Delta H^0{}_{298°}$ formation (cal/mole)	—	7,964[a]	2,239
$\Delta F^0{}_{298°}$ formation (cal/mole)	—	12,275	23,440
$S^0{}_{298.1°}$ (cal/deg/mole)[b]	80.62	57.47	72.73

[a] The heat of formation at 25°C is also reported as 21.8 kcal/mole. W. E. Koerner and F. Daniels, *J. Chem. Phys.* 20, 113 (1952); see also Nat. Bur. Stand. Circular 500.

[b] W. F. Giauque and J. D. Kemp, *J. Chem. Phys.* 6, 40 (1938).

Solid, $\log_{10} p_{cm} = -2460.000/T + 9.58149 + 7.61700 \times 10^{-3}T$
$$-1.51335 \times 10^{-5}T^2$$

Liquid, $\log_{10} p_{cm} = -1753.000/T + 9.00436 - 11.8078 \times 10^{-4}T$
$$+ 2.0954 \times 10^{-6}T^2 \quad (T = \text{abs temp}).$$

Among other numerical properties of N_2O_4 are: the specific conductivity $= 1.3 \times 10^{-12}$ ohm^{-1} cm^{-1} at 17°C, the low conductivity due probably to intermolecular association; dielectric constant $= 2.42$ at 18°C; $n_D = 1.420$ at 20°C; $[P]$ (molar polarization) $= 26.5$ ml; $[R]$ (molar refraction) $= 15.2$ ml, the divergence between the molar polarization and the molar refraction probably due to ion pair formation in the N_2O_4 or $[NO^+][NO_3^-]$.[117] The heat of dissociation of N_2O_4 is reported (see also Table 1.9 above) as 10.204 kcal/mole and the heat of vaporization as being between 6740 and 8274 cal/mole.[118] A number of investigators have studied the equilibrium

$$2NO_{2(g)} \rightleftarrows N_2O_{4(g)}$$

It was found [119] that

$$K_{atm} = \frac{P^2{}_{NO_2}}{P_{N_2O_4}}$$

[117] C. C. Addison *et al.*, *J. Chem. Soc.* **1951**, 1289.
[118] E. D. Coon, *Proc. N. Dakota Acad. Sci.* **7**, 46 (1953).
[119] F. H. Verhoek and F. Daniels, *J. Am. Chem. Soc.* **53**, 1250 (1931).

is not independent of pressure because NO_2 and N_2O_4 are not perfect gases. At 25°, $K_{atm} = 0.1426 - 0.7588C°_{N_2O_4}$, where $C°_{N_2O_4}$ is equal to the concentration of N_2O_4 in moles/liter if all the NO_2 were present in that form. A consideration of the results of several investigators and making corrections to the perfect gas state leads to the following thermodynamic quantities for the equilibrium: $\Delta H°_{298°} = 13,693$ cal/mole, and $\Delta F°_{298°} = 1.110$ cal/mole (see Table 1.9, footnote a).

Nitrogen dioxide is an "odd" molecule and, therefore, contains an unpaired electron, by virtue of which this substance is paramagnetic and has an intense red-brown color. The union of two molecules of NO_2 to give a molecule of the tetroxide results in the pairing of the unpaired electrons; therefore, is diamagnetic and is colorless in the pure state.

At temperatures above 150°C nitrogen dioxide begins to dissociate into nitrogen (II) oxide and oxygen:

$$2NO_2 \rightleftharpoons 2NO + O_2$$

Studies of this equilibrium show that while there is virtually no dissociation of the dioxide at 150°C, dissociation becomes very great at temperatures above 600°C.

Not only do NO_2 molecules react with each other to form N_2O_4 molecules, but they also react with NO molecules (which are also "odd") to give N_2O_3 molecules. The two equilibria

$$NO_2 + NO_2 \rightleftharpoons N_2O_4$$
$$NO_2 + NO \rightleftharpoons N_2O_3$$

are similar in many respects.

The equilibrium mixture of NO_2 and N_2O_4 reacts with water to produce nitric acid and nitrogen (II) oxide:

$$3NO_2 + 3H_2O \rightarrow 2H_3O^+ + 2NO_3^- + NO \quad (a)$$

This reaction is, however, known to proceed in steps. The first step is

$$2NO_2 + 2H_2O \rightarrow H_3O^+ + NO_3^- + HNO_2 \quad (b)$$

However, nitrous acid, particularly in warm, strongly acidic solution, reacts in accordance with the following equation:

$$3HNO_2 \rightarrow H_3O^+ + NO_3^- + 2NO \quad (c)$$

Multiplying the equation (b) by three and adding the result to equation (c) yields the over-all process (equation (a)). The value of $\Delta F^0{}_{298°}$ for the over-all process,

$$3NO_{2(g)} + H_2O \rightleftharpoons 2HNO_{3(aq)} + NO_{(g)}$$

is -5870 calories. The process is an important step in the manufacture of nitric acid and is usually carried out in the presence of oxygen. The oxygen reacts with nitrogen(II) oxide to give nitrogen dioxide and displaces the equilibrium still further to produce HNO_3. Furthermore, the nitrogen dioxide thus produced can then react according to the equation to give more nitric acid and nitrogen(II) oxide, and so on.

Structure of NO_2 and N_2O_4. As has already been pointed out NO_2 is an "odd" molecule.[120] The resonating structure is given as

in which one oxygen is held by a double bond and one is held by a single bond plus a three-electron bond. The configuration of the molecule has been determined by electron diffraction.[121] These studies indicate a N—O bond distance of 1.20 A and a bond angle of $132 \pm 2°$. These values are in excellent agreement with Pauling's prediction of a N—O bond distance of 1.18 A and an O—N—O bond angle of about 140°.

The structure of the N_2O_4 molecule has been much discussed but evidence from Raman spectra, entropy measurements, and x-ray studies support a symmetrical structure of the type

with other similar resonance forms. Pauling suggested that the presence of like formal charges on adjacent atoms in this structure makes it less

[120] L. Pauling, *The Nature of the Chemical Bond*, p. 270, Cornell University Press (1940).

[121] S. Claesson, J. Donohue, and V. Schomaker, *J. Chem. Phys.* **16**, 207 (1948).

stable than the unsymmetrical structure,

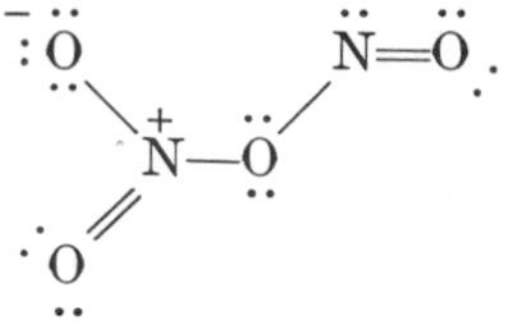

a structure which agrees well with the chemical evidence. However, C. and E. Ingold [122] have presented arguments which strongly support the symmetrical structure. X-ray studies [123] show the N_2O_4 molecule in the solid crystal to have the configuration

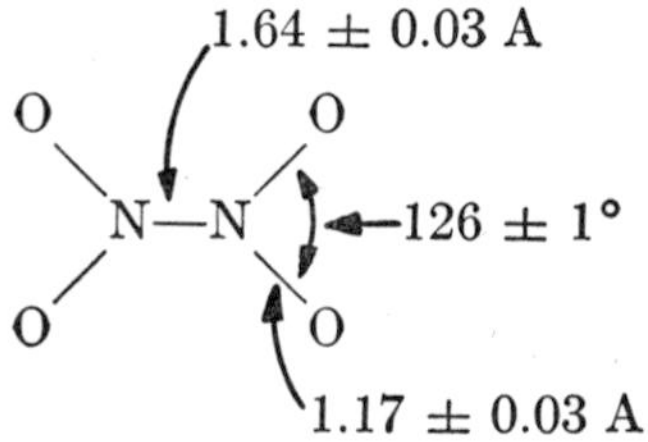

The unusually large N—N distance may be rationalized in terms of the formal positive charges on the two nitrogen atoms as indicated above.

The NO^+—NO_3^- limiting state of the structure $\overset{+\delta}{N}O$—$\overset{-\delta}{N}O_3$ is reached only under the influence of strongly polarizing agents. No abnormalities are observed in molecular weight determinations of N_2O_4 in glacial acetic acid, a result expected if there were appreciable dissociation into the nitrosyl and nitrate ions. The evidence is strong for the existence of these ions when sodium acetate is added to N_2O_4.[124]

Structure analogous to that of N_2O_4 has been suggested for N_2O_3:

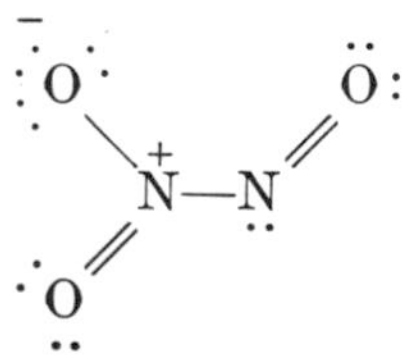

Precession and Weissenberg photographs taken at $-115°C$ show the unit cell of N_2O_3 to be tetragonal with $a = 16.4$ and $c = 8.86$ A. The unit

[122] Nature 159, 743 (1947).
[123] J. Broadley and J. Robertson, Nature 164, 915 (1949).
[124] W. R. Angus et al., Nature 164, 433 (1949).

cell contains 32 molecules and the probable space group is $D_4^{10} - I4_12$. The structure is disordered.[125]

A large number of positively charged N—O and N—O—H ions have been reported but complete characterization is lacking.[126] The existence of such ions as NO_2^+, NO^+ and others through ionization processes in HNO_3, H_2SO_4, $H_2S_2O_7$ has been extensively studied by Ingold and others [127] using physico-chemical methods.

Preparation and Applications of NO_2 and N_2O_4. The chief commercial method for the manufacture of nitrogen dioxide is by the oxidation of nitrogen (II) oxide, which is obtained by the catalytic oxidation of ammonia or by the thermal reaction of N_2 and O_2:

$$2NO + O_2 \rightarrow 2NO_2$$

It may be obtained in the laboratory by the reaction of copper with concentrated nitric acid:

$$Cu + 4H^+ + 2NO_3^- \rightarrow Cu^{++} + 2NO_2 + 2H_2O$$

or by the thermal decomposition of heavy metal nitrates:

$$2Pb(NO_3)_2 \rightarrow 2PbO + 4NO_2 + O_2$$

The chief commercial application of this oxide is as an intermediate in the production of nitric acid.

Metal oxides react with liquid N_2O_4 to form either normal anhydrous nitrates or nitrate-NO_2 addition compounds. Oxides prepared at higher temperatures are much less reactive toward N_2O_4 than are those prepared at lower temperatures. Among NO_2 addition products which have been prepared are $Mg(NO_3)_2 \cdot NO_2$, $Zn(NO_3)_2 \cdot 2.6–3.3NO_2$, $Cu(NO_3)_2 \cdot 2NO_2$ and $Hg(NO_3)_2 \cdot 2NO_2$. These addition compounds decompose to the anhydrous nitrates at low pressures and at temperatures ranging between 90 to 140°C. The zinc compound is actually a mixture of $Zn(NO_3)_2 \cdot 2N_2O_4$ and $Zn(NO_3)_2$. The $Zn(NO_3)_2 \cdot 2N_2O_4$ is intermediate in stability between the copper and the mercury compounds. An abnormal behavior is observed between N_2O_4 and Cu_2O. A voluminous, jade-green microcrystalline solid is formed when the two interact. The most unstable of the Groups IB and IIB—NO_2-addition compounds is $Hg(NO_3)_2 \cdot 2NO_2$.[128]

[125] T. B. Reed and W. N. Lipscomb, *Acta Cryst.* **6**, 781 (1953).

[126] M. Bargalló, *Ciencia* (Mex.) **13**, 257 (1954).

[127] C. K. Ingold *et al.*, *J. Chem. Soc.* **1950**, 2576; G. C. Whitnack, *Anal. Chem.* **23**, 464 (1951); see also N_2O_5 structure, this volume.

[128] J. R. Ferraro and G. Gibson, *J. Am. Chem. Soc.* **75**, 5747 (1953); C. C. Addison *et al.*, *J. Chem. Soc.* **1951**, 2829.

NITRIC ACID, ITS ANHYDRIDE, ACID HALIDE, AND SALTS

Dinitrogen Pentoxide (Nitrogen (V) Oxide). The anhydride of nitric acid, a substance having the molecular formula N_2O_5, is a white, volatile, crystalline solid at room temperature. The substance sublimes under atmospheric pressure at 32.4°C. The vapor pressures of the solid at various temperatures are given by the equation: $\log_{10} p_{mm} = \dfrac{1244}{T}$ $+ 34.1 \log_{10} T - 85.929$, where $T =$ abs. temperature. ΔH^0 for this process is 13,800 cal/mole.

Two convenient methods for the preparation of dinitrogen pentoxide are available. The first involves the dehydration of 100% nitric acid by phosphorus (V) oxide. When a pasty mixture of these two substances is heated to 35–40°C nitrogen pentoxide distills out of the system:

$$2HNO_3 + P_2O_5 \xrightarrow{\text{35–40°C}} N_2O_{5(g)} + 2HPO_3$$

The product may be purified by sublimation in ozonized air in the presence of P_2O_5. The second method consists in the reaction of nitrogen dioxide with ozone. This reaction takes place rapidly and completely in accordance with the equation:

$$2NO_2 + O_{3(g)} \rightarrow N_2O_5 + O_2$$

Another interesting reaction which yields dinitrogen pentoxide is that of chlorine with solid silver nitrate. Nitryl chloride, NO_2Cl, is formed, which then reacts with excess nitrate to give the pentoxide:

$$NO_2Cl + AgNO_3 \rightarrow N_2O_5 + AgCl$$

The pentoxide cannot be obtained synthetically from the lower nitrogen oxides, however, because of its instability.

Gaseous dinitrogen pentoxide exists as N_2O_5 molecules. Electron

diffraction indicates the N—O—N angle in to be

180°. This oxide exists also in the molecular form in such solvents as phosphorus oxychloride, carbon tetrachloride, chloroform, and nitromethane.   Raman,[129] infared,[130] and x-ray crystal studies on the solid[131] show that solid N_2O_5 consists of NO_2^+ and NO_3^- ions.   The N—O distance is 1.15 A in NO_2^+ and 1.24 A in NO_3^-.   The space groups is $D^4{}_{6h} - C6/mmx$, $a = 5.41$ and $c = 6.57$ A at 20°C.[132]   Raman spectra also indicate that solutions of N_2O_5 in sulfuric acid, nitric acid, and phosphoric acid also contain NO_2^+ and NO_3^- ions.[133]

Crystals of nitrogen(V) oxide are hygroscopic, and dissolve readily in water to form nitric acid.   The pentoxide is a strong oxidizing agent and reacts with such reducing agents as metals and various organic substances.   In some cases these reactions are violent.   One of the most interesting chemical properties of nitrogen(V) oxide, however, is its instability.   Even at room temperature the substance slowly breaks down into nitrogen dioxide and oxygen:

$$N_2O_{5(g)} \rightarrow 2NO_2 + \tfrac{1}{2}O_2$$

The study of the kinetics of this reaction has played an important part in the development of the theory of homogeneous reactions, for the decomposition is first order as the following rate equation indicates:

$$-\frac{d[N_2O_5]}{dt} = k[N_2O_5]$$

The mechanism usually proposed for this decomposition is the following:

(1) $\qquad N_2O_5 \rightarrow N_2O_3 + O_2$ (Slow, rate determining)

(2) $\qquad N_2O_3 \rightleftharpoons NO + NO_2$ (Rapid)

(3) $\quad N_2O_5 + NO \rightarrow 3NO_2$ (Rapid)

It is well known that steps (2) and (3) do take place rapidly.   Reaction (3) has been reported as first order; however, at pressures in the order of 1 mm the reaction is second order.   Rate constants and efficiencies vary depending upon admixed gases.   The relative efficiency increases with the molecular weight of monatomic gases (rare gases), and continues to increase on going from rare gases to heavier diatomic and polyatomic gases.   Nitrogen pentoxide itself is the most efficient gas of all.[134]

[129] J. Chedin and J. Pradier, *Compt. rend.* **203,** 722 (1936); D. Millen, *J. Chem. Soc.* **1950,** 2606.

[130] R. Teranishi and J. C. Decius, *J. Chem. Phys.* **22,** 896 (1954).

[131] W. Angus *et al., Nature* **164,** 433 (1949).

[132] E. Grison *et al., Acta Cryst.* **3,** 290 (1950).

[133] See also discussion of NO_2^-.

[134] D. J. Wilson and H. S. Johnston, *J. Am. Chem. Soc.* **75,** 5763 (1953).

Preparation of Nitric Acid.   There are two chief methods by which nitric acid is obtained on an industrial scale.   The older of these involves the reaction of sodium nitrate (Chile saltpeter) with concentrated sulfuric acid.   When a mixture of these two substances is heated in a cast-iron retort, nitric acid distills out of the mixture and is condensed by a silica glass condenser and collected in glass containers:

$$NaNO_{3(s)} + H_2SO_{4(l)} \rightarrow NaHSO_{4(s)} + HNO_{3(g)}$$

The second method involves a reaction which has already been discussed:

$$3NO_{2(g)} + H_2O_{(l)} \rightleftharpoons 2HNO_{3(aq)} + NO_{(g)}$$

Since increasing the concentration of HNO_3 increases the tendency for the above reaction to be reversed, the ratio of the partial pressure of $NO_2(N_2O_4)$ to that of NO required to permit high concentrations of nitric acid to be obtained is such that inconveniently high partial pressures of $NO_2(N_2O_4)$ are required.   This difficulty is overcome by mixing oxygen with the nitrogen dioxide passed into the water.   The oxygen shifts the equilibrium by oxidizing the nitrogen(II) oxide to NO_2.   Since this process is slow, a high concentration of nitric acid is sometimes obtained by passing the NO_2—O_2 mixture into the water under pressure.   Another method for obtaining concentrated nitric acid is by the distillation of dilute solution of nitric acid with concentrated sulfuric acid.   A constant boiling mixture, containing 68.4% HNO_3 and having a boiling point of 121.9°C, is obtained if dilute nitric acid solutions are distilled alone at atmospheric pressure.   Nitric acid which has been saturated with nitrogen dioxide is red in color and is called *fuming* nitric acid.

Physical and Chemical Properties of Nitric Acid.   Absolutely pure nitric acid is a colorless liquid which begins to boil at 86°C under atmospheric pressure (at 35°C under 20 mm), but the boiling point then begins to rise because of the decomposition of the acid.   The pure acid forms colorless crystals which melt at -41.59°C; [135] the liquid has a density at 25°C of 1.50269 g/ml.   The pure liquid acid has a vapor pressure at 25°C of about 60 mm.

On exposure to light or upon heating, 100% nitric acid undergoes reversible decomposition according to the equation:

$$2HNO_3 \rightleftharpoons H_2O + 2NO_2 + \tfrac{1}{2}O_2$$

The equilibrium constant for the above reaction (all substances in the

---

[135] -41.62 ± 0.05 reported by W. J. Dunning and C. W. Nutt, *Trans. Faraday Soc.* **47**, 15 (1951).

gaseous state) is 6.90×10^{-5} at room temperature, so the extent of decomposition is not great. The constant is much larger at higher temperatures, however, being 4.85×10^2 at about 223°C. Pure liquid HNO_3 is reported as dissociating according to the following equilibria: [136]

$$2HNO_3 \rightleftarrows H_2O + N_2O_5$$
$$N_2O_5 \rightleftarrows NO_2^+ + NO_3^-$$
$$HNO_3 + H_2O \rightleftarrows H_3O^+ + NO_3^-$$

and as noted below (for aqueous solutions) the pure substance possibly undergoes the dissociation represented by

$$2HNO_3 \rightleftarrows H_2NO_3^+ + NO_3^-$$

Nitric acid is miscible with water in all proportions and in dilute aqueous solution behaves as a strong acid according to the equation:

$$HNO_3 + H_2O \rightarrow H_3O^+ + NO_3^-$$

Such solutions exhibit all the properties which are characteristic of strong acids. In concentrated solutions the extent of dissociation is much less. In moderately concentrated aqueous solutions there is evidence for the presence of nitronium ions formed in accordance with the equation:

$$2HNO_3 \rightleftarrows \frac{H_2O_3N^+}{(NO_2 \cdot H_2O^+)} + NO_3^-$$

From Raman frequencies, molar intensities and degree of polarization of HNO_3 over the concentration range 0.87 to 24 mole/l, complexes of the type $HNO_3 \cdot nH^+$ and $NO_3^- \cdot nH^+$ are postulated. Values of n may vary from 0 to 3. The equilibrium constant for the pseudo acid, $HNO_3 \cdot nH^+$ is given as 1.7.[137] A similar basic function is exhibited in its reaction with very strong acids such as perchloric [138] in concentrated solutions:

$$HClO_4 + HNO_3 \rightarrow H_2O_3N^+ + ClO_4^-$$
nitronium perchlorate

The number of kinetically separated dissolved particles formed when nitric acid (one mole) is added to sulfuric acid as a solvent have been reported as a v factor.[139] Equations representing the dissociation of nitric

[136] W. J. Dunning and C. W. Nutt, *Trans. Faraday Soc.* 47, 15 (1951).
[137] H. Renner and O. Theimer, *Acta Phys. Austriaco* 6, 78 (1952).
[138] R. J. Gillespie and J. Graham, *J. Chem. Soc.* 1950, 2532.
[139] R. J. Gillespie *et al.*, *J. Chem. Soc.* 1950, 2504.

acid in sulfuric acid are as follows:

$$\begin{aligned}
&&&&v\ factor\\
HNO_3 + 2H_2SO_4 &\rightarrow NO_2^+ + H_3O^+ + 2HSO_4^- &&\ldots\ldots\ldots\ldots\ldots\ldots\ldots\ldots &3.77\\
N_2O_5 + 3H_2SO_4 &\rightarrow 2NO_2^+ + H_3O^+ + 3HSO_4^- &&\ldots\ldots\ldots\ldots\ldots\ldots\ldots\ldots &5.70\\
N_2O_4 + 3H_2SO_4 &\rightarrow NO_2^+ + NO^+ + H_3O^+ + 3HSO_4^- &&\ldots\ldots\ldots\ldots\ldots &5.69\\
N_2O_3 + 3H_2SO_4 &\rightarrow 2NO^+ + H_3O^+ + 3HSO_4^- &&\ldots\ldots\ldots\ldots\ldots\ldots\ldots\ldots &5.69
\end{aligned}$$

The molecular species NO_2HSO_4 and $NOHSO_4$ are both reported as having solvation numbers of 2. The pK for the ionization of 0.025 M HNO_3 in sulfuric acid (90 per cent) is 11.59.[140]

The phase diagram for the system water-nitric acid has been determined.[141] This diagram (Fig. 1.5) indicates that nitric acid forms two

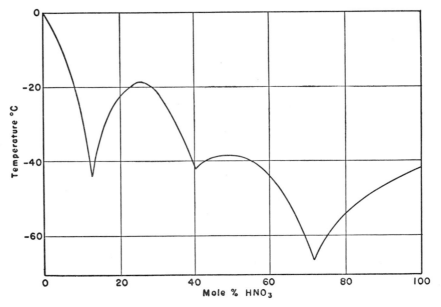

Fig. 1.5.   The system H_2O—HNO_3.

hydrates: $HNO_3 \cdot H_2O$, colorless, opaque crystals which melt at $-37.68°C$, and $HNO_3 \cdot 3H_2O$, large, transparent crystals which melt at $-18.47°C$. The formation of these two hydrates is also reflected in other physical properties of nitric acid solutions, such as electrical conductivity of nitric acid at various dilutions, and expansion of solutions of various concentrations upon heating. Existence of a dimer hydrate, $2HNO_3 \cdot 3H_2O$, has been confirmed.[142] The molecules of nitric acid are held together by

[140] T. G. Bonner and G. Williams, *Chemistry & Industry* **1951**, 820.
[141] F. N. Küster and R. Kremann, *Z. anorg. Chem.* **41**, 1 (1904).
[142] T. G. Berg, *Acta Chem. Scand.* **8**, 374 (1954); **7**, 1045 (1953).

hydrogen bonds. It has been postulated that in the monohydrate, $HNO_3 \cdot H_2O$, there exists an N—O bond that may strengthen into a valence bond to give an ortho acid, H_3NO_4. Liquid $HNO_3 \cdot H_2O$ and pure HNO_3, however, show the same infrared spectrum. Below 2000 cm^{-1} the spectrum of crystallized $HNO_3 \cdot H_2O$ is different from that of the liquid form of the same substance. Bands at 738, 815, and 1381 cm^{-1} may be attributed to the nitrate ion. The crystal is pseudo-hexagonal. The NO_3^- groups are flat and arranged in parallel layers with the oxygen atoms of water molecules.[143] Thermodynamic properties of nitric acid and its hydrates [144] are listed in Table 1.10.

TABLE 1.10. THE THERMODYNAMIC PROPERTIES OF NITRIC ACID
AND ITS HYDRATES

	HNO_3	$HNO_3 \cdot H_2O$	$HNO_3 \cdot 3H_2O$
Mp (°C)	−41.59	−37.68	−18.47
ΔH fusion (cal/mole)	2503	4184	6954
ΔH vap. at 20°C (cal/mole)	9426	—	—
Heat capacity (cal/deg/mole)			
−53.1°C	15.82 (s)	19.81 (s)	35.51 (s)
−33.1°C	26.70 (l)	43.02 (l)	38.67
−13.1°C	26.59	43.32	74.99 (l)
6.9°C	26.42	43.48	76.72
26.9°C	26.24	43.62	77.80
ΔH of infinite diln. (cal/mole)	−7971	−4732	−2132
Entropy of liquid at 298.1°K (cal/deg/mole)	37.19	51.84	82.93
Entropy of gas at 298.1°K (cal/deg/mole)	63.62	—	—

$\Delta H^0_{298.1°} = -41,349$ cal/mole, $\Delta F^0_{298.1°} = -19,030$ cal/mole for HNO_3(l)
$\Delta H^0_{298.1°} = -31,994$ cal/mole, $\Delta F^0_{298.1°} = -17,948$ cal/mole for HNO_3(g)
$\Delta H^0_{298.1°} = -49,320$ cal/mole, $\Delta F^0_{298.1°} = -26,345$ cal/mole for HNO_3 (aq, a = 1)

The chemical reactions of nitric acid may be grouped under three headings: (a) *acid-base reactions*, (b) *oxidation-reduction reactions*, and (c) *substitution reactions*. As far as the first of these groups is concerned it may be noted simply that nitric acid behaves as a typical strong acid and gives the reactions to be expected of such a substance.

In the second classification is placed the large number of reactions in which nitric acid acts as an *oxidizing agent*. The oxidizing power of nitric acid as well as the variety of reduction products obtained from this acid are indicated by the following half equations and the corresponding

[143] D. E. Bethell and N. Sheppard, *J. chim. phys.* 50, C72-4 (1953).
[144] W. R. Forsythe and W. V. Giauque, *J. Am. Chem. Soc.* 64, 48 (1942); G. L. Wilson and F. D. Miles, *Trans. Faraday Soc.* 36, 356 (1940).

standard electrode potentials (25°C):

$$E^0$$

$$H_2O + NO_2 \rightarrow NO_3^- + 2H^+ + e^- \dots\dots\dots -0.81$$
$$H_2O + HNO_2 \rightarrow NO_3^- + 3H^+ + 2e^- \dots\dots\dots -0.94$$
$$2H_2O + NO \rightarrow NO_3^- + 4H^+ + 3e^- \dots\dots\dots -0.96$$
$$5H_2O + N_2O \rightarrow 2NO_3^- + 10H^+ + 8e^- \dots\dots\dots -1.11$$
$$3H_2O + \tfrac{1}{2}N_2 \rightarrow NO_3^- + 6H^+ + 5e^- \dots\dots\dots -1.24$$
$$2H_2O + NH_3OH^+ \rightarrow NO_3^- + 8H^+ + 6e^- \dots\dots\dots -0.73$$
$$6H_2O + N_2H_5^+ \rightarrow 2NO_3^- + 17H^+ + 14e^- \dots\dots\dots -0.84$$
$$3H_2O + NH_4^+ \rightarrow NO_3^- + 10H^+ + 8e^- \dots\dots\dots -0.87$$

A comparison of these potentials with those for nitrous acid indicates that nitric acid is the stronger oxidizing agent of the two. Nitrous acid, however, acts more rapidly. The reaction of nitric acid with pure metals such as copper and silver is slow at first but, once started, continues vigorously. This induction period may be avoided by dissolving a small amount of $NO_2(N_2O_4)$ in the mixture. Furthermore, fuming nitric acid is especially rapid in its action. These facts have lead many chemists to conclude that the mechanism of oxidation of metals by nitric acid involves nitrous acid:

$$N_2O_4 + 2H_2O \rightarrow H_3O^+ + NO_3^- + HNO_2$$
$$Cu + 2HNO_2 + 2H_3O^+ \rightarrow Cu^{++} + 2NO + 4H_2O$$
$$4H_3O^+ + 4NO_3^- + 2NO \rightleftharpoons 3N_2O_4 + 6H_2O$$

The extent of the last reaction depends upon the concentration of the nitric acid. If the acid is dilute, NO is the chief product of the reaction; in concentrated acid, however, the equilibrium is shifted in favor of the formation of $NO_2(N_2O_4)$. This postulated mechanism does not make any provision for the explanation of reduction products such as NH_4^+, NH_3OH^+, $H_2N_2O_2$, N_2, and other compounds of nitrogen such as are obtained with the more vigorous reducing agents as zinc.[145] Further study of this problem is indicated. It is a well-known fact, however, that with a wide variety of reducing agents of moderate strength (metal sulfides, hydrogen sulfide, copper, silver, lead, etc.) the chief reduction product of dilute nitric acid is NO, whereas the concentrated acid yields chiefly $NO_2(N_2O_4)$.

The reactions of mixtures of strong aqueous solutions of nitric and hydrochloric acids with gold and platinum (unaffected by nitric acid alone) are of interest. These metals dissolve readily in this mixture. This fact may not be interpreted as indicating that the mixture of acids has a stronger oxidation potential than nitric acid alone, but rather that the presence of high concentrations of chloride ion increases the solution

[145] A. M. Leko and S. O. Radosavljevic, *Bull. soc. chim. Belgrade* **14**, 47 (1949).

potential of the metal because of its ability to form chloride complexes. Furthermore, the nitrosyl chloride present in the HCl—HNO_3 mixture apparently catalyzes the reactions:

$$4H_3O^+ + 3Cl^- + NO_3^- \leftrightharpoons NOCl + Cl_2 + 6H_2O$$

Mixtures of hydrochloric and nitric acids are commonly called *aqua regia*.

Nitric acid undergoes many *substitution reactions*, several of which are of great industrial importance. For example, nitric acid reacts with aromatic hydrocarbons to form nitro compounds. All these reactions which take place in the liquid phase are catalyzed by Lewis acids, such as concentrated sulfuric acid or boron trifluoride. It is believed that the acid catalyst activates the nitric acid molecule so as to actually produce or at least make potentially available nitryl ions, NO_2^+, and that these ions attack the benzene ring to displace protons:

$$HONO_2 + A \rightarrow A:OH^- + NO_2^+$$
$$NO_2^+ + C_6H_6 \rightarrow C_6H_5NO_2 + H^+$$
$$A:OH^- + H^+ \rightarrow A + HOH$$

(A = Electron acceptor, *i.e.*, a Lewis Acid)

The reaction of toluene to produce trinitrotoluene (T.N.T.) is an example of such a reaction. When such nitration reactions take place in the vapor phase, however, it is believed that a free radical mechanism is involved.

Nitric acid also undergoes substitution reactions with alcohols to produce esters of nitric acid. An important example of this sort of reaction is the esterification of glycerol to produce the explosive glyceryl trinitrate (commonly, but incorrectly, called nitroglycerine):

$$C_3H_5(OH)_3 + 2HONO_2 \rightleftharpoons C_3H_5(ONO_2)_3 + 3H_2O$$

Nitrates. Nitrates may be classified into two groups, (a) covalent nitrates and (b) ionic nitrates. The first group includes the organic esters of nitric acid which may be represented by the general formula $RONO_2$ as well as the explosive gas fluorine nitrate, $FONO_2$. In addition to the general characteristics of covalent molecular substances, the covalent nitrates are characterized by a much lower stability than the ionic nitrates. The explanation for this phenomenon is considered in the next section.

The ionic nitrates include chiefly the salts of nitric acid. Since this acid is a strong one, the nitrate ion undergoes no appreciable hydrolysis in aqueous solution, and the salts may, in general, be easily prepared by the usual reactions of acid with metals, metal oxides, or carbonates. One limitation is that the oxidizing property of the nitric is such as to make difficult the preparation of nitrates of cations which are strong reducing agents.

All known metal nitrates dissolve readily in water. A few nitrates of complex ions have limited solubility in water. The least soluble of all nitrates is that of the complex organic base:

$$C_6H_5N \underline{\hspace{3cm}} N$$

$$N-C_6H_5$$

$$HC \qquad\qquad C$$

$$N$$

$$C_6H_5$$

This base is commonly called "Nitron" and may be used for the quantitative precipitation of nitrates. In general, the solubility of nitrates in water increases with increasing temperature.

The thermal decomposition of the various nitrates is of some interest. Ammonium nitrate yields water and nitrogen (I) oxide. The light-metal nitrates yield the corresponding nitrites plus oxygen, whereas the heavy-metal nitrates yield the metal oxide, nitrogen dioxide, and oxygen. The molten nitrates are strong oxidizing agents. Neutral or alkaline aqueous solutions of the nitrate ion are much poorer oxidizing agents than is nitric acid.

Structure of Nitric Acid and Nitrates. The results of spectroscopic and electron diffraction investigations of nitric acid, as well as entropy considerations, have led to the following coplanar structure for the HNO$_3$ molecule:

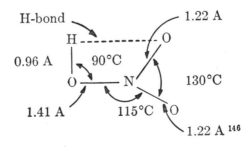

[146] L. R. Maxwell and V. M. Mosely, *J. Chem. Phys.* **8**, 738 (1940).

Electron diffraction investigation of gaseous fluorine nitrate has lead to the assignment of the following structure:

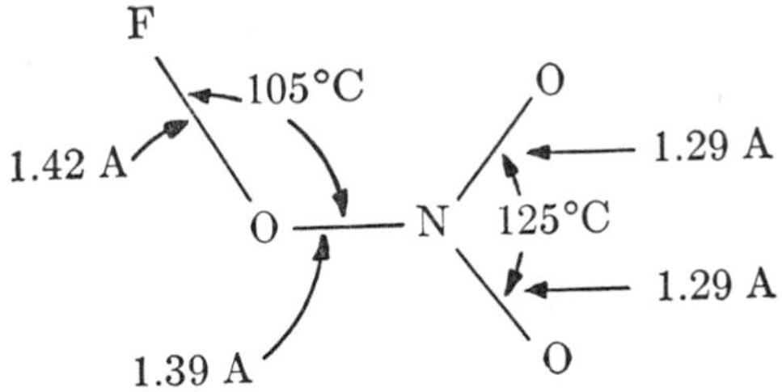

Studies of the structure of the nitrate ion indicate a symmetrical coplanar configuration in which the N to O bond distance is 1.21 ± 0.01 A.[147]

The electronic structure of the nitrate ion may be considered to consist chiefly of resonance among the three equivalent structures of the type:

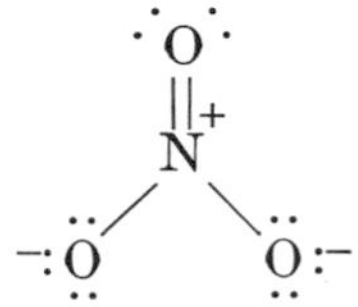

The stability of ionic nitrates arises at least partially from the resonance energy resulting from the interaction of these three equivalent structures. In the covalent nitrates, the resonance of the double bond is restricted to two of the three oxygen atoms,

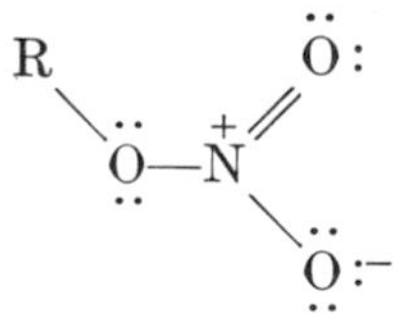

and ,

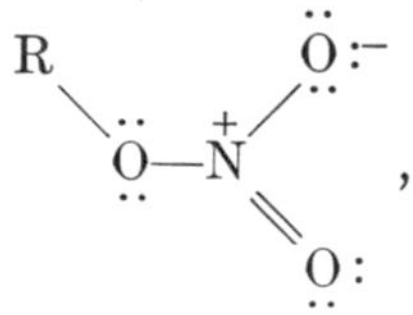

since the structure

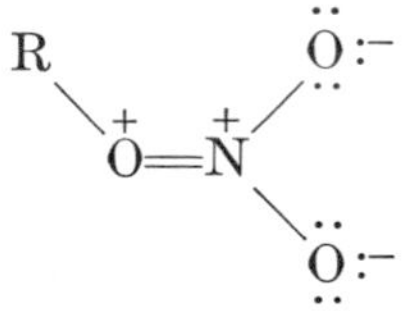

is much less stable than the first two because of the presence of like charge on adjacent atoms. The resonance energy for covalent nitrates is, therefore, considerably less (about 20,000 cal/mole) than for ionic nitrates,

[147] Norman Elliott, *J. Am. Chem. Soc.* **59**, 1380 (1937).

and as a result the latter are more stable.   Similar considerations apply to the covalent and ionic azides.

Nitryl Halides.   Just as the nitrosyl halides, NOX, are acid halides of nitrous acid, so also are the nitryl halides, NO_2X, acid halides of nitric acid.   Of the latter compounds only two are known, NO_2F and NO_2Cl. Nitryl chloride reacts with aqueous sodium hydroxide to give a solution of sodium nitrite and sodium hypochlorite.   Likewise it reacts with gaseous ammonia and liquid ammonia to yield chloramine and ammonium nitrite.[148]   These facts are in accord with the suggestion that in nitryl chloride, the nitryl group is either negative or only slightly positive with the chlorine being either only very slightly negative or else positive in polarity.   The fluoride has been obtained by the reaction of nitrogen(II) oxide with fluorine:

$$4NO + F_2 \rightarrow 2NO_2F + N_2$$

Both nitryl fluoride and nitrosyl fluoride have been prepared in high yields (90%) by the vapor-liquid fluorination of NO_2 and NO respectively.   The reaction is reported to be smooth in each case.[149]   A mechanism for the $NO_2 - F_2$ reaction is proposed as proceeding, first as $NO_2 + F_2 \rightarrow NO_2 + 2F$ (slow, rate determining) and then $NO_2 + F + M \rightarrow NO_2F + M$, where M represents a molecule of any one of the species present.[150]

Nitryl chloride may be converted to the corresponding fluoride, NO_2F, in small yields by the action of AgF on NO_2Cl in the presence of platinum at 240°C.   The reaction between dry HF, BF_3 and N_2O_5 in ethyl nitrite as a solvent results in the formation of NO_2BF_4.   The last mentioned compound decomposes at 240°C in presence of platinum and NaF to give NO_2F.[151]   The chloride has resisted all attempts to prepare it by the reaction of nitrogen dioxide and chlorine.   A number of other methods for preparing nitryl chloride have been worked out, however, including the reaction of nitrosyl chloride with ozone,

$$NOCl + O_3 \rightarrow NO_2Cl + O_2$$

and the reaction of 100% nitric acid with chlorosulfonic acid:

$$HNO_3 + ClSO_3H \rightarrow NO_2Cl + H_2SO_4$$

Both NO_2F and NO_2Cl are colorless gases at room temperature.   The

[148] H. Sisler and H. Batey, *J. Am. Chem. Soc.* **74**, 3408 (1952).
[149] A. V. Faloon and W. B. Kenna, *J. Am. Chem. Soc.* **73**, 2937 (1951).
[150] R. L. Perrine and H. S. Johnston, *J. Chem. Phys.* **21**(12), 2202 (1953).
[151] M. Schmeisser and S. Elischer, *Z. Naturforsch.* **7b**, 583 (1952).

fluoride melts at $-166°C$ and boils at $-72.4°C$ at atmospheric pressure; the chlorine compound melts at $-145°C$ and has a normal boiling point of $-15.9°C$.

The NO_2 group in nitryl chloride is probably (see above) considerably less positive in character than the NO group in nitrosyl chloride. The formation of nitryl perchlorate, NO_2ClO_4, as a white solid of low vapor pressure, has been reported to occur when ozone, oxides of nitrogen, and chlorine dioxide are allowed to react.[152] The substance hydrolyzes to yield nitric and perchloric acids as would be predicted on the basis of the assumption of a positive NO_2 group in NO_2ClO_4:

$$NO_2ClO_4 + H_2O \rightarrow HNO_3 + HClO_4$$

The existence of the nitryl ion, NO_2^+, in the system $HNO_3 - SO_3$ has been proven by Raman spectra investigations.[153] In a $2:1$ mixture of HNO_3 and SO_3, a symmetrical vibration at 1402 cm^{-1} indicates the NO_2^+ ion. Replacing SO_3 by the isosteric molecule, BF_3, leads to the formation of an addition compound, $BF_3 \cdot HNO_3$. There is no evidence of the nitryl ion in this system. In solid $N_2O_5 \cdot 3SO_3$ and $N_2O_4 \cdot 3SO_3$ the NO_2^+ ion is certain and suggests that these substances should be written as $[(NO_2^+)_2S_3O_{10}]^=$ and $[NO^+ \cdot NO_2^+]S_3O_{10}^=$. The Raman line at 2308 cm^{-1} is characteristic of the nitrosyl ion, NO^+.[154]

An anomaly appears to exist with regard to the hydrolysis of NO_2Cl in contrast to its reactions. Hydrolysis studies indicate that it may be written as NO^+OCl^-, or a nitrosyl hypochlorite.[155] The reaction between NO_2Cl and Me_4NN_3, however, gives no indication of the former acting as a nitrosyl compound. The hypochlorite ion is extremely sensitive to the azide ion forming nitrogen, N_2O, and the chloride ion. The products illustrated by the following

$$2NO_2Cl + Me_4NN_3 \rightarrow Me_4NNO_3 + N_2 + N_2O + Cl_2$$

are attributed to the primary decomposition of NO_2Cl to N_2O_4 and chlorine, followed by a reaction of N_2O_4 with N_3^- rather than OCl^- with N_3^-. The assumption, then, based on the above reaction is that the NO_2Cl is a chloride of nitric acid and not a hypochlorite of NO^+.

Nitryl chloride reacts quantitatively with NO according to the equation
$$NO_2Cl + NO \rightarrow NO_2 + NOCl$$

[152] W. E. Gordon and J. W. T. Spinks, *Can. J. Research* 18, Sec. B, 358 (1940).
[153] H. Gerding *et al.*, *J. phys. radium* 15, 406 (1954).
[154] See also, C. K. Ingold *et al.*, *J. Chem. Soc.* 1950, 2576, 2589, 2600, 2606, 2612, 2620.
[155] F. Seel and J. Nograth, *Z. anorg. u. allgem. Chem.* 269, 188 (1952).

The kinetics have been investigated and the reaction is a homogeneous first order one with respect to each of the reactants. The second order rate constant is expressed by the equation $k = 0.83 \times 10^{12} \exp(-6900/RT)$ ml/mole sec. The mechanism proposed is elementary bimolecular.[156]

Comparisons between NO_2^+ and its isoster CO_2 (as well as other triatomic molecules) have been made.[157] The structures of all the substances CO_2, NO_2^+, N_3^-, and CS_2 have been confirmed as linear by the method of linear combinations of atomic orbitals. The order of giving off an atom, as in destruction or substitution, is N_3^-, NO_2^-, CO_2; the order of opening a bond is NO_2^+, CS_2, N_3^-, CO_2; and the order of positive attack on a molecule is NO_2^+, CO_2.

Nitryl chloride reacts with antimony(V) chloride in liquid chlorine to form the compound $NO_2Cl \cdot SbCl_5$. This compound may be considered as nitryl chloroantimonate(V). It is a thermolabile compound, easily decomposed by water and by alcohol. In liquid ammonia there is no solvolysis but the solution does conduct. Chemical evidence is presented for ionization of the compound in its reaction with Me_4NClO_4 and Me_4NBF_4. Nitryl salts are formed in both instances, forming $NO_2^+ClO_4^-$ with the former and $NO_2^+BF_4^-$ with the latter.[158] The reaction between nitryl chloride and metal halides varies depending upon the reducing nature of the halide ion. Thus, there is no reaction between $SnCl_4$ or $SiCl_4$ and NO_2Cl. The reaction with $SnBr_4$ and SnI_4 is rapid liberating the corresponding halogens, Br_2 and I_2 respectively. Ammonia reacts giving a number of oxidation products, among them $ClNH_2$, N_2H_4, NH_2NO_2 but no nitrates. Sulfur trioxide reacts violently giving a voluminous white precipitate. No reaction is observed with WO_3 or MoO_3. Likewise I_2O_5 does not react.[159]

PEROXIDES OF NITROGEN

A number of investigators have reported the production of a higher oxide of nitrogen by the action of an electrical discharge on mixtures of nitrogen dioxide and oxygen.[160] An oxide of the empirical formula NO_3 was prepared by passing a mixture of NO_2 and O_2 in the ratio $1:20$ through an electrical discharge tube at 1 mm pressure and condensing the product in a liquid air trap. The molecular formula also appears to be NO_3 judging from the spectrum and from the difficulty of condensation. The

[156] D. C. Freiling *et al.*, *J. Chem. Phys.* **20**, 327 (1952).
[157] A. Potier, *J. chim. phys.* **48**, 285 (1951).
[158] F. Seel *et al.*, *Z. anorg. u. allgem. Chem.* **269**, 197 (1952).
[159] J. H. Batey and H. H. Sisler, *J. Am. Chem. Soc.* **74**, 3408 (1952).
[160] R. Schwarz and H. Achenbach, *Ber.* **68**, 343 (1935).

oxide is stated to be unstable above about $-140°C$ and decomposes to give products which include NO_2. Apart from its condensation at liquid air temperatures, the production of high concentrations of NO_3 in the gas phase or by the direct action of ozone in N_2O_5 is not favored by equilibrium conditions. Little is known of its chemical properties, except that it liberates iodine from iodides and does not form hydrogen peroxide on hydrolysis.[161] It is reported that the formation of an oxide NO_2O—O—NO_2 takes place by the action of dinitrogen pentoxide on hydrogen peroxide. This substance was reported to yield hydrogen peroxide on hydrolysis.

Kinetic evidence has been reported for the gas-phase existence of the peroxy radicals NO_4 and NO_3.[162] Isotopic exchange between highly enriched oxygen and vapor of isotopically normal N_2O_5 was observed. The rate of exchange was not affected by the initial addition of NO_2. The mechanism proposed for the exchange and interaction of N_2O_5 and O_2 is

$$N_2O_5 \rightleftarrows NO_3 + NO_2$$
$$NO_3 + NO_2 \rightleftarrows N_2O_5$$
$$NO_2 + O_2 \rightleftarrows NO_4$$
$$NO_4 \rightleftarrows NO_2 + O_2$$
$$N^{18}O_4 + NO_3 \rightleftarrows N^{18}O_3 + NO_4$$

The NO_3 molecule refers to the structural isomer $\overset{O}{\underset{O}{N}}NO$, a molecule which has been proven to be important in the pyrolysis of N_2O_5.[163] The species NO_4 is suggested as having the peroxy structure $\overset{O}{\underset{O}{N}}NOO$.

Several reports of the formation of "pernitric" and "pernitrous" acids have been made but none of these reports has sufficient substaniation to warrant their being considered.

THE SULFIDES AND SELENIDES OF NITROGEN

The various oxygen, hydrogen, and halogen compounds of nitrogen discussed have been organized in terms of the oxidation states of nitrogen exhibited in the various compounds. Because of the distinctly different character of the sulfur compounds of nitrogen and their apparent lack of analogy with the oxygen compounds, it is considered desirable to discuss them separately in a special section.

[161] Iw. Trifonow, *Z. anorg. Chem.* **124**, 123 (1922).
[162] R. A. Ogg, *J. Chem. Phys.* **21**, 2079 (1953).
[163] See *Chem. Abs.* **41**, 5004, 7182 (1947).

Two well-defined sulfides of nitrogen have been prepared: (a) tetranitrogen tetrasulfide, N_4S_4, and (b) dinitrogen pentasulfide, N_2S_5. In addition, several different substances supposed to have the empirical formula NS_2 have been reported,[164] and the existence of N_2S_4 [165] has apparently been established.

Nitrogen Tetrasulfide. The most thoroughly investigated of these nitrogen-sulfur compounds is tetranitrogen tetrasulfide. This substance is obtained when sulfur dissolves in liquid ammonia:

$$10S + 16NH_{3(l)} \rightarrow N_4S_4 + 6(NH_4)_2S$$

$$(NH_4)_2S + xS \rightarrow (NH_4)_2S_{(x+1)}$$

These reactions are reversible, however, and in order for the reaction to go to completion the sulfide and polysulfide must be removed. This removal is accomplished by adding silver iodide (soluble in liquid ammonia) which forms insoluble precipitates of silver sulfide and polysulfide. The nitrogen sulfide is isolated by allowing the ammonia to evaporate.[166]

A second method for obtaining N_4S_4 is through the reaction of a mixture of dry air and ammonia with a mixture of sulfur dichloride (SCl_2) and benzene chilled to 0°C:

$$6SCl_2 + 16NH_3 \rightarrow N_4S_4 + 12NH_4Cl + 2S$$

After four of five hours of such treatment, the precipitate which consists of a mixture of N_4S_4, NH_4Cl, and sulfur is filtered off and the N_4S_4 extracted by benzene.[167] On recrystallization from benzene or carbon disulfide, N_4S_4 is obtained as golden yellow, monoclinic crystals which change to deep red upon heating. The compound may be obtained in high purity by sublimation at 100°C under reduced pressure. Another method for making the compound consists in the reaction of ammonia gas with a solution of sulfur monochloride (S_2Cl_2) in ether:[168]

$$6S_2Cl_2 + 16NH_3 \rightarrow N_4S_4 + 12NH_4Cl + 8S$$

Sublimed N_4S_4 has a specific gravity of 2.24 at 18°C. The crystals melt with some decomposition at 179°C. The substance burns without

[164] F. L. Usher, *J. Chem. Soc.* **127**, 730 (1925); W. Moldenhauer and A. Zimmermann, *Ber.* **62**, 2390 (1929).

[165] M. Goehring *et al.*, *Z. anorg. u. allgem. Chem.* **267**, 238 (1952); A. Meuwsen, *ibid.* **266**, 250 (1951).

[166] F. W. Bergstrom, *J. Am. Chem. Soc.* **48**, 2319 (1926).

[167] O. Ruff and E. Geisel, *Ber.* **37**, 1573 (1904); **38**, 2659 (1905).

[168] H. B. Van Valkenburgh and John C. Bailar, Jr., *J. Am. Chem. Soc.* **47**, 2134 (1925).

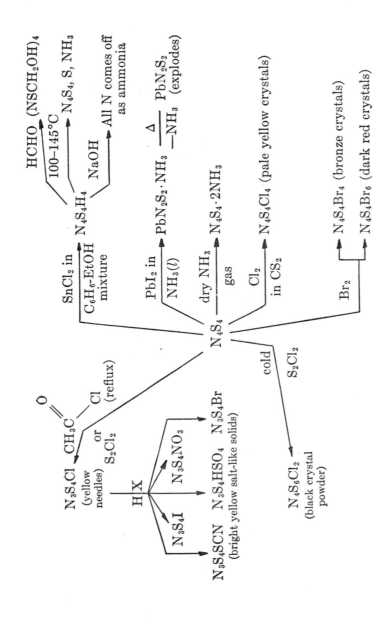

Fig. 1.6. Compounds formed from N_4S_4.

explosion but, on percussion, violent explosions often ensue.   The solid should not, therefore, be kept in glass-stoppered bottles, since explosions may be set off by the opening and closing of the bottles.

The molecular weight of N_4S_4 was determined by cryoscopic measurements in naphthalene and benzene and by ebullioscopic measurements in chloroform, benzene, and carbon disulfide.   Tetranitrogen tetrasulfide is soluble in a variety of organic solvents, and is hydrolyzed with the production of ammonium, sulfite, sulfide, and pentathionate ions; but this reaction takes place only slowly because water does not "wet" N_4S_4 crystals.   In alkaline solutions, hydrolysis takes place more rapidly, principally in accordance with the equation:

$$N_4S_4 + 6OH^- + 3H_2O \rightarrow S_2O_3^= + 2SO_3^= + 4NH_3$$

Some $S^=$ and $S_2O_6^=$ may be produced in the reaction.

The tetrasulfide forms a variety of interesting compounds, some of which are outlined in Fig. 1.6.

The structure of N_4S_4 has not been completely determined.   However, in view of its volatility, of its behavior on hydrolysis, of its diamagnetic properties, of the formation of such compounds as $N_4S_4H_4$ and $N_4S_4Cl_4$, and of their chemical properties, a cyclic structure seems plausible as at least one of the important resonance forms.[169]   Infrared data on the hydrogen derivative, $N_4H_4S_4$, also suggests the cyclic structure, cyclotetrathiotetramine.[170]

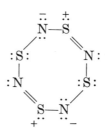

A recent x-ray diffraction study indicates that the molecule has the nonplanar configuration:

N—S = 1.60 A;   S - - - - - S = 2.58 A
S—S (linked by N) = 2.71 A
$\angle$S–N–S = 115°; $\angle$N—S—N = 102°

[169] Margot Goehring, *Chem. Ber.* **80**, 110 (1947).
[170] E. R. Lippincott and M. C. Tobin, *J. Am. Chem. Soc.* **73**, 4990 (1951).

Dinitrogen Pentasulfide. When N_4S_4 is heated in carbon disulfide solution at about 100°C for two hours, it decomposes to yield a compound of the formula N_2S_5 and the solution turns blood red. The N_2S_5 may be separated by distilling the solvent and extracting the residue with dry ether, in which N_2S_5 is soluble. Removal of the ether leaves N_2S_5 as a dark-red oil, which solidifies to gray crystals with a melting point of 11°C and which are similar to iodine in appearance and odor.[171] Dinitrogen pentasulfide undergoes gradual decomposition at room temperature, but explodes when heated. It is stable in solution if protected from the light.[172] It reacts on contact with water to produce ammonia and sulfur —a behavior in marked contrast to the reaction of the corresponding oxide, N_2O_5, which reacts with water to yield nitric acid.

Tetranitrogen Tetraselenide. A compound analogous in properties and molecular formula to N_4S_4 is obtained when selenium monochloride (Se_2Cl_2) in carbon disulfide solution is allowed to react with ammonia. This selenide is an orange-yellow, hygroscopic, very explosive, micro-crystalline mass, which is not appreciably soluble in water.[173]

[171] W. Murthmann and A. Clever, *Z. anorg. Chem.* **13**, 200 (1897); *Ber.* **29**, 340 (1896).

[172] H. B. Van Valkenburgh and John C. Bailar, Jr., *J. Am. Chem. Soc.* **47**, 2134 (1925).

[173] *Cf.* H. B. Van Valkenburgh and John C. Bailar, Jr., *loc. cit.*

CHAPTER 2

PHOSPHORUS, ARSENIC, ANTIMONY, AND BISMUTH

The general characteristics of the elements of the nitrogen family were discussed in the chapter on nitrogen and its compounds. Now is considered in some detail the elements phosphorus, arsenic, antimony, and bismuth, and their compounds.

THE ELEMENTS

It will be observed that the physical (see Table I.3) and chemical properties of the elements illustrate the trend toward increasingly metallic character with increasing atomic number within the family.

Phosphorus. The element phosphorus does not occur in appreciable quantities in nature as the free element, but occurs in large quantities in the form of metal phosphates such as rock phosphate, $Ca_3(PO_4)_2$, and apatite, $CaF_2 \cdot Ca_3(PO_4)_2$. There are a great many varieties of phosphate minerals.

Two forms of elementary phosphorus are commonly encountered in the laboratory. The first of these, white phosphorus, is obtained by heating calcium phosphate, silica (sand), and carbon (coke) in an electric furnace:

$$2Ca_3(PO_4)_2 + 6SiO_2 \rightarrow 6CaSiO_3 + P_4O_{10}$$
$$P_4O_{10} + 10C \rightarrow P_4 + 10CO$$

The phosphorus vapor is condensed under water. The second commonly encountered form, red phosphorus, is obtained by heating white phosphorus to 250°C in the absence of air. The color and vapor pressure of red phosphorus depend upon the temperature and duration of heating. It has been shown that red phosphorus, as it is commonly obtained, is not a true allotrope of phosphorus but consists rather of a mixture of white phosphorus and violet phosphorus. In general, four different true allotropic forms of phosphorus have been established. Their phase relations are indicated in Fig. 2.1, the broken lines referring to equilibria involving metastable forms. Pure violet phosphorus may be obtained by heating a solution of phosphorus in lead at 500°C for 10 hours in the absence of air, allowing the mass to cool, and then dissolving away the lead with acid. The α-form of white phosphorus is the common white form, and is obtained as described above. The β-form of white phosphorus is obtained when α-white phosphorus is cooled to below the transition temperature, −77°C. When white phosphorus is heated at 200°C under a pressure of 12,000 kg/cm², or when it is subjected at ordinary temperature to a pressure of 35,000 atmospheres, another allotrope is obtained, which is called black phosphorus. These four allotropes of phosphorus differ considerably in their chemical and physical

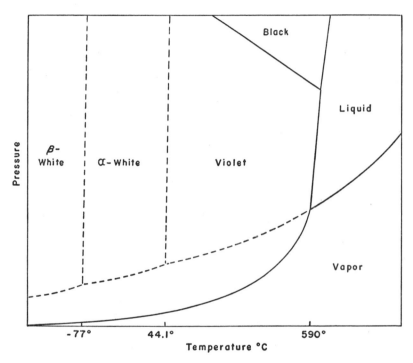

Fig. 2.1. Equilibrium diagram of phosphorus.

properties. Some of their properties are listed in Table 2.1. The white forms are probably made up of P_4 molecules, as is the case with the liquid and with the vapor up to 800°C at which temperature appreciable dissociation into P_2 and P molecules begins to take place. Very pure white phosphorus melts at 44.1°C to give a clear, colorless liquid which boils at 280.5°C. The heat of fusion of α-white phosphorus at its melting point is 601.2 cal/mole(P_4); the heat of sublimation is 13,200 cal/mole and the entropy of solid α-white phosphorus at 25°C is 40.4 cal/deg/mole(P_4). A number of investigators have shown that the molecular formula of phosphorus in organic solvents is P_4.   White phosphorus dissolves also in liquid sulfur dioxide and liquid ammonia.

A structural study on red phosphorus from which residual white phosphorus had been removed has been made.[1]   The microcrystalline or amorphous residue (which is believed to be finely divided violet phosphorus) was subjected to various types of treatment such as thermal aging and crystallization from the melt, and the products were studied by thermal analysis, x-ray diffraction, and microscopic examination.   It was shown that at least four polymorphic forms of red (violet) phosphorus exist.   Triclinic, hexagonal, and tetragonal crystals were grown from phosphorus vapor.

TABLE 2.1.   PROPERTIES OF THE ALLOTROPIC FORMS OF PHOSPHORUS

	β-white	α-white	violet	black
Crystal form	Hexagonal	Cubic	(See below)	Very similar to graphite
Density	1.8	1.85	2.3	2.7
Melting point (°C)	—	44.1°	590°	—
Reactivity	Reactive, but slightly less so than α-white	Very reactive. Ignites spontaneously in air	Considerably less reactive than α-white	Even less reactive than violet
Electrical conductivity	Nonconductor	Nonconductor	Nonconductor	Similar to graphite in conductivity
Solubility in organic solvents	—	High	Insoluble	Insoluble

The transition of white phosphorus to the ordinary red variety takes place also under the action of x-rays, or slowly under the influence of ordinary light.   This transition is catalyzed by a number of substances including iodine.

The electronic and geometrical structures of the P_4 molecule are illustrated respectively by Fig. 2.2, from which it is seen that each phosphorus atom is connected to the other three by single covalent bonds and each phosphorus atom has an unshared pair of electrons.

It is suggested[2] that *spd* bond orbitals are used to account for the relative stabilities of the P_4 molecules.   It does not seem possible for pd^2 bond hybridization to occur as has also been postulated.[3]   The bond

[1] W. L. Roth, T. W. DeWitt, and A. J. Smith, *J. Am. Chem. Soc.* **69**, 2881 (1947).

[2] L. Pauling and M. Simonetta, *J. Chem. Phys.* **20**, 29 (1952).

[3] J. R. Arnold, *J. Chem. Phys.* **14**, 351 (1946).

strain in the P_4 molecule is calculated as 22.8 kcal/mole for a 60° angle. This value is comparable with the value obtained from thermochemical data derived from hydrogenation studies. The difference in enthalpy between white (PIII) and black (stable) phosphorus is 10.3 kcal/mole. The form of white P (PIII) stable below −77°C has an enthalpy 8–9 kcal/mole greater than that of black P.[4] It is suggested that white P_4

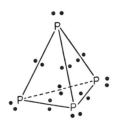 

FIG. 2.2. Electronic and geometrical structure of the P_4 molecule.

is transformed to amorphous red form by the rupture of one bond in each white P_4 tetrahedron. It is further suggested that the red form possesses terminal P atoms which may in turn be attached to other impurity-atoms such as Cl or OH. The different red forms are then explained in terms of different degrees of polymerization and different terminal impurity groups.[5]

In the white form, phosphorus is very reactive. For safety purposes it is stored under water. When it is exposed to air and moisture, it undergoes slow oxidation, part of the energy of this reaction being emitted as light; hence in the presence of air and moisture it glows in the dark. This phenomenon is known as phosphorescence ("light-bearing") whence comes the name of the element. The reactions of phosphorus with various other elements are discussed later. Ordinary red phosphorus is much less reactive than white and is stable in air at ordinary temperatures.

In addition to its use in the production of phosphorus compounds, elementary phosphorus is used in the manufacture of matches and of certain types of bronzes. During World War II large quantities of phosphorus were used in a very effective type of antipersonnel bomb and in the production of smoke screens for the concealment of ships and troops during military maneuvers.

Arsenic. Arsenic sometimes occurs in the free state but is found principally in the form of sulfide ores, such as orpiment, As_2S_3; realgar,

---

[4] See also W. E. Moffitt, *Trans. Faraday Soc.* **44**, 987 (1948).
[5] M. Ya Kraft and V. P. Parini, *Doklady Akad. Nauk S.S.S.R.* **77**, 57 (1951).

As_4S_4; and arsenopyrite, FeAsS. Almost invariably arsenic sulfides occur to some extent wherever metal sulfides are found; hence, arsenic is a common impurity in those metals which are obtained from sulfide ores.   Other arsenic minerals include audetite, As_2O_3, and metal arsenides such as $FeAs_2$, $CoAs_2$, and NiAs.

Free arsenic may be obtained by a reduction of its oxides with carbon,

$$As_4O_6 + 6C \rightarrow As_4 + 6CO$$

or from the sulfide by roasting it to the oxide and then reducing it.

Arsenic exists in two distinct crystalline modifications: (a) the gray, or metallic, arsenic which is the stable form, and (b) yellow arsenic. Metallic arsenic has a density of 5.73 g/ml and forms brittle, hexagonal crystals with a gray, metallic luster.   It is an excellent conductor of heat but its electrical conductivity is rather low.   Under atmospheric pressure, it sublimes at 610°C.   Under 36 atmospheres pressure it melts at 814°C. Gray arsenic is not affected by dry air but when heated to 200°C it exhibits a distinct phosphorescence.   At 400°C it burns with a white flame forming the sesquioxide, As_4O_6.   It takes fire in chlorine and combines, when heated, with most metals to form arsenides.   It is unaffected by hydrochloric acid in the absence of oxygen, but is oxidized by warm, dilute or concentrated nitric acid.   It reacts readily with sulfur when heated.

Yellow arsenic is obtained when arsenic vapor is chilled rapidly, as when arsenic vapor is passed into cold carbon disulfide and the solution cooled to −70°C, or when metallic arsenic is volatilized *in vacuo* and condensed by liquid air.   Yellow arsenic is extremely volatile, and sublimes even from the heat of the hand.   It has the low density of 3.9 g/ml.   The molecular weight of arsenic in a solution formed by dissolving yellow arsenic in carbon disulfide corresponds to the formula As_4.   Yellow arsenic is more reactive than metallic arsenic and phosphoresces at room temperature.   Yellow arsenic is metastable and passes rapidly into the metallic form even at low temperatures; in sunlight at room temperature the change is instantaneous.

A third, apparently amorphous, form of arsenic called black arsenic is obtained by the thermal decomposition of arsine as in the Marsh test. It is not certain that this is a distinct form.   Its properties lie between those of the other two forms.   Measurements of vapor density show that molecules of arsenic in the gaseous state are tetratomic (As_4) and at elevated temperatures begin to dissociate according to the equation:

$$As_4 \rightleftharpoons 2As_2$$

The structure of As_4 is analogous to P_4.

Antimony. Antimony occurs in nature in the free state as well as in the form of its compounds. The principal ore is stibnite, Sb_2S_3, which is obtained chiefly in China. The ore may be roasted to the oxide and reduced with carbon, or may be reduced directly with metallic iron:

$$Sb_2S_3 + 3Fe = 2Sb + 3FeS$$

Antimony forms allotropic modifications similar to those of arsenic. The stable modification, metallic antimony, forms brittle, silvery white, rhombohedral crystals which are considerably less volatile than those of metallic arsenic. It melts at 630.5°C, boils at 1440°C and has a density of 6.7 g/ml. Yellow antimony is even less stable than yellow arsenic, and may be kept only at very low temperatures. It is formed when stibine is oxidized by chlorine or oxygen at very low temperatures. It has a density of 5.3 g/ml.

Several other forms of antimony have been reported, including an explosive form prepared by the electrolysis of a solution of antimony chloride in hydrochloric acid using an antimony anode and a platinum cathode. The product is presumed to be a solid solution of antimony chloride in an unstable form of antimony.

Vapor density measurements give antimony vapor an average formula at 1572°C of $Sb_{2.96}$ and at 1640°C of $Sb_{2.68}$. These values probably correspond to the equilibrium

$$Sb_4 \rightleftharpoons 2Sb_2$$

with perhaps some dissociation according to the equation

$$Sb_2 \rightleftharpoons 2Sb$$

Bismuth. Bismuth occurs in nature most commonly as the free metal, but also as the sulfide Bi_2S_3, called bismuthinite, and as the hydrated oxide $Bi_2O_3 \cdot H_2O$, called bismite. Because of its low melting point, bismuth may be obtained from its native ores simply by heating them; this treatment melts the bismuth which flows off leaving rocky impurities behind.

Bismuth exists in only one form: a light gray metallic, crystalline material having a slight pinkish tinge. Bismuth metal is hard, brittle, and is a poor conductor of heat. It melts at the relatively low temperature of 271°C and boils at 1420°C.

The physical properties of arsenic, antimony, and bismuth are thus seen to reflect their increasingly metallic character. The chemical properties of these elements are in accord with this trend.

Uses of Arsenic, Antimony, and Bismuth. Metallic arsenic is used in the manufacture of arsenic compounds, and in making certain types of bronzes, as well as other varieties of alloys. Its presence in these alloys increases their fluidity, luster, strength, and hardness. Arsenic is used also in the manufacture of lead shot. In this process, molten lead is poured through a screen, and the liquid is thus broken up into drops, which are allowed to fall through a tower into water. A freely falling body tends to assume a spherical form; the presence of arsenic in the lead increases its fluidity and then allows a higher percentage of the drops to attain a spherical form before solidification.

More than half of the antimony consumed in the United States is used in the manufacture of lead storage batteries; antimonial lead being somewhat harder than ordinary lead, and more resistant to the reaction of acids. Lead-antimony grid alloys (*ca.* 6–10% Sb) are in practice a mixed blessing to the battery industry since the latter metal leads to undesirable self-discharge reactions. Antimonial lead is also used for bullets and shrapnel. Alloys of antimony with lead, because of their low melting points, and the fact that they expand upon solidification, are used for type metal. Antimony is likewise a minor constituent in a number of bearing metal alloys containing copper, tin, and lead.

Metallic bismuth also is used in certain types of bearing metals, but its use in the manufacture of low melting alloys for electrical fuses, automatic fire alarms and sprinkler systems, safety plugs on boilers, etc. is more important. Examples of such alloys are Wood's metal (Bi 50%, Pb 25%, Sn $12\frac{1}{2}$%, and Cd $12\frac{1}{2}$%) which melts at 71°C and Rose's metal (Bi 50%, Pb 25%, Sn 25%) which melts at 91°C.

The Hydrogen Compounds of P, As, Sb, and Bi

It was pointed out in the last chapter that all the elements of the nitrogen family form hydrogen compounds corresponding to the electronic formula

$$\text{H} \atop \text{H} : \overset{..}{\underset{..}{\text{M}}} : \text{H}$$

These compounds become less stable as M becomes more metallic.

Thus, bismuthine, BiH_3, is exceedingly unstable.[6] Furthermore, the basicity, which characterizes ammonia in its readiness to take up protons, decreases rapidly with increasing atomic number, and is hardly evident at all in arsine, AsH_3, stibine, SbH_3, and bismuthine, BiH_3. Likewise the reducing properties of these compounds increase in the same order that their stability decreases. Thus phosphine, PH_3, is a much stronger reducing agent than ammonia.

Phosphine. The formation of phosphine takes place in several reactions, some of which are analogous to methods for producing ammonia:

(a) The reaction of calcium phosphide with water:

$$Ca_3P_2 + 6H_2O \rightarrow 3Ca(OH)_2 + 2PH_3$$

(b) The reaction of phosphonium iodide, PH_4I, with alkali.
(c) The direct combination of phosphorus and hydrogen in the gas phase:

$$P_{4(g)} + 6H_{2(g)} = 4PH_{3(g)}$$

As in the case of ammonia, the yield increases with decrease in temperature and increase in pressure. The reaction is so slow at lower temperature, however, that no appreciable amounts of PH_3 are formed at temperatures under 300°C. The value of the equilibrium constant $K = P^4_{PH_3}/P_{P_4} \cdot P^6_{H_2}$ at 404°C is 5.6×10^{-12}. $\Delta H_0^0 = 1530$ cal/mole and $\Delta F^0_{298} = -18,370$ cal/mole.[7]

(d) The reaction of white phosphorus with boiling alkali to produce PH_3 and hypophosphite ion.

$$P_{4(w)} + 3OH^- + 3H_2O \rightarrow PH_3 + 3H_2PO_2^-$$

Phosphine is a colorless, highly poisonous gas which reacts spontaneously with oxygen under certain critical conditions of temperature and pressure. As ordinarily prepared, phosphine ignites spontaneously in air, but this phenomenon is presumed to result from the presence of the much more reactive diphosphine, P_2H_4, as an impurity in the phosphine. Diphosphine is the phosphorus analogue of hydrazine.

The more important physical constants for phosphine are listed in the following table:

[6] F. Paneth, *Ber.* **51**, 1704, 1748 (1918).
[7] D. P. Stevenson and Don M. Yost, *J. Chem. Phys.* **9**, 403 (1941).

TABLE 2.2. PHYSICAL PROPERTIES OF PHOSPHINE

Phase Changes:

Temperature, °C:

$$-242.81 \qquad -223.67 \qquad -185.00 \qquad -133.75 \qquad -89.72$$
$$PH_{3(s\gamma)} \xrightarrow{\qquad} PH_{3(s\alpha)} \xrightarrow{\qquad} PH_{3(s\beta)} \xrightarrow{\qquad} PH_{3(s\delta)} \xrightarrow{\qquad} PH_{3(l)} \xrightarrow{\qquad} PH_{3(g)}$$
$$19.6 \qquad\qquad 185.7 \qquad\qquad 115.8 \qquad\qquad 270.4 \qquad\qquad 3489.$$

ΔH^0, cal/mole:

Vapor pressure of the liquid:

$$\log_{10} p_{cm} = \frac{-1027.300}{T} - 0.0178530T + 0.000029135T^2 + 9.73075 \quad (T = °K)$$

Critical temperature: 51.0°C   Critical pressure: 64 atm

$S^0_{298°}$(exptl) = 50.35 cal/deg/mole $S^0_{298°}$(spectr.) = 50.5 cal/deg/mole

Density of liquid = 0.744 + 0.0005952(186.8 − T)   T = °K

Phosphine and the substituted phosphines have been shown to have a pyramidal structure. The H—P—H bond angle is 93° which would seem to indicate p bonds rather than tetrahedral sp^3 bonds. The P—H distance is 1.42 A.[8] As in the case of the substituted ammonias, no compounds of the type PRR′R″ have ever been resolved into optical isomers. Also as in the case of the substituted ammonias, the potential barrier between d- and l-forms of such molecules is so small that racemization is practically instantaneous.

Phosphine is much less soluble in water than is ammonia (26 ml of the gas in 100 ml water at 17°C) and it undergoes slow decomposition in solution. The ratio (β) of the concentration of PH$_3$ in solution phase to the concentration of solute in the gas phase has been determined and found to follow Henry's law below one atmosphere. In distilled water the mean value for β is 0.201 ± 0.005. The Setchnekow equation, log $(S^0/S) = k_s C_s$, is obeyed in NaCl solution. Acid and basic solutions show little effect on the solubility.[9] It forms the hydrate PH$_3$·H$_2$O (presumably PH$_4$OH), but solutions of phosphine in water are much less basic than solutions of ammonia, and phosphonium salts, [PH$_4$X], are not formed in aqueous solution. Such compounds have been prepared, however, by the direct reaction of phosphine and hydrogen halides. Beautiful, colorless, tetragonal crystals of phosphonium iodide, PH$_4$I, are obtained when gaseous HI and PH$_3$ are mixed, or better, when a carbon disulfide solution of white phosphorus is treated with iodine, the solution evaporated to dryness in a stream of CO$_2$, and the solid residue treated portionwise with water. Phosphonium iodide crystals are deposited on the walls of the container as a result of this reaction; the crystals may be

[8] D. P. Stevenson, *J. Chem. Phys.* 8, 285 (1940).

[9] R. E. Weston, Jr., *J. Am. Chem. Soc.* 76, 1027 (1954).

purified by sublimation (sublimation point = 80°C). Phosphonium compounds undergo ready and complete hydrolysis, thus:

$$PH_4I + H_2O \rightarrow PH_3 + H_3O^+ + I^-$$

If an alkaline solution is used to reduce the vapor pressure of hydrogen iodide this reaction yields very pure phosphine:

$$PH_4I + OH^- \rightarrow PH_3 + H_2O + I^-$$

The relative reducing power of phosphine as compared with other hydrogen compounds of the nitrogen family is indicated by the following electrode potentials:

	E^0 (volts)		
	NH_3	PH_3	AsH_3
$XH_3 = X^* + 3H^+ + 3e^-$	-0.27	-0.06	0.60

When ignited in air phosphine burns to phosphoric acid:

$$PH_3 + 2O_2 \rightarrow H_3PO_4$$

It likewise reduces the usual oxidizing agents, including ions of the nobler metals. Phosphine reacts with a number of metal ions to produce phosphide precipitates of uncertain composition. Metal phosphides are also obtained by the direct reaction of phosphorus and metal (or metal oxide) at elevated temperatures.

Phosphine and substituted phosphines form a large number of co-ordination compounds especially with the platinum group metal ions by sharing the unshared pair of electrons on the phosphorus atom. These compounds are not at all analogous to those of ammonia, particularly with respect to the fact that the former almost invariably are covalent, whereas ammonia is not uncommonly held by ion-dipole forces. It has recently been suggested that the large coordinating tendency of phosphines as compared with ammonia and amines is related to the ability of the metal ion to form π bonds involving d orbitals on the phosphorus atom. Other than a few minor exceptions, all the known addition compounds of phosphine or its derivatives are of the type

$$aM^mX_m \cdot bPR_3$$

in which M represents a metal of oxidation state m, X is a univalent radical, R is H, halogen, alkyl, or alkoxy group.

* ($X = \frac{1}{2}N_2, \frac{1}{4}P_4$, etc.)

Arsine, Stibine, and Bismuthine. These compounds continue the trends, begun with ammonia and phosphine, toward decreasing stability and increasing reducing power. Bismuthine is so unstable that its physical properties have never been determined. Some physical characteristics of arsine and stibine are listed in Table 2.3. The large negative

TABLE 2.3. SOME PHYSICAL PROPERTIES OF AsH_3 AND SbH_3

	AsH_3	SbH_3
Boiling point (°C)	−55	−18
Melting point (°C)	−119	−88
Heat of formation (cal/mole)	−36,700(?)	−81,800(?)

heats of formation are in accord with their lack of stability. They are colorless, very poisonous gases.

Arsine, stibine, and bismuthine are formed by the hydrolysis of metal arsenides, stibides, and bismuthides. The following equations represent examples:

$$Mg_3N_2 + 6H_2O \rightarrow 3Mg(OH)_2 + 2NH_3$$
$$Ca_3P_2 + 6H_2O \rightarrow 3Ca(OH)_2 + 2PH_3$$
$$Na_3As + 3H_2O \rightarrow 3NaOH + AsH_3$$
$$Zn_3Sb_2 + 6H_2O \rightarrow 3Zn(OH)_2 + 2SbH_3$$
$$Mg_3Bi_2 + 6H_2O \rightarrow 3Mg(OH)_2 + 2BiH_3$$

Arsine, stibine, and bismuthine are also formed by the reduction of arsenic, antimony, or bismuth compounds corresponding to higher oxidation states by such reducing agents as zinc in hydrochloric acid:

$$AsO_3^{-3} + 9H^+ + 3Zn = AsH_3 + 3Zn^{++} + 3H_2O$$
$$SbO_3^{-3} + 9H^+ + 3Zn = SbH_3 + 3Zn^{++} + 3H_2O$$

Bismuthine requires the use of a more active metal such as magnesium. These reactions, along with the easy thermal decomposition of arsine and stibine, are used as the basis for an exceptionally sensitive test for arsenic and antimony, known as the Marsh test. A solution of the substance to be tested is added to a flask containing zinc or some other active metal and an acid (usually sulfuric). If arsenic or antimony is present the corresponding hydrogen compound is produced, and leaves the flask through a calcium chloride drying tube. When the delivery tube is heated at some point beyond the drying tube, the arsine or stibine decomposes to give a mirror-like deposit, shiny black in the case of arsenic and brownish black in the case of antimony. The arsenic mirror is readily soluble in hypochlorite solutions but the antimony mirror is not.

Arsine and stibine are likewise detectable through their reducing action on silver nitrate solutions:

$$4AsH_3 + 24Ag^+ + 6H_2O = 24Ag + As_4O_6 + 24H^+$$

The stereochemical configuration of arsine (and presumably of stibine and bismuthine) is very similar to that of phosphine. There is essentially no tendency for arsine, stibine, and bismuthine to accept protons to form "onium" ions. The solubilities of arsine and stibine in water, like that of phosphine, are much less than that of ammonia.

Arsine reacts with most metals at elevated temperatures to form arsenides, which in many cases do not correspond to the usual oxidation states of the metals or of arsenic. A similar statement can be made with respect to antimony. Bismuth forms some compounds with other metals but fewer than antimony. This behavior is not surprising in view of the increased metallic nature of bismuth.

Hypophosphorous Acid and Its Derivatives

Preparation and Properties of Hypophosphorus Acid. The most important inorganic compounds in which phosphorus has an oxidation number of $+1$ are hypophosphorous acid, H_3PO_2, and its salts, the hypophosphites. Hypophosphites are produced when white phosphorus is hydrolyzed in strongly alkaline solution. This reaction, which also yields phosphine, is analogous to the hydrolysis of chlorine and of sulfur to give their hydrogen compounds plus salts of their hypo-acids. If barium hydroxide is used in the reaction with white phosphorus, the excess Ba^{++} ion removed as carbonate by precipitation with carbon dioxide at the end of the reaction, and the solution evaporated to crystallization, crystals of barium hypophosphite, $Ba(H_2PO_2)_2 \cdot H_2O$, are obtained. The acid may be obtained by treating a solution of this salt with an equivalent amount of sulfuric acid, filtering off the barium sulfate, and concentrating the filtrate by evaporation at relatively low temperatures (not above 130°C). Crystals of H_3PO_2 separate when the concentrated solution is cooled below 0°C. Hypophosphorous acid is also produced in the reaction of phosphorus with phosphoric acid at 200°C.

The colorless crystals of hypophosphorous acid are highly soluble in water and are very deliquescent. They melt at 26.5°C. Hypophosphorous acid is a moderately strong acid but is monobasic, ionizing in accordance with the equation:

$$H_3PO_2 = H^+ + H_2PO_2^-$$

The ionization constant [10] at 25°C is about 1.0×10^{-2}. The fact that this acid is only monobasic indicates that two of the hydrogen atoms on the H_3PO_2 molecule are incapable of ionization. This fact is explained by the following electronic structures for hypophosphorous acid and hypophosphite ion in which two hydrogens are connected directly to the phosphorus atom:

$$
\begin{array}{cc}
:\ddot{O}: & :\ddot{O}: \;\; ^{-}\\
H:\ddot{O}:P:H & :\ddot{O}:P:H\\
H & H
\end{array}
$$

These structures are supported by the results of x-ray and exchange investigations [11] and studies of the Raman spectrum of H_3PO_2.[12]

Solutions of hypophosphorous acid are stable at room temperature, but when heated to 140°C or above, decomposition sets in, yielding chiefly phosphine, phosphoric acid, and some hydrogen. Crystals of hypophosphorous acid likewise undergo this reaction when heated. Decomposition also takes place when alkaline solutions of hypophosphites are heated to 100°C or in neutral solutions in the presence of catalysts such as finely divided copper or palladium.

Hypophosphorous acid and its salts are powerful reducing agents as is indicated by the standard potentials for the reactions represented by following half equations:

$$
\begin{array}{ll}
H_3PO_2 + H_2O \rightleftharpoons H_3PO_3 + 2H^+ + 2e^- & E^0 = 0.50 \text{ volt}\\
H_2PO_2^- + 3OH^- \rightleftharpoons HPO_3^{--} + 2H_2O + 2e^- & E^0 = 1.57 \text{ volts}
\end{array}
$$

Reductions of the halogens and of heavy metal salts, such as silver nitrate, mercury(II) chloride, and copper(II) chloride, take place readily though the reaction rates, in certain cases, are rather smaller than might be expected for so powerful a reducing agent. The kinetics of a number of these reactions which proceed at measurable rates have been studied.[13] The mechanisms derived for the reactions with Cl_2, Br_2, I_2, $HgCl_2$, and $CuCl_2$ all involve the assumption of two forms of hypophosphorous acid which are transformable into each other by the slow, reversible

[10] I. M. Kolthoff, *Rec. trav. chim.* **46**, 350 (1927).

[11] W. H. Zachariasen and R. C. L. Mooney, *J. Chem. Phys.* **2**, 34 (1934); A. I. Brodskiï *et al.*, *Doklady Akad. Nauk S.S.S.R.* **75**, 823 (1950); *ibid.* **92**, 589 (1953).

[12] A. Simon and F. Fehér, *Z. anorg. Chem.* **230**, 289 (1937).

[13] A. M. Mitchell, *J. Chem. Soc.* **117**, 1322 (1920); **121**, 1624 (1922); R. O. Griffith and A. McKeown, *Trans. Faraday Soc.* **30**, 530 (1934).

reaction:

$$\text{Form I} \qquad \text{Form II}$$
$$H_3PO_2 + H_3O^+ \rightleftarrows H_5PO_3 + H^+ \quad \text{(slow)}$$
$$H^+ + H_2O \rightleftarrows H_3O^+ \qquad \text{(rapid)}$$

No attempt has been made to isolate two forms of hypophosphorous acid.

Hypophosphorous acid and hypophosphites are very weak oxidizing agents, as the following standard potentials indicate:

$$3H_2O + \tfrac{1}{4}P_4 = H_3PO_2 + H_3O^+ + e^- \qquad E^0 = 0.51$$
$$2OH^- + \tfrac{1}{4}P_4 = H_2PO_2^- + e^- \qquad E^0 = 2.05$$

The acid is reduced to phosphine, however by metallic zinc.

The Hypophosphites. All the hypophosphites are easily soluble in water, but those of the alkaline earth metals are the least soluble. The alkali and alkaline earth salts crystallize with little or no water of hydration, whereas other divalent metal hypophosphites usually form hexahydrates. The hypophosphites are much less poisonous than phosphine or phosphorus.

Hypophosphites may be determined by oxidation to phosphates with hydrogen peroxide and then precipitation by one of the usual procedures, or by treating an acid solution of the hypophosphite with excess standard permanganate and back-titrating with a standard reducing solution. Other oxidimetric methods have been developed.[14]

The Trihalides of Phosphorus, Arsenic, Antimony, and Bismuth

Preparation and Physical Properties of the Phosphorus Trihalides. All the halogens react vigorously and often violently with white phosphorus, and less vigorously with red phosphorus, to form halogen derivatives of the types PX_3, P_2X_4, and PX_5. The nature of the product may be regulated to a considerable degree by the proportions of the reactants, and the conditions of the reaction, but, in any case, the product must be subjected to some sort of separation and purification in order to obtain a pure compound. Phosphorus trichloride and tribromide are usually prepared by the reaction of the gaseous halogen with white or red phosphorus, and the tri-iodide by mixing carbon disulfide solutions of white phosphorus and of iodine in the theoretical atomic ratio (P:I = 1:3). A 1:2 ratio yields chiefly P_2I_4. The trifluoride is made from the tri-

---

[14] I. M. Kolthoff, *Rec. trav. chim.* **46**, 350 (1927).

chloride by treatment with arsenic trifluoride,

$$PCl_{3(l)} + AsF_{3(l)} = PF_{3(g)} + AsCl_{3(l)}$$

antimony trifluoride, or calcium fluoride. A number of mixed trihalides of phosphorus have been prepared and studied.[15] All the trihalides are colorless gases or colorless, volatile liquids except the iodide which is a red, low-melting solid. They are all covalent compounds having the electronic formula

$$:\overset{\cdot\cdot}{X}:$$
$$:\overset{\cdot\cdot}{X}:\overset{\cdot\cdot}{P}:\overset{\cdot\cdot}{X}:$$

Structure determinations by electron diffraction techniques show that all these trihalides have pyramidal configurations in which the phosphorus atom is at the vertex of the pyramid. Furthermore, even in the mixed halides, it has been shown that the bond angles vary only slightly when one halogen is substituted for another; furthermore, the bond distances depend chiefly on the identity of the halogen and not on the particular compound.[16] Important physical properties of the phosphorus trihalides are listed in Table 2.4.[17]

TABLE 2.4. PROPERTIES OF THE PHOSPHORUS TRIHALIDES

	Boiling Point (°C)	Melting Point (°C)	Heat of Vaporization (cal/ mole)	Critical Temp. (°C)	Critical Press. (atm)	$S^0_{298°}$ of Gas (cal/ deg/ mole)	Heat of Formation $-\Delta H^0_{298°}$ (cal/mole)	Bond Angle X–P–X	Bond Distance (A) P–X
PF_3	−101.5	−151.5	3490	−2.05	42.69	64.13	—	104°	1.52
PF_2Cl	−47.3	−164.8	4200	89.17	44.61	—	—	—	—
$PFCl_2$	13.85	−144.0	5950	189.84	49.3	—	—	102°	$\begin{cases} 2.02 \\ 1.55 \end{cases}$
PCl_3	74.2	−111.8	7278	—	—	74.49	$\begin{cases} 69,120\,(g) \\ 76,900\,(l) \end{cases}$	101°	2.00
PF_2Br	−16.1	−133.8	5721	—	—	—	—	—	—
$PFBr_2$	78.4	−115.0	7624	—	—	—	—	—	—
PBr_3	175.3	−40.0	—	—	—	83.11	45,000 (l)	100°	$\begin{cases} 2.23 \\ 1.57 \end{cases}$
PI_3	—	61.0	—	—	—	—	10,900	98°	—
P_2I_4	Dec.	124.5	—	—	—	—	19,800	—	—

[15] H. S. Booth *et al.*, *J. Am. Chem. Soc.* **61**, 3120 (1939) *et ante*.
[16] L. O. Brockway, *Rev. Modern Phys.* **8**, 231 (1936); A. A. Kuz'menko, *Ukrain. Khim. Zhur.* **18**, 589 (1952).
[17] M. L. Delwaulle, J., *chim. phys.* **46**, 87 (1949).

The Preparation and Physical Properties of the Trihalides of Arsenic, Antimony, and Bismuth. Arsenic, antimony, and bismuth form trihalides analogous to those of phosphorus. As in the case of the phosphorus compounds, these trihalides may be prepared by the direct union of the elements. Another method which can be used is the reaction of the oxide or sulfide with the halogen:

$$2Bi_2O_3 + 6Br_2 \rightarrow 4BiBr_3 + 3O_2$$

The physical properties of most of these compounds indicate that their molecules are covalent. The trihalides of arsenic and antimony are

TABLE 2.5. PHYSICAL PROPERTIES OF THE TRIHALIDES OF ARSENIC, ANTIMONY, AND BISMUTH

	Boiling Point (°C)	Melting Point (°C)	Heat of Vaporization (cal/mole)	$S^0_{298°}$ (cal/ deg/mole)	Heat of Formation $-\Delta H^0_{298°}$ (cal/mole)	Color and Physical State at Room Temperature
AsF_3	63 (752 mm)	−8.5	5000 (−53°C)	$\begin{cases} 50.1\pm3\,(l) \\ 69.2\pm2\,(g) \end{cases}$	198,300 (l)	colorless liquid
$AsCl_3$	130	−18	8,692 (25°C)	$\begin{cases} 55.8\pm3\,(l) \\ 78.2\pm2\,(g) \end{cases}$	$\begin{cases} 71,500\,(l) \\ 64,000\,(g) \end{cases}$	colorless liquid
$AsBr_3$	220	35	10,000 (220°C)	—	$\begin{cases} 45,900\,(s) \\ 43,100\,(l) \end{cases}$	yellow solid
AsI_3	403	146	19,200	—	$\begin{cases} 13,600\,(s) \\ 11,400\,(l) \end{cases}$	red solid
SbF_3	sublimes	292	—	—	216,000 (s)	colorless solid
$SbCl_3$	220.2	73.4	10,950 (125°C)	$\begin{cases} 44.8\pm3\,(s) \\ 80.9\pm2\,(g) \end{cases}$	$\begin{cases} 91,400\,(s) \\ 88,400\,(l) \end{cases}$	colorless solid
$SbBr_3$	280	96.6	—	—	$\begin{cases} 60,000\,(s) \\ 56,500\,(l) \end{cases}$	colorless solid
SbI_3	401	167	—	—	22,800 (s)	yellow solid
BiF_3	—	—	—	—	—	colorless solid
$BiCl_3$	447	232	23,177 (25°C)	45.8±4 (s)	90,600 (s)	colorless solid
$BiBr_3$	460	218	—	—	—	yellow solid
BiI_3	439	sublimes	—	—	24,000 (s)	brownish-black solid

soluble in nonpolar solvents such as benzene and carbon disulfide; the bismuth halides, as would be expected from the more metallic character of bismuth, are more polar than the arsenic and antimony compounds, and do not dissolve in such nonpolar solvents. The geometrical and electronic structures of the arsenic and antimony trihalides are similar to those the phosphorus(III) compounds. A table of some of the physical properties of the trihalides of arsenic, antimony, and bismuth is given in Table 2.5.

The Hydrolysis of Trihalides of Phosphorus, Arsenic, Antimony, and Bismuth; Other Reactions. The trihalides of phosphorus are completely hydrolyzed when brought in contact with water to give phosphorous acid and the corresponding hydrohalic acid:

$$PX_3 + 3H_2O = H_3PO_3 + 3H^+ + 3X^-$$

The phosphorus trihalides vary somewhat in the vigor and rapidity with which they undergo hydrolysis in moist air. Qualitatively, it seems to be true that the reactivity of the phosphorus trihalides toward water decreases as the sum of the atomic numbers of the three attached halogens decreases. Thus, $PFBr_2$ is more reactive toward water than is $PFCl_2$ or PF_3. It is interesting to compare the behavior of a phosphorus trihalide, *e.g.*, PCl_3, with the corresponding compounds of the other elements of the family. The reaction of arsenic trichloride with water is analogous to that of the phosphorus compound, except that the $AsCl_3$ reaction may be reversed if sufficiently high concentrations of hydrochloric acid are employed. The hydrolysis of antimony or bismuth chloride does not go to completion, but yields in each case an oxychloride precipitate:

$$SbCl_3 + H_2O = SbOCl_{(s)} + 2H^+ + 2Cl^-$$
$$BiCl_3 + H_2O = BiOCl_{(s)} + 2H^+ + 2Cl^-$$

This decreased tendency toward hydrolysis on the part of the trihalides is another manifestation of the increase in metallic characteristics in the series $P > As > Sb > Bi$. Thus, as the element becomes more metallic, its halogen compounds become more saltlike, and their tendency toward hydrolysis, *i.e.* the tendency for the ion of the element to form a covalent bond with a hydroxide ion from the water, increases.

The trihalides undergo many other reactions to form addition compounds of various types. Some of them are also useful as halogenating agents for organic compounds.

The Sesquioxides and Their Hydrates

Preparation and Properties of Sesquioxides. As in the case of the reaction with the halogens, the combination of phosphorus with oxygen yields a mixture of products, the relative quantities of which depend upon the conditions. F. Wolf and H. Schmager [18] found that the reaction of white phosphorus in a 17-mm quartz tube with a mixture of oxygen (75%) and nitrogen, at about 50°C under 90 mm pressure and with a rate of flow of 30 liters per hour, gives a 56% yield of phosphorus sesquioxide. After purification, phosphorus sesquioxide is obtained as a colorless liquid which solidifies to colorless crystals at 23.8°C and which boils under atmospheric pressure at 175.4°C. Electron diffraction studies [19] on the gas and cryoscopic studies on solutions of phosphorus sesquioxide in naphthalene [20] indicate that the molecular formula of the oxide is P_4O_6 and that it has the geometrical structure illustrated in Fig. 2.3.

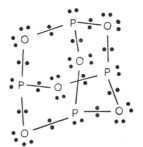 

Fig. 2.3. Electronic and geometrical structure of P_4O_6.

Phosphorus sesquioxide reacts slowly with cold water to form phosphorous acid:

$$P_4O_6 + 6H_2O \rightarrow 4H_3PO_3$$

With hot water the reaction takes place vigorously to yield a mixture of phosphorus, phosphine, phosphoric acid, and other substances. Phosphorus sesquioxide reacts slowly with oxygen at room temperature to yield P_4O_{10}, and is soluble in a variety of organic solvents. When heated at temperatures above 200°C, P_4O_6 undergoes decomposition according

[18] *Ber.* **62**, 771 (1929).
[19] G. C. Hampson and A. J. Stosick, *J. Am. Chem. Soc.* **60**, 1814 (1938).
[20] R. Schenck, F. Mihr, and H. Bathien, *Ber.* **39**, 1506 (1906).

to the equation:

$$2P_4O_6 \rightarrow 3P_2O_4 + 2P\,(red)$$

Phosphorus sesquioxide is a reducing agent and reacts with a variety of oxidizing agents.

Arsenic and antimony each form oxides with molecular formulas analogous to P_4O_6 and presumably have analogous geometrical structures. Bismuth sesquioxide, however, being more nearly ionic, is better represented by its empirical formula, Bi_2O_3. These oxides are obtained when the elements are burned in air; since, unlike phosphorus, these elements do not form pentoxides by direct union with oxygen, an excess of air is not harmful.   They may also be prepared by roasting the sulfides in air, or by heating the corresponding oxide hydrates, *e.g.*:

$$2Sb_2S_3 + 9O_2 \rightarrow Sb_4O_6 + 6SO_2$$
$$2BiO(OH) \rightarrow Bi_2O_3 + H_2O$$

A monoxide of bismuth, BiO, is obtained by heating $(BiO)_2C_2O_4$.   Each of the sesquioxides exists in more than one crystalline form; at room temperature, all forms of the arsenic and antimony compounds are white solids, whereas bismuth sesquioxide is yellow.

The solubility of the sesquioxides in water decreases sharply in the order $P_4O_6 > As_4O_6 > Sb_4O_6 > Bi_2O_3$.   This decrease is indicated in the following table in which some of the physical properties of the last three of these compounds are listed.

TABLE 2.6. SOME PHYSICAL PROPERTIES OF As_4O_6, Sb_4O_6, AND Bi_2O_3

	Mp °C	Bp °C	Solubility (g/100 g H_2O)	Density (g/ml)
As_4O_6	218 (sublimes)	—	2.04 (25°C)	3.7
Sb_4O_6	655	1425	0.002 (15°C)	5.67
Bi_2O_3	817	1900	v. sl. sol.	8.9

Arsenic sesquioxide, commonly known as "white arsenic" and often erroneously referred to simply as "arsenic," is commercially the most important of arsenic compounds; about 60,000 tons of this substance are produced annually.   It is a violent poison and is used in the preparation of insecticides, weed killers, and organic arsenic medicinals.

The reactions of these oxides with acids and alkalies provide an interesting example of the manner in which acidic and basic properties of the oxides of the elements of a given family change from the top to the bottom of the periodic chart. Sesquioxides of nitrogen and phosphorus dissolve in water to form acidic solutions. That the arsenic compound likewise has acidic properties is indicated by the fact that it readily dissolves in solutions of alkalies to form salts called arsenites. Arsenic sesquioxide, however, is somewhat soluble in acids, its solubility in water being increased by the presence of the hydrogen ion, though to a much lesser extent than by the presence of the hydroxide ion. Antimony sesquioxide is definitely amphoteric, dissolving readily in either acids or alkalies. Bismuth trioxide, on the other hand, is insoluble in alkalies, but dissolves in acids; it is thus definitely, though weakly, basic. These relationships are summarized in Table 2.7.

TABLE 2.7. BEHAVIOR OF SESQUIOXIDES WITH ACIDS AND ALKALIES

Oxide	Order of Solubility in		Product Obtained from Solution		Nature of Oxide
	acids	alkalies	in acids	in alkalies	
N_2O_3	—*	↑ increasing	—*	Nitrites	Acidic
P_4O_6	—*		—*	Phosphites	Acidic
As_4O_6	increasing		Compounds such as $AsCl_3$, which are hydrolyzed except in very highly acidic solutions	Arsenites	Weakly acidic
Sb_4O_6			Basic salts only, such as $(SbO)_2SO_4$	Antimonites	Amphoteric
Bi_2O_3	↓		Both basic salts such as $(BiO)_2SO_4$ and normal salts such as $Bi(NO_3)_2$	—	Weakly basic

* Nitrous and phosphorus acids are soluble in pure water, and, hence, also in acid solutions, but this does not indicate reaction with the acid.

The Hydrates of the Sesquioxides, and Their Salts. When water reacts either with phosphorus trihalides or with the sesquioxide, phosphorous acid, a hydrate of the formula H_3PO_3 is formed. Much purer phosphorous acid is obtained from the reaction of hydrogen sulfide with lead phosphite:

$$PbHPO_3 + H_2S \rightarrow H_3PO_3 + PbS_{(s)}$$

When pure, the acid is a colorless solid which melts at about 73°C. It is highly soluble in water, its solubility at 25.4°C being 82.64 g per 100 g of solution. Phosphorous acid is a diprotic acid; salts such as NaH_2PO_3 and Na_2HPO_3 are known, but none of the type M_3PO_3 have been prepared. In contrast to the usual relationship of "ous" and "ic" acids, phosphorous acid is a slightly stronger acid than phosphoric. The equilibrium constants for the ionization of two protons are as follows: [21]

$$H_3PO_3 + H_2O \rightleftharpoons H_3O^+ + H_2PO_3^- \qquad K_1 = 1.6 \times 10^{-2}$$
$$H_2PO_3^- + H_2O \rightleftharpoons H_3O^+ + HPO_3^= \qquad K_2 = 7 \times 10^{-7}$$

The failure of the phosphorous acid molecule to release the third proton is accounted for by the following electronic formulas, in which it is shown that one of the three protons is attached directly to the phosphorus atom:

phosphorous　　　　phosphite
acid　　　　　　　ion

When pure phosphorous acid, or its concentrated solution, is strongly heated decomposition takes place in accordance with the following equation:

$$4H_3PO_3 \rightarrow 3H_3PO_4 + PH_3$$

Phosphorous acid and the phosphite ion are strong reducing agents in aqueous solution as the following standard electrode potentials indicate:

$$H_3PO_3 + H_2O \rightleftharpoons H_3PO_4 + 2H^+ + 2e^- \qquad E^0 = 0.276 \text{ volt}$$
$$HPO_3^= + 3OH^- \rightleftharpoons PO_4^{-3} + 2H_2O + 2e^- \qquad E^0 = 1.12 \text{ volts}$$

Frequently, however, these processes take place only slowly. For example, at room temperature, phosphorous acid reacts at slow, measurable rates with halogens, dichromate, and mercury(II) chloride. It reacts only very slowly, if at all, with a peroxydisulfate under these conditions in the absence of Ag^+ or iodine catalyst. Phosphorous acid readily reduces silver ion to metallic silver, and hot, concentrated sulfuric acid to sulfur dioxide. A number of kinetic studies on phosphorous acid reductions have been carried out, and the slow rate of some of these reactions has been attributed to a mechanism involving the formation of an unstable intermediate H_2PO_3.[22]

[21] I. M. Kolthoff, *Rec. trav. chim. Pays-Bas* **46**, 350 (1927).
[22] G. A. Linhart, *Am. J. Sci.* **35**(4), 353 (1913); Brodskiĭ, *loc. cit.*

Metaphosphorous acid, HPO_2, is obtained when phosphine is burned in air, but this compound changes to the ortho-form, H_3PO_3, when it is dissolved in water.

Arsenous acid has never been isolated, but since the sesquioxide is somewhat soluble in water to give a weakly acidic solution, the free acid presumably exists in aqueous solution. Its ionization constant has been found to be 6×10^{-10}. The formulas of the various arsenites are characterized by great variety and are, in some cases, quite complex. Because of their highly poisonous nature, arsenites are extensively used as insecticides and weed killers. Paris green, $Cu_2(C_2H_3O_2)(AsO_3)$, and Scheele's green, $CuHAsO_3$, are important both as insecticides and as pigments.

Precipitates of hydrous antimony sesquioxide, containing indefinite quantities of water, may be obtained by acidifying an aqueous solution of an antimonite, but there is little evidence for the existence of the definite hydrate antimonous acid. A variety of simple and complex antimonites are obtainable, however. Because of the weakness of the acidic properties of antimony sesquioxide, antimonites are subject to extensive hydrolysis in aqueous solution.

Basic antimony salts containing the group SbO^+ are known as antimonyl compounds. They are obtained by the hydrolysis of normal antimony salts:

$$SbCl_3 + H_2O \rightleftharpoons SbOCl + 2H^+ + 2Cl^-$$

or by crystallization from solutions of antimony trioxide in the appropriate acid:

$$Sb_2O_3 + 2H^+ + 2NO_3^- \rightleftharpoons 2SbONO_3 + H_2O$$

Potassium antimonyl tartrate, $K(SbO)C_4H_4O_6$, is used in medicine under the name tartar emetic.

Bismuth sesquioxide has no acidic properties and, hence, bismuthites are unknown. Basic bismuth salts containing the BiO^+ group, sometimes known as bismuthyl compounds, are obtained when normal bismuth salts are brought in contact with water:

$$Bi^{+3} + H_2O \rightleftharpoons BiO^+ + 2H^+$$

This reaction may be reversed by larger concentrations of acid. Examples of bismuthyl salts include $(BiO)_2SO_4$ and $BiOCl$. Large quantities of basic bismuth salts or oxysalts are prepared for pharmaceutical purposes, especially as antiacids for the treatment of digestive disturbances. Examples of such preparations are the carbonate and nitrate, designated by pharmacists as bismuth subcarbonate and bismuth subnitrate, respectively. Bismuthyl ions are readily reduced to the metal:

$$H_2O + Bi = BiO^+ + 2H^+ + 3e^- \qquad E^0 = -0.32 \text{ volt}$$

Treatment of bismuth salt solutions by alkalies results in the precipitation of bismuthyl hydroxide, BiOOH.

The Tetroxides; Hypophosphoric Acid

Preparation and Properties of the Tetroxides. It has already been pointed out that phosphorus tetroxide, the formula for which is commonly written P_2O_4, is obtained along with red phosphorus when phosphorus sesquioxide is heated, usually in a closed tube at about 290°C. On sublimation the tetroxide forms brilliant crystals, which boil at 180°C in a vacuum. The molecular weight of the compound has not been established with any high degree of accuracy, but the molecular formula, P_8O_{16}, is believed probable by many investigators. The compound has a density of 2.537 g/ml at 22.6°C. It is believed that the tetroxide does not contain quadrivalent phosphorus but contains trivalent and quinquivalent phosphorus in equal amounts. This conclusion is not proved, but is in accord with the fact that phosphorus tetroxide reacts with water to produce phosphorous and phosphoric acids. Phosphorus tetroxide is not affected by moderate heat or light and is not soluble in organic solvents.

Though it is less definitely characterized than the phosphorus compound, antimony tetroxide is apparently a definite substance. Its formula is usually written Sb_2O_4 and it is sometimes considered to be antimony(III) antimonate $Sb^{III}(Sb^VO_4)$. It may conform to an antimony(III, V) oxide. It is formed in small quantities when antimony is burned in air, the chief product being the sesquioxide. It may be prepared by heating the sesquioxide in air to 300 to 400°C. It is an acidic oxide since it dissolves in alkalies, but not in acids.

Hypophosphoric Acid. An acid of the composition represented by the formula $H_4P_2O_6$, known as hypophosphoric acid, may be prepared by a number of methods including: (a) the reaction of nitric acid solutions of copper or silver nitrate with white phosphorus, (b) the anodic oxidation of copper phosphite in 2% sulfuric acid solution, using a copper cathode and a potential of 3 to 10 volts,[23] and (c) the reaction of solutions of sodium hypochlorite in sodium hydroxide with red phosphorus at 5°C.[24]

[23] A. Rosenheim and J. Pinsker, *Ber.* **43**, 2003 (1910).
[24] J. Probst, *Z. anorg. Chem.* **179**, 155 (1929).

A solution of hypophosphoric acid may be obtained by treating lead hypophosphate with hydrogen sulfide, and filtering off the precipitated lead sulfide. On evaporating the solution under vacuum, crystals of the hydrate, $H_4P_2O_6 \cdot 2H_2O$, are obtained. These crystals are colorless and deliquescent, and very soluble in water. On being heated, the solid decomposes into phosphorous and phosphoric acids. Phosphorus tetroxide is the formal anhydride of hypophosphoric acid, but does not yield that acid on reaction with water, presumably because the heat given off in the reaction decomposes the hypophosphoric acid into phosphorous and phosphoric acids as described.

Salts of the type $Li_4P_2O_6 \cdot 7H_2O$, $Na_4P_2O_6 \cdot 10H_2O$, $Na_3HP_2O_6 \cdot 9H_2O$, $Na_2H_2P_2O_6 \cdot 6H_2O$, and $Na_2NiP_2O_6 \cdot 12H_2O$ are known, and their existence indicates that hypophosphoric acid is tetrabasic. The ionization constants are subject to some doubt, but, in general, it is believed that $H_4P_2O_6$ is of about the same strength as $H_4P_2O_7$.

The Halogen Derivatives of the +5 Oxidation State

Halogen Compounds of +5 Phosphorus. The halogen derivatives of +5 phosphorus may be grouped into three general classes: (a) the pentahalides, (b) the oxyhalides, thiohalides, and nitrilic chlorides, and (c) the fluorophosphoric acids. The last of these groups is discussed in a later section.

The pentahalides of phosphorus are formed either by the direct union of the element with an excess of halogen or by the reaction of trihalides with halogen:

$$P_4 + 10Cl_2 \rightarrow 4PCl_5$$
$$PF_3 + Cl_2 \rightarrow PF_3Cl_2$$

The latter method is particularly useful in the preparation of mixed halides. A unique mixed halide, PCl_3Br_4, is formed by heating 40.5 mole per cent PBr_5 with 59.5 mole per cent PCl_5 to 40–50°C and cooling. Orange red crystals (mp = 36.7°C) of the mixed halide are formed as well as liquid PCl_3. Addition of PBr_3 to an excess of PCl_5 gives a red precipitate. At a 3:2 ratio the product is PCl_3Br_4. With an excess of PBr_3 present a yellow solid results analyzing as $PClBr_4$. Addition of PBr_3 to PCl_3Br_4 also gives the yellow mixed halide, $PClBr_4$.[25]

The structures of various pentahalides in the vapor state have been determined by electron diffraction and they have been found to have a trigonal bipyramidal structure such as that shown in Fig. 2.4. In the mixed halides such as PF_3Cl_2 the chlorine atoms are at the apical positions.

[25] A. A. Kuz'menko, *Ukrain. Khim. Zhur.* **18**, 589 (1952).

Some of the physical constants for the pentahalides are listed in the following table.

TABLE 2.8. PHYSICAL CONSTANTS OF PHOSPHORUS PENTAHALIDES

Substance	Bp (°C)	Mp (°C)	$-H^0_{298°}$ (formation)	Interatomic Distance A	Color
PF_5	−75	−83	—	1.57	colorless
PF_3Cl_2	10	− 8	—	P–F 1.59 / P–Cl 2.05	colorless
PCl_5	160 (sublimes)	—	106,500 (s)	P–Cl 2.11* / P–Cl 2.04	colorless
PF_3Br_2	—	−20	—	—	—
PBr_5	Dec.	100°	60,600 (s)	—	two forms { one red / one yellow
PI_5	not known	—	—	—	—

* The apical chlorines in the trigonal bipyramid have P–Cl distances 2.11 A whereas the equatorial chlorines have P–Cl distances of 2.04 A. The electron configuration $3s$, $3p$, $3p$, $3p$, $4s$ accounts for different behavior between 3 equilateral and 2 apical Cl atoms.[26]

As is apparent from their physical properties, as well as from the fact that in the liquid state they are very poor conductors of electricity, these pentahalides are covalent compounds. The question as to their electronic structures is still unsettled. Although one $3d$ orbital may be used

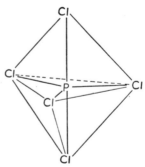

FIG. 2.4. Structure of phosphorus pentachloride.

[26] F. Senent, *Anales real soc. españ. fis. y quim.* **47B**, 665 (1951); H. Siebert, *Z. anorg. u. allgem. Chem.* **265**, 303 (1951).

to form sp^3d hybrid orbitals it is possible that the molecule may resonate among the five possible structures of the type:

The structure and non-equivalence of the chlorine atoms in PCl_5 have been elucidated by measuring the ^{36}Cl exchange with PCl_5 in CCl_4. It is reported that: (1) three chlorine atoms undergo rapid initial exchange; (2) the three equatorial chlorine atoms undergo exchange rapidly but the two chlorine atoms in apical positions exchange but slowly; (3) there is no rapid intramolecular exchange between apical and equatorial positions. A transition state of PCl_5 and Cl_2 of the type

$$\begin{array}{ccc} Cl & Cl & Cl \\ & \diagdown | \diagup & \\ & P & \cdots Cl \\ & \diagup | \diagdown & \\ Cl & Cl & Cl \end{array}$$

is suggested. This state decomposes rapidly to PCl_5 and Cl_2.[27] This resonance would be in qualitative accord with the fact that the stability of the pentahalides decreases rapidly in the order $PF_5 > PCl_5 > PBr_5$. Even PCl_5 is half dissociated into PCl_3 and chlorine at 200°C. The trigonal bipyramidal structure does not persist in the solid pentachloride or pentabromide. The former contains tetrahedral $[PCl_4]^+$ ions and octahedral $[PCl_6]^-$ ions in its crystal lattice and the latter contains $[PBr_4]^+$ and Br^- ions in its crystals. One may surmise that the decreasing stability of the pentahalides is not unrelated to steric effects of the type Pauling considers under the term *radius-ratio effects*.[28]

The pentahalides undergo rapid hydrolysis in contact with an excess of water to yield phosphoric acid and the hydrohalic acids. In the presence of a limited quantity of water, the hydrolytic products are hydrohalic acids and phosphorus oxyhalides, POX_3. Mixed oxyhalides may be obtained by treating $POCl_3$ with calcium fluoride or antimony trifluoride. The oxyhalides have approximately tetrahedral structures

[27] J. Downs and R. E. Johnson, *J. Chem. Phys.* **22**, 143 (1954).

[28] L. Pauling, *The Nature of the Chemical Bond*, Second Edition, Cornell University Press (1940), pp. 380–4.

and have the following electronic formula:

Phosphorus oxychloride serves as a nonaqueous solvent for many metal halides.[29]   An analogy exists between water and $POCl_3$ on the basis of complexes formed between $POCl_3$ and such salts as $SnCl_4$, $TiCl_4$, and $SbCl_5$.   Conductivity measurements have been made before and after the addition of PCl_5 to the $POCl_3$-metal chloride solution.   The PCl_5 serves as a complex destroyer.   A rapid increase in conductivity occurs as the PCl_5 is added indicating a release of the complex-forming chloride from the solvent.   With $SnCl_4$ a drop in conductivity occurs at a $SnCl_4$:PCl_5 mole ratio between 1 and 2 coincident with the precipitation of $[PCl_4]_2{}^+[SnCl_6]^=$.   Such a process has an analogy in the water system in the decomposition of $SnCl_4 \cdot nH_2O$ by $CsCl$ to yield Cs_2SnCl_6. Conductometric titration of BCl_3 in $POCl_3$ with PCl_5 added as the complex destroyer indicates the presence of $BCl_3 \cdot PCl_5$.   The complexes studied all appear to form through an ionic mechanism.   The mechanism is probably related to the autoionization: $2POCl_3 \rightleftarrows POCl_2{}^+ + POCl_4{}^-$. The $SbCl_5 \cdot POCl_3$ complex would then be $[POCl_2{}^+][SbCl_6{}^-]$, the $POCl_3$-complex functioning as a monobasic acid.   The titanium complex, $TiCl_4 \cdot 2POCl_3$, would ionize to $2POCl_2{}^+$ and $TiCl_6{}^=$ or as a dibasic acid. No compounds containing the $POCl_4{}^-$ in the solid state have, however, been isolated.[30]   A number of other solid $POCl_3$ solvates have been reported: $AlI_3 \cdot 2POCl_3$; $SbCl_3 \cdot POCl_3$; $MgCl_2 \cdot POCl_3$; $CaO \cdot 3POCl_3$; $MgO \cdot 2POCl_3$; $ZnO \cdot 3POCl_3$.[31]

Addition compounds of the same type as those described above have been reported with $POFCl_2$ or POF_2Cl and metal(IV) halides.   If contact time of the MCl_4 with excess $POFCl_2$ or POF_2Cl is sufficiently long, complete exchange within the phosphoryl molecule occurs and $2POCl_3 \cdot MCl_4$ is crystallized from solution.[32]   Among the phosphoryl halide and mixed halide complexes prepared are: $2POCl_3 \cdot ZrCl_4$; $2POCl_3 \cdot HfCl_4$; $2POFCl_2 \cdot$ $ZrCl_4$ (mp = 74–8°C); $2POFCl_2 \cdot HfCl_4$ (mp = 80–3°C); $POF_2Cl \cdot HfCl_4$ (mp = 110–13°C); $POF_2Cl \cdot ZrCl_4$ (mp = 106–9°C); $POF_3 \cdot ZrCl_4$; $POF_3 \cdot HfCl_4$ (mp = 85°C).

[29] W. L. Groenveld and H. P. Zuur, *Rec. trav. chim.* **72**, 617, 950 (1953).
[30] V. Gutmann, *Z. anorg. u. allgem. Chem.* **270**, 179 (1952).
[31] *Ibid.* **269**, 279 (1952).
[32] E. M. Larson *et al.*, *J. Am. Chem. Soc.* **74**, 3489 (1952).

Analogous sulfur compounds of the general formula, PSX_3, have been prepared by similar methods. These compounds have geometrical and electronic structures which resemble those of the oxyhalides. The important physical properties of the phosphorus oxy- and thiohalides are listed in the following table:

TABLE 2.9. PROPERTIES OF THE PHOSPHORUS OXY- AND THIOHALIDES

Substance	Bp (°C)	Mp (°C)	ΔH^0 vap. (cal/mole)	$-\Delta H^0_{298°}$ (formation) (cal/mole)	<X–P–X	Distances P–X (A)
POF_3	−39.8	−39.4	5030	—	107°	P–F, 1.52 P–O, 1.56
$POCl_3$	105.1	1.25	8200	138,400 (g) 147,100 (l) 150,300 (s)	106°	P–Cl, 2.02[a] P–O, 1.58
$POBr_3$	189.5	56	—	106,900 (s)	—	—
POF_2Cl	3.1	− 96.4	6090	—	106°	P–O, 1.55 P–F, 1.51 P–Cl, 2.01
$POFCl_2$	52.9	− 80.1	7400	—	106°	P–O, 1.54 P–F, 1.50 P–Cl, 1.94
$POFBr_2$	110.1	−117.2	7520	—	—	—
POF_2Br	30.5	− 84.8	7093	—	—	—
$PSCl_3$	125	− 35	—	—	107°	P–Cl, 2.01 P–S, 1.95
$PSCl_2F$	64.7	− 96.0	6863	—	—	—
$PSClF_2$	6.3	−155.2	5703	—	—	—
PSF_3	−52.3	−148.8	4684	—	—	P–F, 1.51 P–S, 1.85
$PSBr_3$	206	37	—	—	—	—

[a] Electron diffraction and microwave data on $POCl_3$ give the following: P–Cl = 1.99$_5$ ± 0.02 A; P–O = 1.45 ± 0.05 A <Cl–P–Cl = 103.5 ± 1°.[32a]

A series of very interesting products has been obtained by the partial ammonolysis of phosphorus pentachloride, usually by the reaction of the

[32a] G. R. Badgley and R. L. Livingston, *J. Am. Chem. Soc.* **76**, 267 (1954).

pentachloride with ammonium chloride at 150°C in a closed tube. The reaction may be represented by the following equation:

$$nPCl_5 + nNH_4Cl \rightarrow (PNCl_2)_n + 4nHCl_{(g)}$$

where $n = 3, 4, 5, \cdots x$. These phosphonitrilic chlorides, as they are called, are "ammono" analogues of phosphorus oxychloride. It has been found possible to isolate from the reaction mixture various members of this group of compounds and to study their structures and properties. The trimer melts at 114°C, boils at 256°C at atmospheric pressure, and

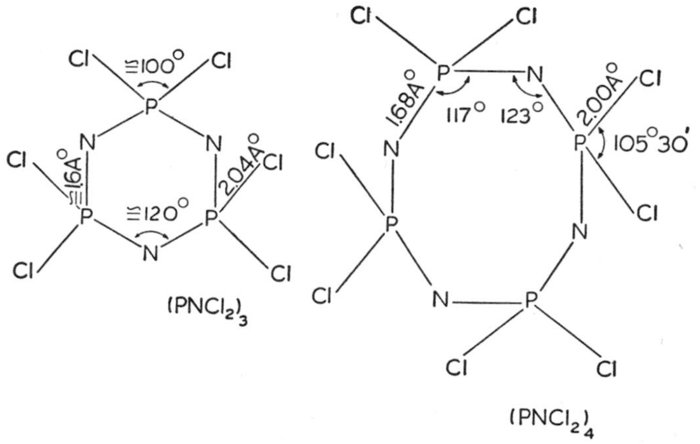

FIG. 2.5. Structure of the trimer and tetramer of phosphonitrilic chloride.

is readily soluble in benzene, ether, and carbon tetrachloride. The tetramer melts at 123.5°C and boils at 328.5°C and has a lower solubility in the above named solvents than the trimer. The pentamer, hexamer, and heptamer have lower melting points, 41°C, 91°C, and −18°C, respectively. The trimer and the tetramer have the cyclic structures in which the six- and eight-membered rings are composed of alternate nitrogen and phosphorus atoms (see Fig. 2.5). The higher polymers presumably have linear structures. All the phosphonitrilic chlorides, when heated to about 300°C, are converted to an elastic product, possessing many of the properties of rubber. Unfortunately, the applicability of this elastomer to practical problems is limited by the considerable chemical activity of its chlorine atoms. Some characteristic solvolytic reactions of trimeric phosphonitrilic chloride are represented by the following equations:[33]

$$(PNCl_2)_3 + 6H_2O = [PN(OH)_2]_3 + 6HCl$$
$$(PNCl_2)_3 + 4NH_3 = (PN)_3Cl_4(NH_2)_2 + 2NH_4Cl$$
$$\downarrow + 8NH_3$$
$$[PN(NH_2)_2]_3 + 4NH_4Cl$$
$$(PNCl_2)_3 + 6HY = [PN(Y)_2]_3 + 6HCl \quad (Y = N_2H_3, OR, NHR, NR_2)$$

The Halogen Compounds of +5 Arsenic and Antimony. Although it is by no means clear why, arsenic forms no pentahalide other than the fluoride AsF_5. Antimony forms the pentafluoride SbF_5 and the pentachloride $SbCl_5$ but no pentabromide or pentaiodide. Bismuth forms no pentahalides at all.

The properties of AsF_5, SbF_5, and $SbCl_5$ are similar to those of the phosphorus pentahalides, though the increasingly metallic character of the central elements is exhibited by the decreasing tendency of these compounds to undergo hydrolysis, SbF_5 being quite resistant to the action of water. The physical constants for the three pentahalides of arsenic and antimony are listed in the following table:

TABLE 2.10. PHYSICAL PROPERTIES OF THE PENTAHALIDES OF
ARSENIC AND ANTIMONY

	Mp (°C)	Bp (°C)	Specific Gravity	Color
AsF_5	−88.7	−58.2		colorless gas
SbF_5	6	150	$2.99^{23°}$	colorless oily liquid
$SbCl_5$	− 6	102 at 68 mm	$2.346^{20°}$	yellow liquid

Although $SbBr_5$ and BiF_5 do not exist, the compounds $HSbF_6$ and $HBiF_6$ have been prepared.

THE +5 OXIDES

Phosphorus(V) Oxide. The chief product of the oxidation of phosphorus in an excess of air or oxygen is a fairly nonvolatile, white, amorphous powder known as phosphorus(V) oxide and having the molecular formula P_4O_{10} rather than P_2O_5. Several modifications of this substance exist, but the substance described above is the β-form, which is the form familiar to commerce. A crystalline, volatile α-form is ob-

[33] L. Audrieth, R. Steinman, and A. Toy have published an excellent review of these unusual substances, *Chem. Rev.* **32,** 109–33 (1943); R. Klement and O. Koch, *Chem. Ber.* **87,** 9253 (1954); E. S. Scott and L. F. Audrieth, *J. Chem. Educ.* **31,** 173 (1954); H. Specker, *Z. anorg. Chem.* **263,** 133 (1950).

tained by subliming P_4O_{10}; a glassy γ-form is obtained by melting the β-form at about 570°C; and a crystalline δ-form is obtained as fine needles by prolonged heating of the γ-form at 500°C.   The δ-form melts at 569°C. The α-form has a density of 2.30 g/ml and the δ-form a density of 2.72 g/ml.

Structural investigations show that the α-form contains distinct P_4O_{10} molecules packed together.   The dimensions and configuration of these molecules are the same as in the vapor state (see below).   The δ-form, however, has a continuous structure made up of linked PO_4 tetrahedra. Of the four forms of the oxide the α-form is least stable and the δ-form most stable.   The high volatility of the α-form as compared with the δ-form as well as the lower density of the former is readily understood in terms of the differences in their structures.[34]   Electron diffraction studies of the vapor phase confirm the existence of P_4O_{10} molecules, and show that the O—P—O bond angle is 101.5°.[35]   The geometrical arrangement of the atoms in the oxide molecule is shown in Fig. 2.6.

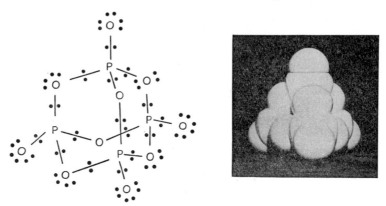

Fig. 2.6.   Structure of phosphorus (V) oxide, P_4O_{10}.

The most notable chemical property of phosphorous(V) oxide is the rapidity and completeness with which it undergoes hydration to form various phosphoric acids.   The oxide, therefore, is a strong dehydrating or drying agent.

The +5 Oxides of Arsenic, Antimony, and Bismuth.   Arsenic(V) oxide is a white, amorphous, fusible powder.   The corresponding antimony compound is a pale yellow, infusible, insoluble solid.   Both are prepared by the dehydration of the corresponding hydrate which in each

[34] C. H. McGillavry and H. C. J. de Decker, *Rec. trav. chim.* **60**, 153 (1941); H. C. J. de Decker, *ibid.* **60**, 413 (1941).

[35] G. C. Hampson and A. J. Stosick, *J. Am. Chem. Soc.* **60**, 1814 (1938).

case is obtainable by the oxidation of the corresponding sesquioxide (M_2O_3 or M_4O_6) with nitric acid.

Bismuth(V) oxide, mixed with lower oxides and alkali, is obtained as a reddish brown solid by the oxidation of alkaline suspensions of the sesquioxide with strong oxidizing agents such as permanganate, hexacyanoferrate(III), peroxide, peroxydisulfate, or hypochlorite. The fusion of Bi_2O_3 with caustic potash and potassium chlorate in the air also leads to bismuth(V) oxide.

The Phosphoric Acids and Their Salts

Phosphoric Acids. When phosphorus pentoxide reacts with an excess of water, a solution of orthophosphoric acid, H_3PO_4, is obtained:

$$P_4O_{10} + 6H_2O \rightarrow 4H_3PO_4$$

When, however, less than an excess of water is used or when concentrated solutions of H_3PO_4 are dehydrated, or when H_3PO_4 is allowed to react with phosphorus pentoxide, in such proportions as to yield compositions in the range between $P_4O_{10} \cdot 6H_2O$ (orthophosphoric acid—H_3PO_4) and $P_4O_{10} \cdot 2H_2O$ (metaphosphoric acid—HPO_3), a series of exceedingly viscous, semisolid products are obtained. These products, commonly called "polyphosphoric" acids, have been the subject of much research. It seems fairly certain, as a result of recent studies,[36] that such products are equilibrium mixtures, containing at least the following components: orthophosphoric acid, shown to be present over the entire range ($P_4O_{10} \cdot 6H_2O$ to $P_4O_{10} \cdot 2H_2O$), triphosphoric acid, $H_5P_3O_{10}$, likewise present over the entire range, pyrophosphoric acid, $H_4P_2O_7$, present up to 85 weight per cent P_4O_{10}, and one or more polymers of metaphosphoric acid, $(HPO_3)_n$, present at P_4O_{10} compositions above 83%. The so-called pure metaphosphoric acid (88.7% P_4O_{10}) contains at least three different components including ortho- and triphosphoric acids.

Only two phosphoric acids have been prepared in the crystalline state: orthophosphoric and pyrophosphoric. Orthophosphoric acid is obtained as a white solid of the composition H_3PO_4 which melts at 42.3°C or in the form of the hemihydrate, $2H_3PO_4 \cdot H_2O$ which melts at 29.35°C. The thermodynamic constants for orthophosphoric acid are only approximately known. The heat of formation of this substance in dilute aqueous solution from H_2, red phosphorus, and O_2 is 302,000 cal/mole. $\Delta F^0_{298°}$ for this process is $-270,000$ cal/mole. The electronic formula for ortho-

---

[36] P. N. Bell, *Anal. Chem.* **19**, 97 (1947); T. Fuwa, *J. Chem. Soc. Japan, Ind. Chem. Sect.* **56**, 10 (1953).

phosphoric acid is[36a]

$$
\begin{array}{c}
\text{H} \\
\ddot{\text{O}}\ddot{:} \\
\text{H}:\ddot{\text{O}}:\text{P}:\ddot{\text{O}}:\text{H} \\
\ddot{\text{O}}\ddot{:}
\end{array}
$$

and, as would be expected from this formula, the acid is triprotic, its successive ionization constants being 7.5×10^{-3}, 6.2×10^{-8}, and (approximately) 2×10^{-13}.[37] The best laboratory method for the production of orthophosphoric acid is by the oxidation of pure white phosphorus with nitric acid of specific gravity 1.2 (concentrated nitric acid reacts explosively), and evaporating the solution to crystallization. Commercial "syrupy" phosphoric acid (whose composition corresponds to 85% H_3PO_4 by weight) is obtained by the action of concentrated sulfuric acid on calcium phosphate (rock phosphate or bone ash):

$$Ca_3(PO_4)_2 + 3H_2SO_4 \rightarrow 3CaSO_{4(s)} + 2H_3PO_4$$

Solid pyrophosphoric acid, $H_4P_2O_7$, is obtained when a suspension of copper pyrophosphate in water is treated with hydrogen sulfide, the precipitated copper sulfide filtered off, and the filtrate subjected to careful evaporation. Crystalline $H_4P_2O_7$ melts at about 61°C. In acid solution, particularly when heated, it undergoes hydrolysis to the orthoacid:

$$H_4P_2O_7 + H_2O \rightarrow 2H_3PO_4$$

Pyrophosphoric acid is believed to have the electronic formula

$$
\begin{array}{c}
\text{H}\qquad\text{H} \\
\ddot{\text{O}}\ddot{:}\quad\ddot{\text{O}}\ddot{:} \\
\text{H}:\ddot{\text{O}}:\text{P}:\ddot{\text{O}}:\text{P}:\ddot{\text{O}}:\text{H} \\
\ddot{\text{O}}\ddot{:}\quad\ddot{\text{O}}\ddot{:}
\end{array}
$$

and is tetraprotic. The values 1.4×10^{-1}, 1.1×10^{-2}, 2.9×10^{-7}, and 3.6×10^{-9} have been given for its four ionization constants. It will be noted that the first and second constants are very close together. This

[36a] S. Furberg, *Acta Chem. Scand.* 8, 532 (1954).

[37] H. S. Harned and B. B. Owen, *Chem. Rev.* 25, 31 (1939); M. Jowett and H. Millett, *J. Am. Chem. Soc.* 51, 1004 (1929).

accounts for the existence of many salts of the types $M_2H_2P_2O_7$ and $M_4P_2O_7$ and some of the type $M_3HP_2O_7$, but few, if any, of the type $MH_3P_2O_7$.

Structure of the Phosphates. A study of the salts of the various phosphoric acids reveals great variety in structure and properties. In discussing these substances, it is convenient to use the very helpful classification proposed by L. F. Audrieth and O. F. Hill.[38] In this classification the phosphates are first divided into crystalline *phosphates* and those which are commonly called *phosphate glasses*.

The first group is further subdivided, from the structural point of view, into (a) the *linear* phosphates and polyphosphates and (b) the *cyclic* polyphosphates. The *linear* phosphates and polyphosphates include:

(1) orthophosphates, containing the PO_4^{-3} ion,

(2) pyrophosphates, containing the $P_2O_7^{-4}$ ion,

(3) triphosphates, containing the $P_3O_{10}^{-5}$ ion.

These three ions have the following electronic structures:

$$\left[\begin{array}{c} :\overset{..}{O}: \\ :O:P:O: \\ :\overset{..}{O}: \end{array}\right]^{-3} \quad \left[\begin{array}{c} :\overset{..}{O}: \ :\overset{..}{O}: \\ :O:P:O:P:O: \\ :\overset{..}{O}: \ :\overset{..}{O}: \end{array}\right]^{-4} \quad \left[\begin{array}{c} :\overset{..}{O}: \ :\overset{..}{O}: \ :\overset{..}{O}: \\ :O:P:O:P:O:P:O: \\ :\overset{..}{O}: \ :\overset{..}{O}: \ :\overset{..}{O}: \end{array}\right]^{-5}$$

and phosphates containing these ions are derivatives of orthophosphoric, pyrophosphoric, and triphosphoric acids, respectively. While claims have been made for the existence of tetraphosphates and higher linear polyphosphates, these claims are not in accord with the results of either x-ray or chemical investigations. In the linear polyphosphates, tetrahedra, in which the phosphorus atom is surrounded tetrahedrally by four oxygen atoms, are linked together through a common oxygen atom, as in the linear polysilicates. The P–O distance in the PO_4^{-3} ion is 1.54 A, and is 1.56 A for the end oxygens and 1.52 A for the middle oxygen in the $P_2O_7^{-4}$ ion.

The cyclic polyphosphates result from the fact that it is possible for the PO_4 tetrahedra to be linked to form cyclic anions, again as in the case of analogous polysilicates. The best characterized anion of this group

[38] *J. Chem. Educ.* **25**, 80 (1948).

is the trimetaphosphate ion, which has the following structure:

$$
\left[\begin{array}{c}
\ddot{\text{:O}} \quad \ddot{\text{O}}\text{:} \\
\text{:P:} \\
\text{:O} \quad \text{O:} \\
\text{:O:P:O:P:O:} \\
\text{:O:} \quad \text{:O:}
\end{array}\right]^{-3}
$$

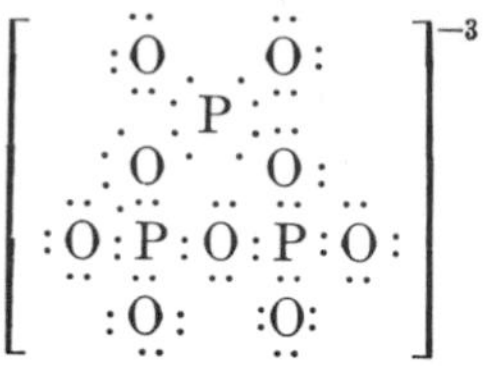

The existence of this anion in the solid trimetaphosphates and in their aqueous solutions has been definitely established. The preparation of cylic tetrametaphosphates, *e.g.*, $Al_4(P_4O_{12})_3$, has been announced.[39] These compounds contain the anion $[P_4O_{12}]^{-4}$ which has the following structure:

$$
\left[\begin{array}{c}
\ddot{\text{:O:}} \quad \ddot{\text{:O:}} \\
\text{:O:P:O:P:O:} \\
\text{:O:} \quad \text{:O:} \\
\text{:O:P:O:P:O:} \\
\text{:O:} \quad \text{:O:}
\end{array}\right]^{-4}
$$

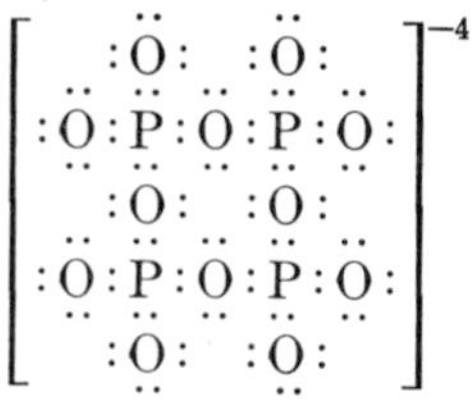

The question as to the existence of even larger rings such as $[P_6O_{18}]^{-6}$ remains unsettled. It seems definite, however, that the single PO_3^- ion is incapable of more than transitory existence, since it would react immediately with PO_4^{-3} or $P_2O_7^{-4}$ to form $P_2O_7^{-4}$ or $P_3O_{10}^{-5}$, respectively, or would combine with other PO_3^{-3} groups to form cyclic anions such as those mentioned above. Claims have been made for the existence of the ion of the structure

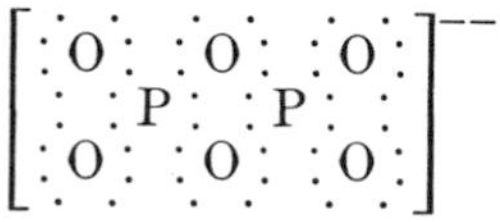

$$
\left[\begin{array}{c}
\text{:O:} \quad \text{:O:} \quad \text{:O:} \\
\text{:P:} \quad \text{:P:} \\
\text{:O:} \quad \text{:O:} \quad \text{:O:}
\end{array}\right]^{--}
$$

but this has not yet been established.[40] Work has been done, however,[41] which indicates that branched chain polyphosphate anions do not exist.

The polyphosphates are prepared, in general, by heating the acid salts of simpler phosphoric acids; condensation takes place with the loss of water. Representative processes involving the sodium salts are

[39] Pierre Bonneman, *Compt. rend.* **204**, 865 (1937); R. S. Hisar, *Bull. soc. chim. France* 1951, 806; A. E. R. Westman and A. E. Scott, *Nature* **168**, 740 (1951); B. Andersen and K. Lehmann, *Acta Chem. Scand.* **6**, 613 (1952).

[40] A. Travers and Yu Kwong Chu, *Compt. rend.* **198**, 2100 (1934).

[41] J. R. Van Wazer, Paper presented at 111th meeting of the American Chemical Society, 1947; G. Saini, *Ann. chim.* **42**, 227 (1952).

summarized in the following diagram:

$$2Na_2HPO_4 \rightarrow Na_4P_2O_7 + H_2O$$

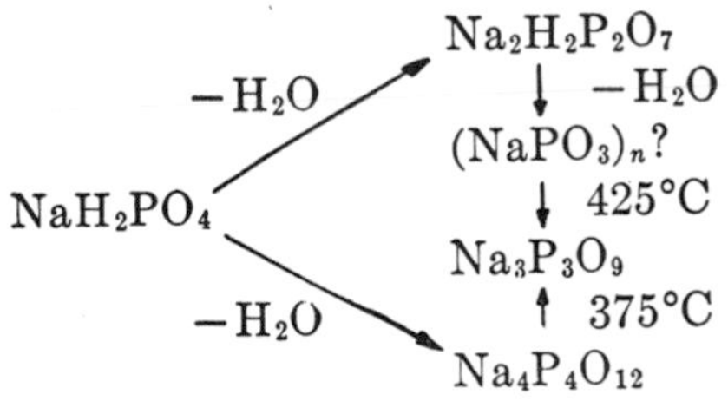

$$
\begin{array}{ccc}
 & & Na_2H_2P_2O_7 \\
-H_2O \nearrow & & \downarrow\ -H_2O \\
 & & (NaPO_3)_n? \\
NaH_2PO_4 & & \downarrow\ 425°C \\
 & & Na_3P_3O_9 \\
-H_2O \searrow & & \uparrow\ 375°C \\
 & & Na_4P_4O_{12}
\end{array}
$$

$$2Na_2HPO_4 + NaH_2PO_4 \rightarrow Na_5P_3O_{10} + 2H_2O$$

The cyclic trimetaphosphate ion is the most stable of the cyclic phosphates. All the metaphosphates, if heated to fusion and allowed to cool slowly, are converted to crystalline polymetaphosphates, preferentially, though not exclusively, to the cyclic trimetaphosphate. Rapid cooling yields glasses of the type discussed below.

All of the polyphosphates undergo hydrolysis to yield simpler anions. In the case of the linear polyphosphates the rate of hydrolysis increases with increasing chain length, increasing acidity of the solution, and rise in temperature. The presence of excess base increases the stability of linear polyphosphates. On the other hand, the rupture of metaphosphate rings is facilitated by the presence of alkali. Typical hydrolysis reactions in aqueous solution include:

$$P_3O_9^{-3} + H_2O \rightarrow H_2P_3O_{10}^{-3} \xrightarrow{+2H_2O} 3H_2PO_4^-$$

cyclic trimetaphosphate · · · · · dihydrogen triphosphate · · · · · dihydrogen orthophosphate

$$P_3O_{10}^{-4} + H_2O \rightarrow HP_2O_7^{-3} + HPO_4^{-2}$$

triphosphate · · · · · monohydrogen pyrophosphate · · · · · monohydrogen orthophosphate

$$H_2P_2O_7^{-2} + H_2O \rightarrow 2H_2PO_4^-$$

dihydrogen pyrophosphate · · · · · dihydrogen orthophosphate

$$HP_2O_7^{-3} + H_2O \rightarrow HPO_4^{-2} + H_2PO_4^-$$

$$P_2O_7^{-4} + H_2O \rightarrow 2HPO_4^{-2}$$

pyrophosphate

When a fused metaphosphate, such as that obtained by the dehydration of NaH_2PO_4, is rapidly cooled a glassy material first described by

Graham, and hence called Graham's salt, is obtained. In fact a clear glass is obtained by the quenching of any fused sodium phosphate mixture having $Na_2O:P_4O_{10}$ ratio between 2:1 and 10:3. Higher proportions of Na_2O result in the formation of a matrix of crystalline material suspended in a glass. A variety of experimental results leads to the definite conclusion that these glassy metaphosphates are true glasses, composed of mixtures containing high molecular weight anions. Unpublished observations of Audrieth and coworkers indicates an average ionic weight of between 4000 and 23,000, depending upon the history of the sample and the nature of the starting material. There is no evidence for the existence of "hexametaphosphates" in these materials. The process of solution of these metaphosphate glasses in water undoubtedly involves some hydration and hydrolysis.

Chemical and Physical Properties of the More Familiar Phosphates: Industrial Applications. Since orthophosphoric acid is a triprotic acid, there are three series of orthophosphates. Representatives of these three series, with their names (there are several ways of naming them) are listed in the following table:

TABLE 2.11. NOMENCLATURE OF ORTHOPHOSPHATES

Sodium Salt		*Calcium Salt*	
NaH_2PO_4	monosodium orthophosphate sodium dihydrogen orthophosphate primary sodium orthophosphate	$Ca(H_2PO_4)_2$	primary calcium orthophosphate
Na_2HPO_4	disodium orthophosphate sodium monohydrogen orthophosphate secondary sodium orthophosphate	$CaHPO_4$	secondary calcium orthophosphate
Na_3PO_4	trisodium orthophosphate tertiary sodium orthophosphate normal sodium orthophosphate	$Ca_3(PO_4)_2$	tertiary calcium orthophosphate

The alkali metal phosphates and the primary alkaline earth metal phosphates are readily soluble in water, but most other phosphates dissolve to only a slight extent. Even the less soluble phosphates dissolve readily in acid solutions, however, because of the tendency for phosphate and monohydrogen phosphate ions to take up protons.

Orthophosphoric, pyrophosphoric, and triphosphoric acids are strong with respect to the first ionization, first two ionizations, and first three ionizations, respectively, but are weak with respect to the rest of the ionizable hydrogens. Hence, their normal salts, and some of their acid salts undergo considerable hydrolysis in aqueous solution, *e.g.*:

$$PO_4^{-3} + H_2O = HPO_4^{--} + OH^-$$
$$HPO_4^- + H_2O = H_2PO_4^- + OH^-$$

Because of the strongly alkaline nature of its aqueous solution, trisodium orthophosphate has considerable use as a cleansing agent.

The most important use of phosphates is in the production of fertilizer. Tertiary calcium phosphate, $Ca_3(PO_4)_2$, which occurs in nature and is marketed as rock phosphate, is too slightly soluble in water to be of much value as a fertilizer. When rock phosphates are treated with sulfuric acid, however, a mixture of calcium sulfate and the more soluble primary calcium phosphate, $Ca(H_2PO_4)_2$, is obtained:

$$Ca_3(PO_4)_2 + 2H_2SO_4 + 4H_2O \rightarrow Ca(H_2PO_4)_2 + 2CaSO_4 \cdot 2H_2O$$

This product, commonly known as "superphosphate of lime," is used in tremendous quantities as a fertilizer. By the use of phosphoric acid in place of sulfuric an even more concentrated phosphate fertilizer is obtained. Nitric acid has also been suggested to give phosphorus and nitrogen-containing salts. Primary calcium phosphate is used in certain types of baking powder. Phosphates are used also in the weighting of silk, as well as in the fireproofing of certain fabrics.

The phosphate ion is capable of taking part in the formation of a number of complex compounds. For example, the addition of excess phosphoric acid to a solution of a iron(III) salt results in the formation of soluble complexes such as $H_3[Fe(PO_4)_2]$ and $H_6[Fe(PO_4)_3]$. When a solution containing the phosphate ion is treated with a solution of ammonium molybdate in nitric acid, a yellow precipitate of ammonium phosphomolybdate is obtained. This substance is a typical salt of a heteropolyacid and has a very complex structure. Its composition corresponds approximately to the empirical formula $(NH_3)_4PO_4 \cdot 12MoO_3 \cdot 3H_2O$. A number of other phosphomolybdates, as well as a series of phosphotungstates, are known also. The formation of the yellow phosphomolybdate precipitate is used as an analytical test for the PO_4^{-3} ion. Arsenate ion gives a similar reaction.

A number of reactions are available for distinguishing qualitatively between orthophosphoric acid, pyrophosphoric acid, and the polymeric metaphosphoric acids. Some of these are summarized in Table 2.12.

Just as metaphosphoric acid may be converted to orthophosphoric by the reaction with water, so may metaphosphates be converted, to a

TABLE 2.12. DISTINGUISHING REACTIONS OF THE PHOSPHORIC ACIDS

Reagent	H_3PO_4	$H_4P_2O_7$	$(HPO_3)_n$
$AgNO_3$	yellow ppt. Ag_3PO_4	white ppt. $Ag_4P_2O_7$ (cryst.)	white ppt. (gelatinous)
$Zn(C_2H_3O_2)_2$	no ppt.	white ppt. $Zn_2P_2O_7$	no. ppt.
$(NH_4)_2MoO_4$ in HNO_3	yellow ppt.	no ppt.	no ppt.
$BaCl_2$ (acid)	no ppt.	no ppt.	white ppt.
$BaCl_2$ (alkali)	white ppt. $Ba_3(PO_4)_2$	white ppt. $Ba_2P_2O_7$	white ppt.
Al^{+3}	ppt. soluble in acetic acid	ppt. insoluble in acetic acid	ppt. insoluble in acetic acid
$[Co(NH_3)_6]Cl_3$	no immediate ppt.	reddish-yellow ppt.	no immediate ppt.

greater or lesser degree, to orthophosphates or other linear polyphosphates by reactions in the fused state with metal oxides:

$$Ca(PO_3)_2 + 2CaO \rightarrow Ca_3(PO_4)_2$$

The colored orthophosphate or polyphosphate mixtures formed when beads of sodium metaphosphate are heated with metal compounds are of use in identifying the metals:

$$NaPO_3 + CuO \rightarrow NaCuPO_4$$
$$\text{(blue)}$$
$$NaPO_3 + NiSO_4 \rightarrow NaNiPO_4 + SO_3$$
$$\text{(green)}$$

Some of the complex metaphosphates are useful as water softeners because of their ability to tie up or sequester such metal ions as Ca^{++} and Mg^{++}, and prevent these ions from forming soap precipitates.

THE FLUO-, AQUO AMMONO, AND AMMONO PHOSPHORIC ACIDS

The Fluophosphoric Acids. If the hydroxide radicals on the phosphoric acid molecule are replaced one by one with the isosteric fluorine radical the following series of molecules are obtained:

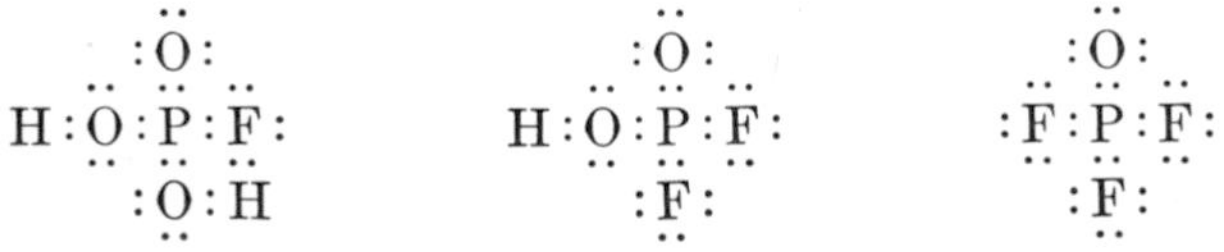

The last of these is phosphorus oxyfluoride which has already been discussed. The first two, however, are new compounds which are called monofluophosphoric acid and difluorophosphoric acid, respectively.

Knowledge of the chemistry of these two acids and their derivatives is largely the result of the work of Lange and his coworkers.[42]   The types of methods by which these acids and their salts are obtained are illustrated by the following equations:

$$POF_3 \xrightarrow{H_2O} HPO_2F_2 \xrightarrow{H_2O} H_2PO_3F$$

$$H_3PO_4 + HF \rightleftarrows H_2PO_3F + H_2O$$

$$H_2PO_4^- + HF \rightleftarrows HPO_3F^- + H_2O$$

$$6NH_4F + P_4O_{10} \xrightarrow{fusion} 2NH_4HPO_3F + 2NH_4PO_2F_2 + 2NH_3$$

$$(HPO_3)_n + nHF \xrightarrow{(anhyd.)} nH_2PO_3F \text{ (+ some } HPO_2F_2)$$

$$Na_4P_2O_7 + 2HF_{(aq)} \rightleftarrows 2Na_2PO_3F + H_2O$$

Anhydrous H_2PO_3F and HPO_2F_2 are available commercially.[43]   Monofluophosphoric acid is an oily, practically odorless liquid similar in appearance and viscosity to concentrated sulfuric acid; it undergoes moderate decomposition at 185°C under reduced pressure and may not be distilled. It is exceedingly viscous at lower temperatures and is a solid glass at −80°C.   The density (d_4^{25}) of the liquid is 1.818.   It will be noted that this acid is both isoelectronic and isoprotic with sulfuric acid.   Furthermore, the monofluophosphate ion has the same charge as, and is similar in size and structure to, the sulfate ion.   It is not surprising, therefore, that monofluophosphoric acid and its salts are similar in their chemistry to sulfuric acid and the sulfates—except for the much stronger oxidizing properties of sulfuric acid.   The correlation is particularly strong with respect to the solubilities of respective salts of the two acids.   Monofluophosphoric acid reacts with water according to the equilibrium:

$$H_2PO_3F + H_2O \rightleftarrows H_3PO_4 + HF$$

Difluophosphoric acid is a mobile, colorless, fuming liquid, similar in appearance to concentrated perchloric acid.   It boils with slight decomposition at 115.9°C at atmospheric pressure, and freezes at −96.5 ± 1°C. Its density (d_4^{25}) is 1.583 and its heat of vaporization is 7925 cal/mole. It is more highly corrosive than monofluophosphoric acid and attacks glass rapidly at its boiling point or in the presence of traces of moisture. The correspondence in properties between sulfuric acid and the sulfates and monofluophosphoric acid and its salts is matched by a similar corre-

[42] W. Lange and R. Livingston, *J. Am. Chem. Soc.* **69**, 1073 (1947) *et ante*.
[43] Ozark-Mahoning Co., Tulsa, Okla., *Technical Bulletin FPA-1*, May 15, 1944.

spondence between perchloric acid and the perchlorates and difluophosphoric acid and its salts. The strong oxidizing and explosive properties of perchloric acid and its salts are, however, missing from the attributes of difluophosphoric acid and its salts. Difluophosphoric acid reacts with water according to the equilibrium:

$$HPO_2F_2 + H_2O \rightleftarrows H_2PO_3F + HF$$

Numerous salts of both the monofluo- and difluo-acids have been prepared. Both mono- and difluophosphate ions undergo hydrolysis.

In addition to the fluoderivatives discussed above, salts of hexafluophosphoric acid, HPF_6, have been prepared by such reactions as the following:

$$PCl_5 + 6MF \rightarrow MPF_6 + 5MCl \quad (M = NH_4^+, \text{etc.})$$

$$PCl_5 + 6MF \xrightarrow[HF]{\text{liq.}} 5MCl + MPF_6$$

Sixty-five per cent aqueous solutions of the free acid are commercially available. The acid exists in stable equilibrium in concentrated solution, but when diluted to the concentration of 50% HPF_6 or less, considerable hydrolysis takes place. The PF_6^- ion is quite stable in neutral or alkaline media. The acid is useful in electrolytic brightening and polishing metals and alloys. Brass, Ni-Ag, stainless steel are polished at 50–75 amp/sq ft at 20–50°C.[44]

Ammono and Aquo Ammono Phosphoric Acids. The concepts of the nitrogen system of compounds and of ammono and aquo ammono analogues of compounds in the oxygen system were discussed in the preceding chapter. A number of ammono and aquo ammono phosphoric acids are known, either in the free state or in the form of their salts or esters. A few of the more important of these are listed in Table 2.13. Those not known in the free state but only in the form of salts or esters are boxed in.

The Acids and Salts of +5 Arsenic, Antimony, and Bismuth. When elementary arsenic or arsenic sesquioxide is oxidized with concentrated nitric acid or with chlorine water, orthoarsenic acid, H_3AsO_4, is produced and may be obtained as the crystalline hemihydrate $2H_3AsO_4 \cdot H_2O$ by concentrating the resulting solution at temperatures under 100°C. This substance is a white, deliquescent solid which melts at 36°C and is iso-

[44] H. F. Martin and C. B. F. Young, *Metal Finishing* 48, 70 (1950); see also Vol. III, this Series.

TABLE 2.13.   THE AQUO, AQUO AMMONO, AND AMMONO DERIVATIVES OF PHOSPHORIC ACID

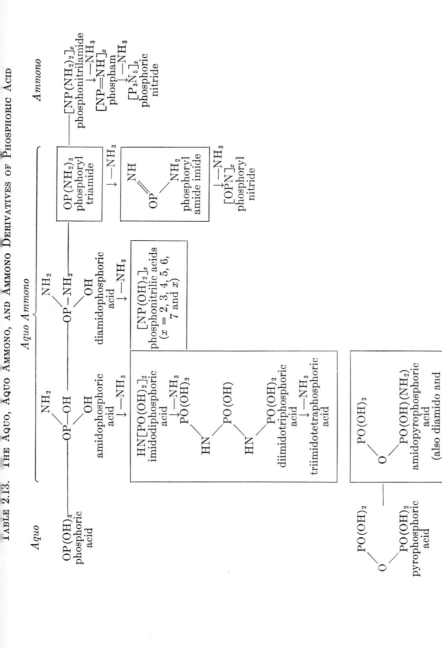

L. F. Audrieth and O. F. Hill, *J. Chem. Educ.* **25**, 85 (1948).

morphous with the corresponding hydrate of phosphoric acid. If the concentration is carried out at 100°C needle-like crystals of the anhydrous acid, H_3AsO_4, are obtained. When the acid is heated, it readily loses water to form the oxide, As_4O_{10}. It is somewhat weaker than phosphoric acid and, for corresponding salts of the two acids, the arsenate ion hydrolyzes to the greater extent. Primary, secondary, and tertiary orthoarsenates are known, as well as meta-arsenates and pyroarsenates. The arsenates strongly resemble corresponding phosphates in solubility and crystal form, many phosphate-arsenate pairs being isomorphous. Like phosphoric acid, arsenic acid has a strong tendency to form poly acids and a large number of heteropoly and isopoly acids of $+5$ arsenic are known. The arsenate ion gives a reaction with ammonium molybdate in nitric acid solution entirely analogous to that of the phosphate ion. Arsenate may be distinguished from phosphate by the chocolate brown Ag_3AsO_4 precipitate which it forms (Ag_3PO_4 is yellow), and by the formation of a yellow sulfide precipitate with hydrogen sulfide in strongly acid solution. Of the tertiary orthoarsenates, only the alkali-metal salts are soluble in water. Lead and calcium arsenates, $Pb_3(AsO_4)_2$, $Ca_3(AsO_4)_2$, $PbHAsO_4$, and $CaHAsO_4$, are used extensively in the preparation of insecticides. All the arsenates are highly poisonous.

Arsenates in acid solution are moderately strong oxidizing agents as is indicated by the following standard potential:

$$HAsO_2 + 2H_2O = H_3AsO_4 + 2H^+ + 2e^-, \quad E^0 = -0.559 \text{ volt}$$

Antimonic acid has not been well characterized; in fact, it is not certain that it exists as a definite compound. When antimonates are treated with strong acids, when antimony is vigorously oxidized with nitric acid, or when antimony pentachloride is completely hydrolyzed a gelatinous precipitate of a "hydrated" antimony pentoxide is obtained. This precipitate is not of constant composition, however, and may be the pentoxide with more or less adsorbed water. This precipitate, as well as the anhydrous pentoxide, dissolves readily in alkali to give solutions of salts whose formulas indicate that they are derived from an acid of the formula $HSb(OH)_6$. Among these are the salts $KSb(OH)_6$ and $NaSb(OH)_6$. The latter salt, the formula for which was long written $Na_2H_2Sb_2O_7 \cdot 5H_2O$ and the name sodium pyroantimonate applied, is one of the least soluble of all sodium salts, and its precipitation is sometimes used as a test for sodium ion.

In no case is there any structural similarity between phosphates and antimonates. The ion SbO_4^{-3} does not exist, and the so-called pyroantimonates, such as the sodium salt just mentioned, do not contain pyroantimonate ion, $Sb_2O_7^{-4}$. The salt $Mg(SbO_3)_2 \cdot 12H_2O$ which has been called hydrated magnesium metaantimonate, is shown by x-ray studies to be correctly formulated $[Mg(H_2O)_6][Sb(OH)_6]_2$. Similar cobalt and nickel salts are known. Furthermore, $Cu(NH_3)_2(SbO_3)_2 \cdot 9H_2O$ is $[Cu(NH_3)_3(H_2O)_3][Sb(OH)_6]_2$ and $LiSbO_3 \cdot 3H_2O$ is $Li[Sb(OH)_6]$.

A solution of an antimonate is a good oxidizing agent as is indicated by the electrode potential for the half-reaction represented by:

$$SbO^+ + 5H_2O = HSb(OH)_6 + 3H^+ + 2e^-, \quad E^0 = ca. -0.7 \text{ volt}$$

Antimonic acid is considerably weaker than arsenic acid and the antimonates undergo extensive hydrolysis in aqueous solution.

The compound $NaSbF_6$ (analogous to $NaPF_6$) is known and, upon partial hydrolysis, yields the salt $Na[SbF_4(OH)_2]$ analogous in structure to $Na[Sb(OH)_6]$.

Bismuthic acid is unknown, but Bi_2O_5 dissolves in strong alkali to yield metabismuthates such as $NaBiO_3$, commonly known simply as sodium bismuthate. The bismuthate ion in the presence of acids is an exceedingly strong oxidizing agent, as is indicated by the highly negative standard potential corresponding to the following half-equation:

$$BiO^+ + 2H_2O = HBiO_3 + 3H^+ + 2e^-; \quad E^0 = ca. -1.6 \text{ volts}$$

For example, bismuthate ion readily oxidizes manganese(II) ion to permanganate. Orthobismuthates are unknown.

THE SULFIDES OF PHOSPHORUS, ARSENIC, ANTIMONY, AND BISMUTH

The Sulfides of Phosphorus. It has been definitely established that phosphorus forms four sulfides, *viz.* P_4S_3, P_4S_5, P_4S_7, and P_4S_{10}; in addition, there is some evidence for the existence of P_3S_6. It will be noted that only one of these corresponds to any of the oxides which phosphorus forms. The important physical characteristics of the sulfides of phosphorus are listed in Table 2.14.

Tetraphosphorus trisulfide is made by heating a slight excess of red phosphorus with sulfur in a glass tube gradually to 100°C and then more strongly until the reaction starts and spreads throughout the mixture. The reaction must be carried out in the absence of oxygen. An impure form of this compound is used in the manufacture of certain types of matches. On being warmed in the presence of oxygen P_4S_3 luminesces. P_4S_3 is almost unaffected by cold water, and is only gradually attacked by boiling water; it forms, however, a reddish brown solution in liquid ammonia which is gradually transformed into a brown jelly. It dissolves in ether and alcohol without reaction.

TABLE 2.14. PHYSICAL PROPERTIES OF THE SULFIDES OF PHOSPHORUS

	P_4S_3	P_4S_5	P_4S_7	P_4S_{10}
Melting point (°C)	171–172.5	170–220	305–310	286–290
Boiling point (°C)	407–408	—	523	513–515
Density of solid at 17°	203	217(25°)	2.19	2.09
Color:				
solid	yellow	yellow	almost white	yellow
liquid	brownish yellow	—	light yellow	reddish brown
Solubility at 17°:				
in CS_2(g/100 g.)	100	≈10	0.029	0.222
in C_6H_6 (solvent)	2.5	—	—	—
in toluene	31.2	—	—	—

Tetraphosphorus pentasulfide, P_4S_5, is obtained by the reaction of P_4S_3 with slightly more than the theoretical quantity of sulfur in the presence of iodine under the influence of diffuse sunlight, or by slowly cooling a molten mixture of red phosphorus and sulfur in the atomic ratio 2:3. It is separated from the P_4S_7, also formed in these reactions, by extraction with carbon disulfide in which it is moderately soluble.

Tetraphosphorus heptasulfide, P_4S_7, is also obtained by heating red phosphorus and sulfur in the atomic ratio of 4:7 and a little (5%) P_4S_3 until distillation becomes evident. It is also formed by the reaction of P_4S_3 and P_4S_{10} in carbon disulfide at 100°C. The heptasulfide is more reactive towards water than are the other phosphorus sulfides.

Phosphorus(V) sulfide, whose molecular formula has been shown to be P_4S_{10}, is best obtained by heating red phosphorus and sulfur in the atomic ratio 2:5 plus 1% excess of sulfur to 700°C in a pressure tube, previously evacuated.[45] The pentasulfide is extracted from the reaction mixture with carbon disulfide and is recrystallized from the same solvent. Phosphorus pentasulfide hydrolyzes in water or in alkaline solution to yield chiefly phosphoric acid plus hydrogen sulfide. It is used as reagent in organic chemistry to bring about the substitution of sulfur in certain classes of compounds.

Phosphorus Oxysulfide. When phosphorus sesquioxide and sulfur in theoretical proportions are heated under an inert atmosphere to 160°C a vigorous and sometimes violent reaction takes place to yield phosphorus oxysulfide in accordance with the following equation:

$$P_4O_6 + 4S \rightarrow P_4O_6S_4$$

Phosphorus oxysulfide is a colorless to pale yellow solid depending upon its purity. It melts at 102°C and boils at 295°C. It is soluble in carbon

[45] A. Stock and B. Herscovici, *Ber.* **43**, 1223 (1910).

disulfide but reacts with benzene. The substance is deliquescent and is readily hydrolyzed:

$$P_4O_6S_4 + 6H_2O \rightarrow 4HPO_3 + 4H_2S$$

The structure of $P_4O_6S_4$ is analogous to that of P_4O_{10}.

Arsenic and Antimony Sulfides; Their Thiosalts. Both arsenic and antimony form sulfides of the general formulas M_2S_3 and M_2S_5. In addition arsenic forms the sulfide of the empirical formula AsS (which occurs in nature as the abundant red-colored mineral, *realgar*) as well as the unimportant yellow compound As_4S_3. The sulfide As_2S_3 is a bright yellow compound which occurs in nature as the mineral *orpiment* which is obtained by treatment of +3 arsenic with hydrogen sulfide. It is readily obtained in the colloidal state if the precipitation is carried out in solutions of low ionic strength, as when a solution of arsenous acid is saturated with hydrogen sulfide. The sulfide As_2S_5 likewise bright yellow in color, is obtained by treatment of strongly acidic solutions of arsenates with hydrogen sulfide. This reaction is relatively slow, and a mixture of As_2S_3 and As_2S_5 is usually obtained because of the reduction of +5 arsenic to +3 by hydrogen sulfide. In the presence of certain catalysts such as iodide ion, only As_2S_3 is obtained.

The sulfide Sb_2S_3 occurs in nature as the black mineral *stibnite*, but when precipitated from solutions of +3 antimony it is orange red in color. It, Sb_2S_3, and Sb_2S_5 are usually obtained by methods analogous to those used for the corresponding arsenic compounds.

The sulfides of arsenic and antimony, like their oxygen analogues, have acidic properties and dissolve readily in strong bases such as the alkali hydroxides, and undergo such reactions as:

$$As_2S_3 + 9OH^- \rightarrow 2AsO_3^{-3} + 3HS^- + 3H_2O$$

Of particular interest, is the fact that these sulfides dissolve readily in solutions of sulfide ion. These reactions may be considered as manifestations of the acidic properties of the sulfides, the sulfide ion in the solution acting as base. The equations for the respective reactions and the names of the resulting ions are as follows:

$$As_2S_3 + 3S^= \rightarrow 2AsS_3^{-3}$$
thioarsenite

$$As_2S_5 + 3S^= \rightarrow 2AsS_4^{-3}$$
thioarsenate

$$Sb_2S_3 + 3S^= \rightarrow 2SbS_3^{-3}$$
thioantimonite

$$Sb_2S_5 + 3S^= \rightarrow 2SbS_4^{-3}$$
thioantimonate

The thio-ions obtained are quite stable in neutral or alkaline solution, but since the corresponding acids H_3AsS_3, H_3AsS_4, H_3SbS_3, and H_3SbS_4 are unstable, acidification of the solutions results in the reprecipitation of the sulfides and the liberation of hydrogen sulfide.

These sulfides of arsenic and antimony are amphoteric for they likewise dissolve in concentrated acid though, in the case of the arsenic sulfides, the acid must be very concentrated and the rate is slow.

When solutions of bismuth salts are treated with hydrogen sulfide, bismuth sesquisulfide, Bi_2S_3, is obtained as a black precipitate. This compound occurs in nature as the mineral *bismuthinite*. Like the sesqui-oxide, it possesses no acidic properties, and hence dissolves in moderately concentrated acids but not in bases.

THE PEROXY ACIDS OF PHOSPHORUS

Acids of phosphorus are known which are analogous to peroxymono-sulfuric and peroxydisulfuric acids. They have the formulas H_3PO_5 and $H_4P_2O_8$, and are called, respectively, peroxymonophosphoric acid and peroxydiphosphoric acid. Their electronic formulas are the following:

$$
\begin{array}{cc}
\ddot{\text{O}}: & \ddot{\text{O}}: \qquad \ddot{\text{O}}: \\
\text{H}:\ddot{\text{O}}:\ddot{\text{O}}:\text{P}:\ddot{\text{O}}:\text{H} & \text{H}:\ddot{\text{O}}:\text{P}:\ddot{\text{O}}:\ddot{\text{O}}:\text{P}:\ddot{\text{O}}:\text{H} \\
\ddot{\text{O}}: & \ddot{\text{O}}: \qquad \ddot{\text{O}}: \\
\text{H} & \text{H} \qquad \text{H}
\end{array}
$$

As these formula indicate, each molecule contains a peroxy group. Since the oxygen atoms in this group are customarily assigned an oxidation state of -1, the oxidation state of phosphorus in the peroxyphosphoric acids is $+5$ just as in the phosphoric acids. By virtue of the peroxy group which they contain, the peroxy phosphoric acids and their salts are strong oxidizing agents.

The peroxyphosphoric acids are prepared by the reaction of hydrogen peroxide with P_4O_{10} or metaphosphoric acid,

$$P_4O_{10} + 4H_2O_2 + 2H_2O \rightarrow 4H_3PO_5$$
$$2HPO_3 + H_2O_2 \rightarrow H_4P_2O_8$$

or by the electrolysis of solutions of potassium monohydrogen ortho-phosphate, using low current density and avoiding cathodic reduction by the addition of chromate ion.

PART II

NONAQUEOUS CHEMISTRY

by Alfred R. Pray

School of Chemistry, University of Minnesota

CHAPTER 3

NONAQUEOUS CHEMISTRY

GENERAL

Several hundred thousand substances are known to the chemist and perhaps half might have potential use as media for chemical reactions. Nevertheless, the number actually employed for the purpose has been disappointingly small. Attention is repeatedly drawn in the literature to the paucity of information on nonaqueous media and the need for data in the field. For "the more we learn about water, the clearer it becomes that this liquid holds an exceptional position among solvent media, but research workers the world over persist in studying aqueous systems, and then attempt to base broad generalization on this limited range of experience." [1] "Much important chemistry . . . has been obscured by our slavish devotion to water." [2] Probably not more than a few dozen liquids have been investigated, and of these, few with any thoroughness.

One of the early observations on a solvent other than water pointed out that carbonates in contact with anhydrous acids dissolved in absolute alcohol remained undecomposed. [3] It was later shown that the reaction is possible but very slow. [4]

Observations on liquefied ammonia, the nonaqueous solvent most studied to date, began with Faraday's researches on the liquefaction of gases in 1805. It was soon noted that the gas was easy to liquefy, and by the middle of the century systematic investigations on this solvent were under way [*vide infra*].

Many suggestions for classifying solvents have been made. [5] These

---

[1] R. M. Fuoss and A. S. Fuoss, *Annual Review of Physical Chemistry* 4, 49 (1953).

[2] J. B. Conant and N. F. Hall, *J. Am. Chem. Soc.* 49, 3062 (1927).

[3] M. J. Pelouze, *Pogg. Ann.* 26, 343 (1832) and *Ann. chim. et phys.* (2) 50, 314 and 434 (1832).

[4] C. Vallee, *Compt. rend.* 132, 677 (1901).

[5] C. A. Kraus, *Properties of Electrically Conducting Systems*, Chemical Catalog Co., N. Y. (1922); P. Walden, *Elektrochemie Nichtwässriger Lösungen*, J. A. Barth, Leipzig (1924); P. Walden, *Salts, Acids, and Bases*, McGraw-Hill, N. Y. (1929) (translated by L. F. Audrieth); E. C. Franklin, *Nitrogen System of Compounds*, Reinhold, N. Y. (1935); W. F. Luder and S. Zuffanti, *Electronic Theory of Acids and Bases*, J. Wiley and Sons, N. Y. (1946); L. F. Audrieth, *Acids, Bases, and Nonaqueous Systems*, University Litho-printers, Ypsilanti, Mich. (1949); L. F. Audrieth and J. Kleinberg, *Nonaqueous Solvents*, J. Wiley and Sons, N. Y. (1953).

suggestions often arose out of attempts to elucidate on the nature of acids, bases and neutralization reactions.

At present the most important properties of a potentially useable solvent seem to be the dipole moment and the dielectric constant; the second is dependent on the first. A large value for the dipole moment expresses the idea that the solvent molecule has a positively charged part well separated from a negatively charged part. If such a molecule is placed in an electric field, *e.g.*, by placing some of the solvent between the plates of a condenser connected to a battery, the molecule will orient itself in such a way as to have the negatively charged part pointing toward the positive plate of the condenser, and the positive part correspondingly pointing toward the negative plate. This orientation tends to neutralize the field, and the extent to which it occurs is expressed by the dielectric constant, a vacuum arbitrarily being assigned a value of unity. A large value for the dipole moment thus implies a large value for the dielectric constant, and *vice versa*.

If a charged body, such as an ion, is introduced into a solvent which has a large dipole moment, combination between ion and solvent molecule promptly occurs. Ions in such solvents are thus solvated and solubility is enhanced by solvation. If the dipole moment is small, solvation of an ion is also small, and the solubility will correspondingly be small.

In a salt, positive ions are associated with negative ions. When a pair of such ions is introduced into a solvent of high dielectric constant, the force of attraction between the pair is lessened, the force depending inversely on the dielectric constant. It should be pointed out that the dielectric constant of the solvent in the vicinity of an ion may be very different from the dielectric constant of the solvent as determined in the absence of ions. Until very recently this dependence was an unsolved problem, in fact it was not known for certain whether the dielectric constant was increased or decreased. This obstacle arises from the difficulty of measuring the dielectric constant of a conducting medium. Water has been the only solvent thus far studied; for water the dielectric constant in the vicinity of a point charge is very low (unity) up to about 2 A from the charge, where the dielectric constant has the value of four or five, this condition arising from electron (and atom) polarization only. From 2 A up to about 4 A the rise is very rapid, reaching the value for the bulk of the liquid at that distance.[6] More specifically, if two ions attract each other with a certain force in a vacuum, the distance between them being specified, then in a solvent with a dielectric constant of ϵ the

[6] See D. M. Ritson and J. B. Hasted, *J. Chem. Phys.* **16**, 11 (1948).

attractive force between them will be only $1/\epsilon$ as much for the same distance. This statement is of course, Coulomb's law, or

$$f = \frac{1}{\epsilon} \left(\frac{q_1 q_2}{r^2} \right)$$

in which f is the force of attraction between two ions of charge q_1 and q_2, separated by a distance r, in a medium of dielectric constant ϵ. This relation leads to the important idea that solvents with large dielectric constants promote ionization of their solutes, or dissociation of solutes already ionized. This idea is usually referred to as the Nernst-Thomson rule.[7] Thus a solvent of large dipole moment and large dielectric constant not only readily solvates ions but also reduces the attraction between them. This conclusion has been given qualitative acknowledgment in the principle of *similia similibus solvuntur*, or like dissolves like. However, the phenomenon of solubility depends not only on properties of the solvent but equally upon properties of the solute.[8] It will be reasonable to expect that solvents with small dielectric constants will be poor solvents for salts, and, when these substances are soluble, that the ions will be highly associated into neutral pairs or large charged aggregates (ion doublets, ion triplets, etc.). Experiment amply confirms this expectation.[9] Few solvents have dielectric constants larger than 50. Water, *e.g.*, has a dielectric constant of 78.54 at 25°C; that of hydrogen cyanide is also very high, 106.8 at 25°C; that of formanide is 109.5 at 25°C; that of anhydrous hydrogen sulfate is 110 at 20°C; and the value for hydrogen fluoride is 83.6 at 0°C. However, most polar liquids have values much lower. Acetamide has a value of 59 at 83°C, hydrazine 52 at 25°C, and ammonia about 22 at −33.5°C. Nonpolar liquids, which are by far the commonest ones encountered, have dielectric constants around the value 2.

The charges on a solvent molecule, whose magnitude and separation are expressed by the dipole moment, likewise give rise to the phenomenon of association in solvents, of which hydrogen bonding is perhaps the best known example. Solvent molecules with large dipoles tend to associate into strands or clusters, leading to anomalously high boiling points. Temperature effects run counter to the tendency.[10] Associated solvents,

[7] W. Nernst, *Z. physik. Chem.* **13**, 531 (1894); J. J. Thomson, *Phil. Mag.* **36**, 320 (1894).

[8] J. H. Hildebrand and R. L. Scott, *Solubility of Non-electrolytes*, 3rd Ed., Reinhold, N. Y. (1953).

[9] C. A. Kraus and R. M. Fuoss, *J. Am. Chem. Soc.* **55**, 21 (1933); R. M. Fuoss and C. A. Kraus, *ibid.* **55**, 2387 (1933); *idem, ibid.* **57**, 1 (1935).

[10] J. N. Wilson, *Chem. Revs.* **25**, 377 (1939).

because of the large dielectric constants and large dipole moments, are often referred to as ionizing solvents and as levelling solvents. These terms refer to the tendency of such solvents to ionize or dissociate strong acids, *etc.*, to about the same degree. Solvents of low dielectric constant and small dipole moment are sometimes referred to as differentiating solvents.[11] As a result of the low dielectric constant such solvents do not promote ionization of their solutes and such solutes are then free to exhibit the intrinsic differences between them. This difference is more easily described as a particular case: in water with a dielectric constant of about 80, the acids $HClO_4$, HBr, HCl, HNO_3, and Cl_3CCOOH, all exhibit about the same strengths. It should be noted that the effect of these upon the inversion of sucrose is clearly ordered, even in water, however.[12] In glacial acetic acid on the other hand, with a dielectric constant of slightly less than 10, trichloroacetic acid is an extremely weak acid while perchloric acid is moderately weak, the others being in the series just presented. How little data of this kind are available in the literature and the tremendous field awaiting study will be apparent in the sections to follow.[13]

In an approximate way, each solvent here treated has been described in terms first of its properties and then of the solubility relations existing in it. Next come acid-base behavior and oxidation-reduction phenomena. Miscellaneous observations on solvolysis and amphoterism come next, followed by organic reactions and physical chemistry. The nonaqueous chemistry of certain other solvents (as HF, interhalogens, halogens, phosphorus compounds, sulfuric acid, nitric acid, *etc.*) than those herein treated have been considered in previous volumes or will be considered in future volumes under the chemistry of the specific compounds. The treatment of the solvent systems in this section will serve to give a broad background to the general nature of nonaqueous chemistry.

AMMONIA

Although ammonia can be obtained in the liquid state with little trouble, the low normal boiling point, $-33.35°C$, requires that work with

[11] A. Hantzch, *Z. Elektrochem.* **24**, 201 (1918); *ibid.* **29**, 221 (1923); *ibid.* **30**, 194 (1924); *Ber.* **60B**, 1933 (1927); A. Hantzch and A. Weissberger, *Z. physik. Chem.* **125**, 251 (1927); A. Hantzch, *ibid.* **134**, 406 (1928); *Ber.* **63B**, 1789 (1930); N. F. Hall, *Chem. Revs.* **8**, 191 (1931).

[12] See A. Hantzch and A. Weissberger, *Z. physik. Chem.* **125**, 251 (1927).

[13] An especially good treatment of conductance, chemical potential, and diffusion in solutions of simple electrolytes will be found in R. A. Robinson and R. H. Stokes, *Electrolyte Solutions*, Butterworths, London (1955), while for the general case see the work of H. S. Harned and B. B. Owen, *Physical Chemistry of Electrolytic Solutions*, 2nd Ed., Reinhold, N. Y. (1950).

it be carried on at low temperatures or high pressures. The heat of vaporization is high, however, which makes it possible to handle the liquid in ordinary laboratory apparatus, which in use is soon coated over with insulating rime. The literature should be consulted for details [14] including apparatus suitable for titrations.[15]

The following table lists some of the properties of this solvent.

TABLE 3.1. SOME PHYSICAL PROPERTIES OF AMMONIA

Normal boiling point	$-33.35\,^{\circ}C$
Freezing point	$-77.7\,^{\circ}C$
Dielectric constant	22 (at $-34\,^{\circ}C$)
Conductivity	1.3 (10^{-9}) mho (at $-79\,^{\circ}C$)
Dipole moment	1.47 D
Viscosity	0.00265 dyne-sec./cm^2 (at $-33.5\,^{\circ}C$)
Density	0.683 g/ml (at $-33.4\,^{\circ}C$)
Heat of vaporization	5.64 kcal/mole
Heat of fusion	1.43 kcal/mole

PROPERTIES OF ANHYDROUS AMMONIA

As a Solvent. Liquid ammonia is able to dissolve a wide variety of substances and observations on it began very early.[16] Among the organic materials the alcohols, halogen compounds such as chloroform, compounds containing nitrogen such as amines, nitriles, *etc.*, ketones, esters, simple ethers, and phenol and its derivatives are readily soluble. Paraffins are generally insoluble, the most unsaturated among them being the most soluble. The aromatic hydrocarbon compounds are in general only sparingly soluble. Among inorganic substances, oxides, hydroxides, sulfates, sulfites, sulfides (except ammonium and arsenic(III) sulfides), carbonates, phosphates, and fluorides are insoluble. Metal chlorides and bromides are generally only slightly soluble, oftentimes with solvolysis. Iodides, nitrates, nitrites, sodium chloride, sodium sulfide, and other sodium salts are fairly soluble. The ammonium halides and pseudo-

[14] W. C. Johnson and W. C. Fernelius, *J. Chem. Educ.* **6**, 441 (1929); G. W. Watt and T. E. Moore, *J. Am. Chem. Soc.* **70**, 1197 (1948); G. W. Watt and C. Keenan, *J. Am. Chem. Soc.* **71**, 3833 (1949); E. C. Franklin, *The Nitrogen System of Compounds*, Am. Chem. Soc. Monograph No. 68, Chemical Catalog Company, N. Y., 1935, appendix, pp. 317–330.

[15] A. J. Shattenshtein, *Acta Physicochim. U.R.S.S.* **7**, 691 (1937); *ibid.* **13**, 604 (1940); G. Watt and C. Keenan, *J. Am. Chem. Soc.* **71**, 3833 (1949).

[16] H. V. Regnault, *Pogg. Ann.* **111**, 402 (1860); E. Weyl, *ibid.* **121**, 601 (1894); *ibid.* **123**, 350 (1864); E. Seeley, *Chem. News* **23**, 169 (1871); *J. Frank. Inst.* **91**, 110 (1871); G. Gore, *Proc. Royal Soc.* **20**, 441 (1872); *ibid.* **21**, 140 (1873); M. Joannis, *Compt. rend.* **109**, 900 and 965 (1890); *ibid.* **112**, 337 and 392 (1891); *ibid.* **113**, 795 (1892); *ibid.* **114**, 585 (1892); *ibid.* **116**, 1370 and 1518 (1893); *ibid.* **118**, 713 and 1149 (1894); *ibid.* **119**, 557 (1895); E. C. Franklin and C. A. Kraus, *Am. Chem. J.* **20**, 820 (1898).

TABLE 3.2. SOME SOLUBILITIES OF INORGANIC SALTS IN AMMONIA [a]

Solute	Solubility [b]	Solute	Solubility
$AgCl$	0.8	MnI_2	0.02
$AgBr$	5.9	NaF	0.4
AgI	206.8	$NaCl$	3.0
$AgNO_3$	86.0	$NaBr$	138.0
$BaCl_2$	0	NaI	161.9
$Ba(NO_3)_2$	97.2	$NaNO_3$	97.6
$BiCl_3$	0	$NaNH_2$	0.004
$Bi(NO_3)_3$	0	Na_2SO_3	0.2
$Ca(NO_3)_2$	80.2	$NaHSO_3$	0.088
$Cd(NO_3)_2$	0	$NaCNS$	205.5
$Co(NO_3)_2$	0	Na_2SO_4	0
$Cu(NO_3)_2$	Sol. with react.	NH_4Cl	102.5
$FeBr_3$	0	NH_4Br	237.9
$Hg(NO_3)_2$	0	NH_4I	368.5
HgI_2	Sol. with react.	NH_4NO_3	390
H_3BO_3	1.9	$(NH_4)_2SO_3$	0
I_2	Sol. with react.	NH_4HCO_3	0
KCl	0.04	NH_4ClO_4	137.9
KBr	13.5	$NH_4C_2H_3O_2$	253.2
KI	182.0	$(NH_4)_2HPO_4$	0
KNO_3	10.4	$(NH_4)_2S$	120.0
KNH_2	3.6	NH_4CNS	312.0
$KClO_3$	2.52	$Ni(NO_3)_2$	0
$KBrO_3$	0.002	$Pb(NO_3)_2$	Sol. with react.
KIO_3	0	$Pb(C_2H_3O_2)_2$	0
K_2CO_3	0	S	0
K_2SO_4	0	$SbBr_3$	0
$KCNO$	1.7	$SnCl_4$	0
$LiNO_3$	243.7	$Sr(NO_3)_2$	87.1
Li_2SO_4	0	ZnI_2	0.1
Mg_3N_2	0	ZnO	0

[a] H. Hunt, *J. Am. Chem. Soc.* **54**, 3509 (1932); *ibid.* **55**, 3528 (1933).
[b] Solubilities given in g per 100 g of NH_3 at 25°C under unspecified pressures.

halides (*e.g.*, thiocyanates) and also the substituted ammonium halides (*e.g.*, tetraethylammonium chloride) prove to be extremely soluble.

One of the surprising features of liquid ammonia is its ability to dissolve the alkali metals unchanged. This fact was very early observed, and quite possibly led to the development of ammonia as a medium of unusual interest.[17] The alkaline earth metals are also dissolved by liquid ammonia, but evaporation of the solvent yields the metal in the form of a hexammonate, $M \cdot 6NH_3$.

[17] E. Weyl, *Pogg. Ann.* **121**, 601 (1864); *ibid.* **123**, 350 (1864); C. A. Seely, *Chem. News* **23**, 169 (1871); *J. Frank. Inst.* **91**, 110 (1871); H. P. Cady, *J. Phys. Chem.* **1**, 707 (1897); E. C. Franklin and C. A. Kraus, *Am. Chem. J.* **20**, 820 (1898).

Solutions of lithium, sodium, potassium, rubidium, and cesium are alike in their deep blue color and in other properties. They are all less dense than the parent solvent, are excellent electrical conductors, and are strongly paramagnetic in concentrated solutions. However, the magnetic susceptibility is negative at low temperatures for moderate concentrations (*ca.* 0.2 *M.*) and becomes positive again for solutions still more dilute. At high concentrations, the electrical conductance approaches that of metals; at low concentrations it approaches that of electrolytic solutions. Transference measurements show that at high concentrations, the negative "ion" moves about 280 times as fast as the positive ion; at great dilutions, it only moves seven times as fast. Conductance data also show that the negative ion is the same for all solutions of metals. The light absorptions of all solutions of metals, at equivalent concentrations in the dilute region, are identical. The alkali metals are also soluble in amines of low molecular weight, as methylamine and ethylamine, to give blue solutions, and sodium dissolved in fused caustic soda or in fused sodamide is similarly blue.

The electrolysis of substituted ammonium halides, NH_4X, leads to the formation of a blue solution of the free inorganic radical NR_4. It had been supposed that the formation of the free radical "ammonium" might be effected in the same way but the evidence appears, however, to be limited. When a saturated solution of ammonium chloride is electrolyzed (in water) with a mercury cathode, the mercury gradually becomes pasty, swells, and finally congeals. If this solid mass is removed from the solution and exposed to the air, it little by little evolves ammonia and hydrogen, in the proportion of two to one by volume. It is thus concluded that an amalgam of the unstable pseudo-metal ammonium is present, but efforts to prepare free ammonium not amalgamated have not been successful.

The solutions of alkali metals in liquid ammonia are stable even at room temperature (at an appropriate pressure) for a considerable time. The tendency is present, however, for the following reaction to occur:

$$2NH_3 + 2Na \rightarrow 2NaNH_2 + H_2$$

The introduction of small amounts of catalysts, such as iron(III) oxide or platinum black, cause it to proceed rapidly. It has been suggested that the stability of these metal solutions can be attributed to the low electrode potentials of these metals against ammonia as compared to the corresponding potentials against water, which are greater, and also to the small auto-ionization of the solvent [*vide infra*].

It is now supposed that the blue solutions of metals in liquid ammonia are solutions containing two species—the metal ions and electrons. It is to the latter that the blue color is due, as well as the quasimetallic electrical conduction and the other properties which the solutions have in common among themselves. The view that in concentrated solutions of metals the electrons are largely free,[18]

$$M \rightarrow M^+ + e^-$$

while in dilute solutions the electrons are solvated,

$$e^- + x\mathrm{NH}_3 \rightarrow (\mathrm{NH}_3)_x e^-$$

has been questioned on thermodynamic grounds.[19] The electrons appear to be trapped in cavities in the solvent of a size very near to that of a single ammonia molecule. These cavities thus resemble the familiar type of electron traps in molecular crystals.[20]

It follows from the existence of "free" electrons in solutions of the alkali metals that these solutions should be among our most powerful reducing agents; this conclusion is borne out by experiment.

In water, the strongest reducing agents reduce hydrogen ions to free hydrogen. In liquid ammonia, this tendency is low. The reduction reaction is characterized by the addition of an electron to an atom or ion; the positive metal ion, conjugate to the electron originally, is nonreactive. The equation

$$2\mathrm{Na}^+ + 2e^- + \mathrm{S} \rightarrow \mathrm{S}^{-2} + 2\mathrm{Na}^+$$

presents this concept.

In some cases, products are obtained that are impossible to prepare in any other way. For example, the reduction of sodium nitrite leads to sodium nitroxylate:

$$2\mathrm{NaNO}_2 + 2\mathrm{Na} \rightarrow \mathrm{Na}_4\mathrm{N}_2\mathrm{O}_4$$

This latter is a yellow powder of limited solubility.

Reaction of Elements in Liquid Ammonia. The table below presents the principal products formed when solutions of the alkali metals are

[18] C. A. Kraus, *Properties of Electrically Conducting Systems*, Chemical Catalog Co., N. Y. (1922).

[19] R. A. Ogg, Jr., *J. Chem. Phys.* **13**, 533 (1945); *J. Am. Chem. Soc.* **68**, 155 (1946); *J. Chem. Phys.* **14**, 114 (1946); *ibid.* **14**, 295 (1946); *Phys. Rev.* **69**, 243 and 668 (1946); *J. Chem. Phys.* **14**, 399 (1946); H. A. Boorse, D. B. Cook, R. B. Pontius, and M. W. Zemansky, *Phys. Rev.* **70**, 92 (1946); R. A. Ogg, Jr., *ibid.* **70**, 93 (1946); W. N. Lipscomb, *J. Chem. Phys.* **21**, 52 (1953).

[20] N. F. Mott and R. W. Gurney, *Electronic Processes In Ionic Crystals*, Clarendon Press, Oxford (1940).

TABLE 3.3. ACTION OF ALKALIES ON OTHER ELEMENTS IN LIQUID AMMONIA

Element	Metal	Product
As	Li	Li_3As
As	Na	Na_3As
As	K	$K_3As \cdot NH_3$ (potassium in excess)
		$K_2As_4 \cdot NH_3$ (arsenic in excess)
Bi	Na	Na_3Bi (insoluble)
Ge	Na	Na_4Ge_x
Hg	Na	$NaHg_3$
Hg	K	KHg_{18}
O_2	Li	Li_2O and Li_2O_2
O_2	Na	$NaOH$, $NaNH_2$, and $NaNO_2$
O_2	Na	Na_2O_2
O_2	Na	NaO_2 (at $-77°$)
P	Li	LiP [When alkali metal solutions are treated with phosphorus in toluene, normal phosphides do not form. Instead one obtains such compounds as Li_2P, Na_2P, K_3P_2, and some polyphosphides. E. Evers, *J. Am. Chem. Soc.* **73**, 2038 (1951)]
P	Na	$Na_3P_2H_3$ and $NaNH_2$ (sodium in excess)
P	Na	$NaP_3 \cdot 3NH_3$ (phosphorus in excess)
P	K	$KP_5 \cdot 3NH_3$ (phosphorus in excess)
Pb	Li	Li_4Pb_x (soluble)
Pb	Na	$NaPb$ (insoluble)
Pb	Na	$NaPb_2$ (soluble)
Pb	Na	Na_4Pb_9 (soluble)
Pb	K	KPb_2 (soluble)
Pb	K	K_4Pb_9 (soluble)
Pb	Rb	(?) (soluble)
Pb	Cs	(?) (soluble)
S	Li	Li_2S (slightly soluble)
S	Li	Li_2S_2 (slightly soluble)
S	Li	Li_2S_4 (soluble)
S	Li	Li_2S_x (?) (soluble)
S	Na	Na_2S (slightly soluble)
S	Na	Na_2S_2 (?) (slightly soluble)
S	Na	Na_2S_4 (soluble)
S	K	K_2S (slightly soluble)
S	K	K_2S_2 (slightly soluble)
S	K	K_2S_4 (soluble)
S	Rb	Rb_2S_2
S	Rb	Rb_2S_4
S	Cs	Cs_2S_2
S	Cs	Cs_2S_4
Sb	Li	Li_3Sb (insoluble)
Sb	Na	Na_3Sb (insoluble)
Sb	Na	Na_3Sb_{5-7}
Se	Li	Li_2Se (slightly soluble)
Se	Li	Li_2Se_{2-5} (soluble)
Se	Na	Na_2Se (slightly soluble)
Se	Na	Na_2Se_{2-6} (soluble)

TABLE 3.3—*Continued*

Element	Metal	Product
Se	K	K_2Se (slightly soluble)
Se	K	K_2Se_x (soluble)
Se	Rb	Rb_2Se
Se	Cs	Cs_2Se
Sn	Na	(?) (soluble)
Te	Na	Na_2Te (insoluble)
Te	Na	Na_2Te_2 (soluble)
Te	Na	Na_2Te_3 (soluble)
Te	Na	Na_2Te_4 (soluble)
Te	K	K_2Te (insoluble)
Te	K	K_2Te_3 (soluble)
Te	Rb	Rb_2Te
Te	Cs	Cs_2Te

brought into contact with a number of elements. It will be observed that while the expected products are obtained in most cases, *e.g.*, K_2Se, nevertheless many of the products are unexpected, *e.g.*, Na_4Pb_9.[21]

REACTIONS OF COMPOUNDS WITH ALKALI METALS IN LIQUID AMMONIA

The reduction of a great variety of salts by the alkali metals and calcium has been attempted and Table 3.4 presents this in summary.

It should be noted that a number of the formulas presented as products in this table, *e.g.*, $NaZn_{12}$, were arrived at by titrating a solution of the salt with a solution of the alkali metal or alkaline earth metal. The course of such titrations was followed potentiometrically and in some cases conductometrically. Such titrations do not lead to an unambiguous formulation for the product, as is well known. They are reported in the literature, however, and are presented here without further *caveat*.[22] Recently, some of these older titrations have been repeated. Very careful reinvestigation of the formation of alkali metal sulfides has shown that sodium, potassium, rubidium, and cesium all form sulfides with the formula M_2S_4. In addition, potassium, rubidium, and cesium form sulfides with the formula M_2S_2, and sodium and potassium only form sulfides with the formula M_2S. No other polysulfides of these alkali

[21] G. W. Watt, *Chem. Rev.* **46**, 289 (1950).

[22] C. A. Kraus, *J. Am. Chem. Soc.* **44**, 1220 (1922); *Trans. Am. Electrochem. Soc.* **45**, 175 (1924); F. W. Bergstrom, *J. Phys. Chem.* **30**, 12 (1926); W. C. Johnson and W. C. Fernelius, *J. Chem. Educ.* **7**, 981 (1930); E. Zintl and A. Harder, *Z. physik. Chem.* **A154**, 47 (1931); E. Zintl and W. Dullenkopf, *Z. physik. Chem.* **B16**, 183 (1932); E. Zintl and H. Kaiser, *Z. anorg. u. allgem. Chem.* **211**, 113 (1933); and W. C. Fernelius and R. F. Robey, *J. Chem. Educ.* **12**, 66 (1935) for a full discussion of these intermetallic compounds.

TABLE 3.4. REACTIONS OF ALKALI METALS ON SALTS IN LIQUID AMMONIA

Salt	Metal	Product (principal)
AgCl	Na	Ag
AgCl	K	Ag
AgI	Na	Ag
AgI	K	Ag
AgI	Ca	Ag
AgCN	Na	Ag
AgCN	K	Ag
AgCN	Ca	Ag
$AgNO_3$	Na	Ag
$AgNO_3$	K	Ag
AgCNO	Na	Ag
AgCNO	K	Ag
AgCNO	Ca	Ag
AgCNS	Na	Ag
AgCNS	K	Ag
AgCNS	Ca	Ag
$AlX_3 (X = Cl^-, Br^-, I^-)$	K	Al
$BiCl_3$	Na	$NaBi_{3.3}$ (?)
BiI_3	Na	Bi
BiI_3	Na	Na_3Bi (insoluble)
BiI_3	Na	Na_3Bi_3 (soluble)
BiI_3	Na	Na_3Bi_5 (soluble)
BiOI	Na	Bi (with excess bismuth)
BiOI	Na	Na_3Bi_x (with excess sodium)
BiOI	K	Bi (with excess bismuth)
BiOI	K	K_3Bi_x (with excess potassium)
CdI_2	Na	NaCd
CdI_2	Na	$NaCd_{5-7}$
$Cd(CN)_2$	Na	NaCd
$Co(NO_3)_2$	Na	Co
CuI	Na	Cu
$Cu(NO_3)_2$	Na	Cu
$Fe(NO_3)_3$	Na	Fe
$GaBr_3$	Na	Ga
HgI_2	Ca	Ca_3Hg_2
$Hg(CN)_2$	Na	NaHg
$Hg(CN)_2$	Ca	Ca_3Hg_2
$InX_3 (X = Cl^-, Br^-, I^-)$	K	In
KNO_2	Na	$KNaNO_2$
KNO_3	K	K_2NO_2
MnI_2	Na	Mn, then $Mn(NH_2)_2$ and $Mn(NHNa)_2 \cdot 2NH_3$
$NaNO_2$	Li	$LiNaNO_2$
$NaNO_2$	Na	Na_2NO_2
$NaNO_3$	Na	Na_2NO_2
$Ni(NH_2)_2$	Na	Ni
$Ni(NH_2)_2$	K	Ni
$Ni(NH_2)_2$	Ca	Ni
$NiCl_2$	Na	Ni, then $Ni(NH_2)_2$ and NaCl
$NiBr_2$	K	Ni, then $Ni(NH_2)_2$ and KBr
NiI_2	Ca	Ni, then $Ni(NH_2)_2$ and CaI_2

[See text.]

TABLE 3.4—*Continued*

Salt	Metal	Product (principal)
$PbBr_2$	Na	Pb and Na_4Pb
PbI_2	Na	Na_4Pb
PbI_2	Na	Na_4Pb_7
PbI_2	Na	Na_4Pb_9
PbI_2	K	K_4Pb_9
PbI_2	Ca	Ca_2Pb_3
ZnI_2	Na	$NaZn_4$
ZnI_2	Na	$NaZn_{12}$
$Zn(CN)_2$	Na	$NaZn_4$
$Zn(CN)_2$	Na	Zn (if $Zn(CN)_2$ in excess)
$Zn(CN)_2$	Ca	Ca_7Zn

metals appear to exist although a complex polysulfide, M_6S_4, has been reported for potassium and rubidium when titrated in the presence of sodium iodide.   Each is likely a mixed metal sulfide.   The formulas were established by titrating a polysulfide, M_2S_x, with the alkali metal, M, following the course of the titration potentiometrically and extremely slowly to ensure attainments of equilibrium (up to 40 hours).[23]   The differential electrode of Müller was used.[24]

The reaction between nickel salts and an alkali metal presents some complexities (in the laboratory).   At the start, the nickel salt is reduced to elementary nickel:

$$NiCl_2 + 2Na \rightarrow Ni + 2NaCl$$

This nickel, however, promptly catalyzes the reaction between sodium and ammonia:

$$Na + NH_3 \rightarrow NaNH_2 + \tfrac{1}{2}H_2$$

The sodamide then reacts with any of the nickel salt not yet reduced:

$$2NaNH_2 + NiCl_2 \rightarrow Ni(NH_2)_2 + 2NaCl$$

Nickel(II) amide is insoluble and precipitates as the ammonate, $Ni(NH_2)_2 \cdot 2NH_3$.   It is possible to interrupt this sequence of reactions by removing the nickel as it appears.   Nickel so prepared, and cobalt and iron also, exhibit some unusual properties.   Prepared in this way, the products are pyrophoric and exhibit some catalytic activity in hydrogenations, inferior, however, to the Raney nickel.[25]   Allowing the reac-

[23] G. W. Watt and J. Otto, Jr., *J. Electrochem. Soc.* 98, 1 (1951).

[24] E. Müller, *Z. physik. Chem.* 135, 102 (1928).

[25] G. Watt and D. Davies, *J. Am. Chem. Soc.* 70, 3753 (1948); G. Watt and W. Jenkens, Jr., *ibid.* 73, 3275 (1951); G. Watt, W. Roper, and S. Parker, *ibid.* 73, 5791 (1951); G. Watt and C. Keenan, *ibid.* 74, 2048 (1952); G. W. Watt and P. I. Mayfield, *ibid.* 75, 1760 (1953).

tions to continue has produced the compounds, Fe_3N, $Co(NH_2)_2$, $Co(NO_2)(NH_2)$, $Ni(NH_2)_2$, Ni_3N, and Ni_3N_2.

When carbon monoxide is passed into solutions of lithium, sodium, potassium, rubidium, calcium, barium, and strontium, carbonyls of these metals are formed.[26] These products are unstable white solids, insoluble in the solvent, decomposing when heated *in vacuo* at 350°C,

$$4NaCO \rightarrow Na_2CO_3 + Na_2O + 3C$$

and soluble in water. Lithium carbonyl, $LiCO$, detonates violently when thrown into water, the carbonate and soot being formed, as well as hydrogen and some carbon monoxide. It should be noted that these substances are not the same as the salts of hexahydroxybenzene, *e.g.*, $K_6C_6O_6$,[27] which are often described as the "carbonyls" of the alkali metals. The properties of the two sets of substances make them entirely different. An unstable "grape-colored" reaction product of sodium and carbon monoxide has been converted into a number of products by treatment with ammonium chloride, of which three appear to have been identified: rhodizonic acid (as the ammonium or sodium salt), glycollic acid, and the acid amide of glycollic acid.[28]

An interesting use of the reducing power of the alkali metals in solution in liquid ammonia is found [29] in the reduction of potassium tetracyanonickelate(II) with potassium to potassium tetracyanonickelate(0).

$$K_2[Ni(CN)_4] + 2K \rightarrow K_4[Ni(CN)_4]$$

Potassium tetracyanopalladate(II) is similarly reduced to potassium tetracyanopalladate(0).[30] These compounds are chemical curiosities in that the nickel atom (or palladium atom) has an oxidation state of zero. This condition is not unheard of, of course, as the metal carbonyls are similar in that particular. It is of interest to note [31] that the existence of $K_4[Ni(CN)_4]$ was predicted from purely thermodynamical considerations.

The reactions of the alkali metals with organic molecules are inherently very complex. Further complications arise because for the most part attention has been focussed on the winning of a particular product, rather than on generalized reactions. Only the reduction of organometallic compounds will be referred to here; for the rest, the

[26] T. G. Pearson, *Nature* **131**, 166 (1933).
[27] R. Nietzki and T. Benckiser, *Ber.* **18**, 499 and 1833 (1885).
[28] A. Scott, *Science* **115**, 118 (1952).
[29] J. W. Eastes and W. M. Burgess, *J. Am. Chem. Soc.* **64**, 1187 (1942).
[30] J. J. Burbage and W. C. Fernelius, *J. Am. Chem. Soc.* **65**, 1484 (1943).
[31] B. Ormont, *Acta Physicochim. U.R.S.S.* **12**, 759 (1940).

literature, which is extensive, must be searched.[32] For organic reactions in which the reduction by sodium (or other alkali metal) is hesitant, the addition of an easily reduced alcohol promotes the reduction of the organic compound [Birch, *op. cit.*]. This expedient appears not to have been tried by the inorganic chemist, although it is highly promising.

A few reactions between organic compounds of antimony and the alkali metals have been studied. For example, $(C_6H_5)_2SbI$ reacts with sodium in liquid ammonia to form $(C_6H_5)_2SbNa$ and perhaps $(C_6H_5)_2Sb$.[33]

Diphenyl bismuth iodide, $(C_6H_5)_2BiI$, is similarly reduced to $(C_6H_5)_2Bi$.[34] The initial step in this reaction produces a product useful in further syntheses of bismuth compounds:

$$(C_6H_5)_2BiI + 2Na \rightarrow (C_6H_5)_2BiNa + NaI$$

Boron compounds have been little studied as oxidants toward the alkali metals. Triphenyl boron ammine reacts with sodium by addition:[35]

$$(C_6H_5)_3B \cdot NH_3 + Na \rightarrow (C_6H_5)_3BNa \cdot NH_3$$

Trimethyl boron adds ammonia on solution and then when treated with sodium evolves hydrogen:[36]

$$(CH_3)_3B \cdot NH_3 + Na \rightarrow (CH_3)_3B \cdot NH_2Na + \tfrac{1}{2}H_2$$

If the product is treated with ammonium bromide, trimethyl boron ammine is reformed:[37]

$$(CH_3)_3B \cdot NH_2Na + NH_4Br \rightarrow (CH_3)_3B \cdot NH_3 + NaBr + NH_3$$

[32] General:—E. C. Franklin and C. A. Kraus, *Am. Chem. J.* 20, 820 (1898); F. de Carli, *Gazz. chim. ital.* 57, 347 (1927); W. C. Fernelius and G. W. Watt, *Chem. Revs.* 20, 195 (1937); W. C. Fernelius and G. B. Bowman, *Chem. Revs.* 26, 3 (1940); A. J. Birch, *Nature* 158, 585 (1946); G. W. Watt, *Chem. Revs.* 46, 317 (1950); A. J. Birch, *Quart. Revs.* 4, 69 (1950); In solvent mixtures:—P. M. Dean and G. Berchet, *J. Am. Chem. Soc.* 52, 2823 (1930); T. H. Vaughn and J. A. Nieuwland, *Ind. Eng. Chem. Anal. Ed.* 3, 274 (1931); C. B. Wooster and J. F. Ryan, *J. Am. Chem. Soc.* 56, 1133 (1934); G. F. White, *J. Am. Chem. Soc.* 45, 779 (1923). Reduction mechanism:—A. J. Birch, *J. Proc. Roy. Soc. N. S. Wales* 83, 245 (49); *J. Chem. Soc.* 1950, 1551; A. J. Birch and S. M. Mukherji, *J. Chem. Soc.* 1949, 2531; A. J. Birch, *J. Chem. Soc.* 1947, 102 and 1642.

[33] L. A. Woods and H. Gilman, *Proc. Iowa Acad. Sci.* 48, 251 (1941); L. A. Woods, *Iowa State Coll. J. Sci.* 19, 61 (1944).

[34] L. A. Woods, *Iowa State Coll. J. Sci.* 19, 61 (1944).

[35] C. A. Kraus, *Contemporary Developments in Chemistry*, Columbia Univ. Press, N. Y. (1927).

[36] J. E. Smith and C. A. Kraus, *J. Am. Chem. Soc.* 73, 2751 (1951).

[37] *Ibid.*

Dimethyl gallium chloride is at first reduced and then slowly evolves hydrogen on treatment with sodium in ammonia:

$$(CH_3)_2GaCl + Na + NH_3 \rightarrow (CH_3)_2Ga \cdot NH_3 + NaCl$$
$$(CH_3)_2Ga \cdot NH_3 \rightarrow (CH_3)_2GaNH_2 + \tfrac{1}{2}H_2$$

If an excess of sodium is used, a different product is obtained: [38]

$$(CH_3)_2GaCl + 2Na + NH_3 \rightarrow (CH_3)_2GaNH_2Na + \tfrac{1}{2}H_2 + NaCl$$

Triethyl germanyl reacts with lithium in liquid ammonia: [39]

$$\tfrac{1}{2}[(C_2H_5)_3Ge]_2 + Li + NH_3 \rightarrow (C_2H_5)_3GeH + LiNH_2$$

Diphenyl germanyl forms a disodium salt: [40]

$$[(C_6H_5)_2Ge]_4 + 8Na \rightarrow 4(C_6H_5)_2GeNa_2$$

Tetraphenyl germane is substituted by sodium:

$$(C_6H_5)_4Ge + Na + NH_3 \rightarrow (C_6H_5)_3GeNa + NaNH_2 + C_6H_6$$

The disubstitution product, $(C_6H_5)_2GeNa_2$, may also form.[41]

The chemistry of organo lead compounds, so far as reductions by the alkali metals go, is similar to that of germanium. Thus triphenyl plumbyl is reduced to triphenyl sodium plumbide by sodium: [42]

$$\tfrac{1}{2}[(C_6H_5)_3Pb]_2 + Na \rightarrow (C_6H_5)_3PbNa$$

Reduction with other alkali metals and the alkaline earth metals gives corresponding products.[43]   Reductions of lead compounds appear to have been studied more than other organometallics.[44]

Only one mercury organic compound, ethyl mercury(II) chloride, appears to have been reduced by an alkali metal to yield simple products: [45]

$$C_2H_5HgCl + 3Na + NH_3 \rightarrow NaHg + C_2H_6 + NaCl + NaNH_2$$

[38] C. A. Kraus and F. E. Toonder, *J. Am. Chem. Soc.* **55**, 3547 (1933).
[39] C. A. Kraus and E. A. Flood, *J. Am. Chem. Soc.* **54**, 1635 (1932).
[40] C. A. Kraus and C. L. Brown, *J. Am. Chem. Soc.* **52**, 4031 (1930).
[41] C. A. Kraus and E. A. Flood, *J. Am. Chem. Soc.* **54**, 1635 (1932); C. A. Kraus and L. S. Foster, *ibid.* **49**, 457 (1927).
[42] L. S. Foster *et al.*, *J. Am. Chem. Soc.* **61**, 1685 (1939).
[43] R. W. Leeper, *Iowa State Coll. J. Sci.* **18**, 57 (1943).
[44] L. D. Apperson, *Iowa State Coll. J. Sci.* **16**, 7 (1941); J. C. Bailie, *ibid.* **14**, 8 (1939); E. Bindschadler, *ibid.* **16**, 33 (1941): G. Calingaert and H. Soroos, *J. Org. Chem.* **2**, 537 (1937); L. S. Foster, W. M. Dix, and I. J. Gruntfest, *loc. cit.;* H. Gilman and J. C. Bailie, *J. Am. Chem. Soc.* **61**, 731 (1939); R. W. Leeper, *loc. cit.*
[45] C. A. Kraus and H. F. Kurtz, *J. Am. Chem. Soc.* **47**, 43 (1925).

Silicon organic compounds behave much in the same way toward the reducing action of the alkali metals in ammonia as do those of germanium. Some exceptions appear.   While triethyl germanyl reacts with lithium (*vide supra*) the analogous triethyl silicyl does not.[46]   Triphenyl silane is reduced to sodium *bis*(triphenylsilicyl)imide: [47]

$$2(C_6H_5)_3SiH + Na + NH_3 \rightarrow [(C_6H_5)_3Si]_2NNa + 2\tfrac{1}{2}H_2$$

A number of organo-tin compounds have been reduced by the alkali metals.   Diethyl tin yields *bis*(diethylstannyl sodium),

$$2(C_2H_5)_2Sn + 2Na \rightarrow [NaSn(C_2H_5)_2]_2$$

while tetraethyl tin yields triethylstannyl sodium and ethane: [48]

$$(C_2H_5)_4Sn + 2Na + NH_3 \rightarrow (C_2H_5)_3SnNa + C_2H_6 + NaNH_2$$

Behavior of tetramethyl tin and of tetraphenyl tin is correspondent.[49]

Franklin, in the monograph referred to earlier,[50] draws a formal analogy between the "aquo" and the "ammono" systems.   Autoionization in these two systems is given by the equations:

$$2H_2O \rightleftharpoons H_3O^+ + OH^-$$
$$2NH_3 \rightleftharpoons NH_4^+ + NH_2^-$$

For water, hydroxides are to be regarded as derived by the replacement of one hydrogen atom and oxides by the replacement of both.   For ammonia, the replacement of one hydrogen atom leads to the formation of amides, the replacement of two hydrogen atoms to imides, and the replacement of all three hydrogen atoms to nitrides.   Ammonium salts are to be regarded as acids, amides as monoacidic bases, imides as diacidic bases, and nitrides as triacidic bases.   Long ago the acidic nature of ammonium salts in ammonia was revealed in the observation that a concentrated solution of ammonium nitrate in liquid ammonia was able to dissolve metal oxides and hydroxides.[51]   Other ammonium salts can behave as acids and their ammonia solutions can attack metals or metal oxides (Table 3.5).

[46] C. A. Kraus and W. K. Nelson, *J. Am. Chem. Soc.* **56**, 195 (1934).

[47] H. H. Reynolds *et al.*, *J. Am. Chem. Soc.* **51**, 3067 (1929).

[48] T. Harada, *Sci. Papers Inst. Phys. Chem. Research* (*Tokyo*) **35**, 290 (1939).

[49] C. A. Kraus and A. M. Neal, *J. Am. Chem. Soc.* **52**, 695 (1930); C. A. Kraus and W. V. Sessions, *ibid.* **47**, 2361 (1925); R. F. Chambers and P. C. Scherer, *ibid.* **48**, 1054 (1926).

[50] Footnote, p. 155.

[51] F. Divers, *Proc. Roy. Soc.* **21**, 109 (1875).

TABLE 3.5. REACTIONS OF AMMONIUM SALTS IN LIQUID AMMONIA

Ammonium Salt	Reactant	Products
NH_4Cl	NaOH	$NaCl$, NH_3, H_2
NH_4NO_3	CaO	$Ca(NO_3)_2$, NH_3, H_2O
NH_4NO_3	MgO	$Mg(NO_3)_2$, NH_3, H_2O
NH_4NO_3	ZnO	$Zn(NO_3)_2$, NH_3, H_2O
NH_4NO_3	CdO	$Cd(NO_3)_2$, NH_3, H_2O
NH_4NO_3	PbO	$Pb(NO_3)_2$, NH_3, H_2O
NH_4NO_3	CuO	$Cu(NO_3)_2$, NH_3, H_2O
NH_4NO_3	HgO	$Hg(NO_3)_2$, NH_3, H_2O
NH_4NO_3	Ca	$Ca(NO_3)_2$, NH_3, H_2
NH_4NO_3	Fe	$Fe(NO_3)_2 \cdot 6NH_3$, H_2
NH_4N_3	Li	LiN_3, NH_3, H_2
NH_4I	Mg	$MgI_2 \cdot 6NH_3$, H_2
NH_4I	La	$LaI_3 \cdot xNH_3$, H_2
NH_4I	Ce	$CeI_3 \cdot 8NH_3$, H_2
NH_4Cl	Be	$BeCl_2 \cdot 4NH_3$, $BeCl_2 \cdot 2NH_3$, H_2
NH_4Br	Mn	$MnBr_2 \cdot 6NH_3$, H_2
NH_4CN	Fe	$(NH_4)_4[Fe(CN)_6] \cdot xNH_3$, H_2

Reactions are possible between ammonium salts and the bases of the ammonia system. They occur in the following ways:

$$NH_4NO_3 + KNH_2 \rightarrow KNO_3 + 2NH_3$$

$$NH_4N_3 + KNH_2 \rightarrow KN_3 + 2NH_3$$

In these two reactions both reactants and products are soluble in the ammonia. In the following case potassium chloride, which has only limited solubility in the solvent, precipitates:

$$NH_4Cl + KNH_2 \rightarrow KCl + 2NH_3$$

The reaction

$$2NH_4I + PbNH \rightarrow PbI_2 + 3NH_3$$

is an example involving a diacidic base, lead imide, which is not soluble but which is taken into solution by the acid, ammonium iodide. An analogous reaction takes place between calcium oxide and hydrochloric acid in water. The triacidic base, bismuth nitride, BiN, is similarly insoluble but is taken into solution by ammonium iodide:

$$3NH_4I + BiN \rightarrow BiI_3 + 4NH_3$$

Insoluble hydroxides are precipitated in water by the addition of a soluble base to a solution of an appropriate salt. Amides which are insoluble in ammonia can be precipitated in much the same way:

$$KNH_2 + AgNO_3 \rightarrow AgNH_2 + KNO_3$$

The formation of imides and nitrides in ammonia corresponds to the formation of oxides in water:

$$2KNH_2 + PbI_2 \rightarrow PbNH + 2KI + NH_3$$
$$3KNH_2 + BiI_3 \rightarrow BiN + 3KI + 2NH_3$$
$$6KNH_2 + 3HgI_2 \rightarrow Hg_3N_2 + 6KI + 4NH_3$$

Oxidizing and reducing reactions occur in liquid ammonia even as they do in water, although not always in parallel ways. It is observed [52] that when oxygen is passed into a solution of metallic potassium in liquid ammonia, potassium hydroxide and potassium amide are first formed, followed by further oxidation of the potassium amide to potassium nitrite:

$$2K + \tfrac{1}{2}O_2 + NH_3 \rightarrow KOH + KNH_2$$
$$4KNH_2 + 3O_2 \rightarrow 2KNO_2 + 2KOH + 2NH_3$$

When potassium ammonostannite is treated with elementary iodine oxidation to potassium ammonostannate occurs: [53]

$$K_4Sn(NH_2)_6 + I_2 \rightarrow K_2Sn(NH_2)_6 + 2KI$$

Powerful oxidizing agents in liquid ammonia have been little sought for and perhaps do not exist. Nitric acid in ammonia (*i.e.*, ammonium nitrate) has no oxidizing powers, and alkali permanganates and chromates have very limited power. The formal analog of nitric acid in the nitrogen system of compounds appears to be hydrazoic acid. In liquid ammonia it acts, however, as an ordinary acid, and with metals it gives metal azides and hydrogen gas, the azide group remaining intact:

$$2HN_3 + Ca \rightarrow Ca(N_3)_2 + H_2$$

This behavior is in contrast to that in water, where hydrazoic acid acts similarly to nitric acid in that free hydrogen is not formed. Thus, metallic calcium is acted on by an aqueous solution of hydrazoic acid to give the azide, nitrogen, and ammonia:

$$3HN_{3(aq)} + Ca \rightarrow Ca(N_3)_{2(aq)} + N_2 + NH_{3(aq)}$$

A potential series for metals in liquid ammonia has been established.[54]

[52] C. A. Kraus and E. F. Whyte, *J. Am. Chem. Soc.* **48**, 1781 (1926).
[53] F. W. Bergstrom, *J. Phys. Chem.* **32**, 433 (1928).
[54] F. M. G. Johnson and N. T. M. Wilsmore, *Trans. Faraday Soc.* **3**, 70 (1907); W. A. Pleskov and A. M. Monossohm, *Acta Physicochim.* **1**, 871 (1934); **6**, 1 (1937); **21**, 235 (1946).

The series is given in Table 3.6. All values are referred to the cadmium electrode (cadmium metal dipping into a saturated solution of cadmium nitrate in liquid ammonia) as standard, *i.e.*, of zero voltage.

TABLE 3.6. POTENTIALS OF METALS IN LIQUID AMMONIA [a]

Metal	Solution	Concentration	EMF
Li	$LiNO_3$	N/10	2.47 v
K	KNO_3	N/10	2.21
Cs	$CsNO_3$	N/10	2.18
Rb	$RbNO_3$	N/10	2.16
Na	$NaNO_3$	N/10	2.07
Ca	$Ca(NO_3)_2$	N/10	1.87
Zn	$Zn(NO_3)_2$	N/10	0.353
Cd	$Cd(NO_3)_3$	Satd.	0.000
Cd	$Cd(NO_3)_2$	N/10	−0.047
H_2 (Pt)	NH_4NO_3	N/10	−0.104
Pb	$Pb(NO_3)_2$	N/10	−0.515
Cu	$Cu(NO_3)_2$	N/10	−0.700
Hg	HgI_2	N/10	−0.895
Ag	$AgNO_3$	N/10	−0.963

[a] The first column gives the metal comprising the opposing electrode, the second column the solution into which the metal dips, the third column the concentration of that solution, and the fourth the electromotive force.

The phenomenon of solvolysis is well known in liquid ammonia, the conduct of halides and oxyhalides, *e.g.*, ranging from complete ammonolysis for the covalent halides such as silicon tetrachloride to no ammonolysis at all for some salts. Some differences between the ammonia system and the water system are encountered. For instance, bismuth halides are notably hydrolyzed, yet are hardly if at all ammonolyzed. In a family, ammonolysis decreases with increasing atomic weight, the boron halides as an example being completely ammonolyzed, aluminum halides only slightly so, and gallium halides not at all. In terms of the equilibria involved, this difference in behavior means that, for the first reaction as expressed by the following equations, the equilibrium favors the reaction products; for the second reaction neither products nor reactants are favored conspicuously; and, for the third, the reactants are favored:

$$BX_3 + 6NH_3 \rightarrow B(NH_2)_3 + 3NH_4X$$
$$AlX_3 + 6NH_3 \rightarrow Al(NH_2)_3 + 3NH_4X$$
$$GaX_3 + 6NH_3 \rightarrow Ga(NH_2)_3 + 3NH_4X$$

With silicon tetrachloride ammonolysis occurs as follows:

$$SiCl_4 + 8NH_3 \rightarrow Si(NH_2)_4 + 4NH_4Cl$$

If the silicon tetramide is warmed to 0°C it loses ammonia:

$$Si(NH_2)_4 \rightarrow SiNH(NH_2)_2 + NH_3$$

At 100°C further loss of ammonia occurs:

$$SiNH(NH_2)_2 \rightarrow SiN(NH_2) + NH_3$$

At 900°C a still further loss takes place:

$$2SiN(NH_2) \rightarrow (SiN)_2NH + NH_3$$

Finally, at 1200°C, only silicon nitride remains:

$$3(SiN)_2NH \rightarrow 2Si_3N_4 + NH_3$$

These reactions have their counterparts in the progressive dehydration of orthosilicic acid, $Si(OH)_4$, to silica, SiO_2.

The reactions of ammonia with the inorganic halides are summarized in the next table. All reactions occur in the liquid phase, *i.e.*, below the boiling point, $-34°C$.

TABLE 3.7. REACTIONS OF AMMONIA WITH INORGANIC HALIDES

Substance	*Product formed*
$AuCl$	$AuCl \cdot 12NH_3$
BCl_3	$B(NH_2)_3$
AlI_3	$AlI_3 \cdot 6NH_3$
CCl_4	no reaction
$SiCl_4$	$Si(NH_2)_4$
$SnCl_4$	$2Sn(NH_2)_3Cl \cdot NH_4Cl$
PbI_2	$PbNH \cdot Pb(NH_2)I$
$TiCl_4$	$TiNCl \cdot xNH_3$
$ZrBr_4$	$3Zr(NH)_2 \cdot 7NH_4Br \cdot xNH_3$
$NOCl$	$NO(NH_2)$
PCl_3	$P(NH_2)_3, P_2(NH)_3$
PCl_5	$P(NH)_2NH_2$
AsX_3 (X is Cl, Br, I)	$As(NH_2)_3$
$VOCl_3$	$VO(NH_2)_3$
VCl_3	$[V(NH_3)_6]Cl_3$
$TeBr_4$	Te_3N_4
$CrCl_3$	$[Cr(NH_3)_6]Cl_3, [Cr(NH_3)_5Cl]Cl_2$

The alkali hydrides are ammonolyzed,

$$MH + NH_3 \rightarrow MNH_2 + H_2$$

and the alkali oxides are also:

$$M_2O + NH_3 \rightarrow MNH_2 + MOH$$

The hydrolysis of normal salts, as $BiCl_3$, to oxysalts as $BiOCl$, has a counterpart in liquid ammonia. When lead nitrate is treated with liquid ammonia the compound $Pb(NH_2)NHPbNO_3$ forms. Addition of the base, KNH_2, causes more of this compound to precipitate while the addition of an ammonium salt causes the compound to redissolve. This behavior is paralleled by the effect of alkalies and acids on $BiOCl$ in water. Many examples of ammonolysis are known.[55]

A reaction which is encountered early in professional training, and about which much speculation has been published, namely the action of ammonia on mercury(I) chloride,[56]

$$Hg_2Cl_2 + NH_3(liq.) \rightarrow Hg + HgNH_2Cl \text{ ("infusible white precipitate")}$$
$$+ Hg(NH_3)_2Cl_2 \text{ ("fusible white precipitate")}$$
$$+ NH_4Cl$$

has been established in such a way that the products are no longer in doubt.[57] Combined chemical and physical methods, particularly x-ray diffraction, applied in aqueous solution and in gaseous and liquefied ammonia, all serve to illustrate the artificiality of the common division of chemistry into "analytical," "physical," *etc.*, components, and in addition provide a model for other investigators. It is now known [58] that only four products are formed which contain mercury, depending on conditions, and of these one is the product of an aqueous reaction: $Hg(NH_3)_2Cl_2$, $Hg(NH_2)Cl$, $Hg_2NCl \cdot H_2O$, and the dehydration product of this last, Hg_2NCl. No mercury(I) material forms, which was a major point of disagreement in the past.

The phenomenon of amphiprotism is exhibited in liquid ammonia to a surprising degree. When zinc iodide is treated in liquid ammonia with potassium amide, insoluble zinc amide forms. Addition of still more potassium amide dissolves the precipitate:

$$ZnI_2 + 2KNH_2 \rightarrow Zn(NH_2)_2 + 2KI$$
$$Zn(NH_2)_2 + 2KNH_2 \rightarrow K_2Zn(NH_2)_4$$

In the water system, the compound analogous to potassium tetramido-

[55] W. C. Fernelius and G. B. Bowman, *Chem. Revs.* **26**, 3 (1940).

[56] H. Freche and M. C. Sneed, *J. Am. Chem. Soc.* **60**, 518, 1938; T. F. Egidius, *Z. anorg. Chem.* **240**, 97 (1938); E. Gleditsch and T. F. Egidius, *ibid.* **228**, 249 (1936); *ibid.* **226**, 265 (1936); this series, Vol. IV.

[57] S. D. Arora, W. N. Lipscomb, and M. C. Sneed, *J. Am. Chem. Soc.* **73**, 1015 (1951); W. N. Lipscomb, *Anal. Chem.* **25**, 737 (1953).

[58] Arora, Lipscomb and Sneed, *loc. cit.*

zincate, $K_2Zn(NH_2)_4$, is potassium tetrahydroxyzincate, $K_2Zn(OH)_4$. It is true that ZnI_2 hydrolyzes to a greater extent than it ammonolyzes.

Aluminum (amalgam) reacts with potassium amide in liquid ammonia, forming $KAl(NH_2)_4$. The reaction takes place in two steps, the first of which forms aluminum amide, $Al(NH_2)_3$, which then dissolves in the excess of potassium amide.

Even the amides of elements such as magnesium, barium, strontium, calcium, lithium, and sodium behave in a way strongly suggesting amphiprotism. That is, magnesium iodide reacts with potassium amide to form potassium tetramido-magnesiate, $K_2Mg(NH_2)_4$. Ammonium nitrate converts it into potassium nitrate and magnesium nitrate. Metals which have been shown to undergo reactions of the same type are contained in the following list: Be, Mg, Zn, Cd, Ca, Sr, Ba, La, Ce, Mo, W, Mn, Ni, Cu(I), Ag, Al, Tl, Sn(II), Sn(IV), Pb(II). Reactions of this kind have been fully reviewed.[59]

Titrations in liquid ammonia have been carried out, but, as might be inferred from the difficulty of keeping standard solutions in this solvent, they are not common. Apparatus is available for the carrying out of titrations in liquid ammonia at room temperature and elevated pressure.[60] With it ammonium nitrate may be titrated against potassium amide, using *o*-nitroaniline as an indicator.

In apparatus of different form, silver bromide has been reduced to metallic silver by titrating the former with a solution of potassium, in the total absence of air or moisture. The blue potassium solution served as its own indicator.[61]

The colors of a large number of indicators in liquid ammonia have been investigated.[62] Among them are the ortho-, meta-, and para-nitrophenols, 2,4, and also 2,5 dinitrophenol, picric acid, the ortho-, meta-, and para-nitroanilines, 2,4 dinitroaniline, 2,4,6 trinitroaniline, azobenzene, para-benzoazoaniline, para-benzoazodimethylaniline, methyl orange, ortho-toluazo-ortho-toluidine, para-toluazodimethylaniline and benzyl-azo-alpha-naphthylamine, each in the following solvents: ammonia, sulfur dioxide, benzene, formic acid, acetic acid, aniline, and water. For each indicator the color was noted in the pure solvent, in an (appropriate) acid solution, and in a basic solution. For the acid in ammonia, ammonium nitrate was used, and potassium amide for the base.

[59] F. W. Bergstrom, *Chem. Revs.* 12, 51 (1933); W. C. Fernelius, *Chem. Revs.* 20, 416 (1937).

[60] A. J. Shattenshtein, *Acta Physicochim. U.R.S.S.* 7, 691 (1937).

[61] G. W. Watt and C. Keenan, *J. Am. Chem. Soc.* 71, 3833 (1949).

[62] A. J. Shattenshtein, *Acta Physicochim. U.R.S.S.* 10, 121 (1939).

TABLE 3.8. THERMODYNAMIC PROPERTIES OF IONS IN LIQUID AMMONIA *

Ion	ΔH^0_f	ΔF^0_f	S^0
Ag^+	26	17.5	23
Br^-	− 59	− 39.9	−30.3
Ca^{++}	−100	−100	−21
Cl^-	− 65.7	− 44.1	−30.3
ClO_3^-	− 47.7	− 17.7	15
Cs^+	− 40.5	− 48	29
F^-	—	− 80.8	—
H^+	0	0	0
Hg^{++}	45.2	31	35
I^-	− 45.3	− 29	−25
IO_3^-	—	− 42.4	—
K^+	− 40.5	− 47.0	21.4
Li^+	− 49	− 54	8
Na^+	− 38.1	− 43.6	15.1
NH_2^-	10.1	34	−10
NH_4^+	− 16.1	− 2.7	24.7
NO_3^-	− 77.6	− 42.8	− 5
Pb^{++}	21	13	11
Rb^+	− 39	− 47.5	29
e^-	40.5	44.4	2
(NH_3)	(-16.1)	(-2.7)	(24.7)

* ΔH^0_f is the heat of formation, ΔF^0_f is the free energy of formation, and S^0 is the entropy of formation, all referred to 25°C and expressed in kcal per mole (S^0 in eu). This temperature was selected to allow intercomparison with water. The entropies are uncertain by *ca.* ±10 entropy units.

Although scattered articles dealing with the thermodynamic quantities have appeared in the literature of nonaqueous chemistry, the only systematic compilation is a recent one on heats of solution and heats of formation, free energies of formation, and entropies, for ions in liquid ammonia.[63]   Table 3.8 lists some of these values.

The equilibrium constant for the autoionization of liquid ammonia at 25°C has been calculated [64] from heats of formation and entropies, recorded in this table, and found to be $K = 1(10^{-28})$. A computation from free energies gives $3(10^{-30})$. A value (at −50°C) [64a] obtained from electrochemical cells is $2(10^{-33})$. These values correspond to the following equilibrium:

$$2NH_3 \rightleftharpoons NH_4^+ + NH_2^-$$

It is also possible to compute from values in the table the free energy change for the reaction:

$$e^- + NH_3 \rightleftharpoons \tfrac{1}{2}H_2 + NH_2^-$$

[63] W. M. Latimer and W. L. Jolly, *J. Am. Chem. Soc.* **75**, 4147 (1953).
[64] W. L. Jolly, *Chem. Revs.* **50**, 351 (1952).
[64a] W. A. Pleskov and A. M. Monoszon, *Acta Physicochim. U.S.S.R.* **2**, 621 (1935).

This one turns out to be a trifle less than -8 kcal leading to a value for the equilibrium constant of a little more than 10^5.

The heat of neutralization in ammonia

$$NH_4G + KNH_2 \rightarrow KG + 2NH_3 \quad \text{(where } G = I^-, NO_3^-, Br^-, \text{ or } SCN^-)$$

has been measured [65] and found to average 26.5 kcal. [The corresponding value for water is about 13.7 kcal.]

It had previously been supposed that in ammonia, calcium alone among the alkali and alkaline earth metals was largely diatomic.[66] This view now appears to have been incorrect. The heats of reaction for each of the alkali metals, Li, Na, K, and Cs, and the alkaline earth metals, Ca, Sr, and Ba, reacting with various ammonium salts, and the heat of solution for each of these metals in ammonia, not known previously, have been measured.[67] The values lead to a heat for the reaction

$$e^- + NH_4^+ \rightarrow \tfrac{1}{2}H_2 + NH_3$$

of very nearly -40.1 kcal in each case, including that of calcium. It is thus to be concluded that this latter metal is dissolved by ammonia as the monatomic species, relinquishing two electrons, rather than otherwise.[68]

It has been conjectured that aluminum metal is oxidized anodically to the Al(I) or Al(II) valence, in liquid ammonia.[69]

In the experiment, salts containing the nitrate ion were electrolzed on an aluminum anode. The loss in weight of this anode, and the current passing a coulometer, led to a mean oxidation state for aluminum of 2.7. Nitrogen was evolved at both anode and cathode.

In the same kind of experiment, gallium is supposed to be oxidized to the Ga(I) and Ga(III) states (the mixture is said to be stable), thallium to the Tl(I) and Tl(III) states, and indium converted to the In(0) and In(III) states (through disproportionation of intermediate oxidation states). However, potentiometric titrations of salts of these metals by potassium indicate only three-electron changes for the metal atoms in question, i.e., that potassium reduced aluminum to the metal directly, showing no intermediate.[70] The dropping mercury electrode reduction of aluminum salts [71] provides no evidence for Al(I) or Al(II).

[65] H. D. Mulder and F. C. Schmidt, *J. Am. Chem. Soc.* **73**, 5575 (1951).
[66] D. M. Yost and H. Russell, Jr., *Systematic Inorganic Chemistry of the Fifth and Sixth Group Non-Metallic Elements*, Prentice-Hall, N. Y. (1944).
[67] L. V. Coulter, *J. Phys. Chem.* **57**, 553 (1953).
[68] S. P. Wolsky, E. J. Zdanuk, and L. V. Coulter, *J. Am. Chem. Soc.* **74**, 6196 (1952).
[69] W. E. Bennett, A. W. Davidson, and J. Kleinberg, *J. Am. Chem. Soc.* **74**, 732 (1952); A. W. Davidson and J. Kleinberg, *J. Phys. Chem.* **57**, 571 (1953).
[70] G. W. Watt, J. L. Hall, and G. R. Choppin, *J. Phys. Chem.* **57**, 567 (1953).
[71] A. D. McElroy and H. A. Laitinen, *J. Phys. Chem.* **57**, 564 (1953).

ACETIC ACID

Acetic acid is a substance which has been known from very early times, at least in the form of impure solutions in water. As wine vinegar it has been made in Orleans (France) for centuries; Lavoisier noted the formation of acetic acid from alcohol. It occurs in nature as the free acid in some plant juices and frequently as the calcium or potassium salt. Stable at ordinary and moderately high temperatures, it often results from the decomposition of complex substances (*e.g.*, wood) by heat. Yet, notwithstanding common acquaintance with the acid, it has been the subject of comparatively little research, the great bulk of which has been in the direction of its use as a reagent. In this discussion "acetic acid" stands for "anhydrous hydrogen acetate." Some early references to its use as a solvent have been collected.[72]

As a solvent its properties make it easy to use; it freezes at 16.6°C and boils at 118°C, it is nontoxic and not decomposed by water. However, it ought not be overlooked that the liquid is not easy to free of water; simple distillation or fusion is ineffective, allowing up to half a per cent of water to remain. In a solution containing half a per cent of water by weight, nearly two per cent of the molecules are this contaminant. It is necessary to distill the liquid under reduced pressure in the presence of P_2O_5, and then distill and freeze alternately, in order to obtain a product of the highest purity.[73] Most of the studies on acetic acid have been made on a more-or-less dry liquid.

The following table lists some of the properties of this solvent.

TABLE 3.9. SOME PHYSICAL PROPERTIES OF ACETIC ACID

Normal boiling point	118.1°C
Freezing point	16.63°C
Dielectric constant	6.17 (20°C)
Conductivity	0.5×10^{-8} mho
Dipole moment	0
Viscosity	1.314 poise (15°C)
Density	1.049 g/ml (20°C)
Heat of vaporization	5.81 kcal/mole
Heat of fusion	2.68 kcal/mole

Properties of Acetic Acid. It is surprising to find that the dipole moment of acetic acid is zero [74] in view of the unsymmetrical structure of the molecule. The explanation resides in the well-known fact, however,

[72] A. W. Davidson, *J. Am. Chem. Soc.* **50**, 1890 (1928).
[73] J. Timmermans, *Physico-chemical Constants of Pure Organic Compounds*, Elsevier, N. Y. (1950).
[74] C. P. Smyth and H. E. Rogers, *J. Am. Chem. Soc.* **52**, 1824 (1930).

TABLE 3.10.* SOLUBILITY OF SALTS IN ACETIC ACID

Insoluble	Slightly Soluble	Sparingly Soluble	Readily Soluble
AgCl	NaCl	AgNO₃	LiNO₃
AgBr	KCl	AlCl₃	NH₄NO₃
AgI	KBr	HgCl₂	Ca(NO₃)₂
AgCN	KI	HgI₂	Cu(NO₃)₂
AgSCN	NH₄Cl	CoCl₂	CaCl₂
PbCl₂	NH₄Br		ZnCl₂
PbI₂	NH₄I		SbCl₃
Hg₂Cl₂	NaNO₃		FeCl₃
CdI₂	KNO₃		BaI₂
Ba(NO₃)₂	BaCl₂		ZnI₂
Ca₃(PO₄)₂	KClO₃		NH₄SCN
Cu₃(PO₄)₂	Na₂SO₄		KCN
CaCO₃	(NH₄)₂SO₄		LiC₂H₃O₂
Zn(C₂H₃O₂)₂	Cu(C₂H₃O₂)₂		KC₂H₃O₂
sulfates (all)			NH₄C₂H₃O₂
			Pb(C₂H₃O₂)₂
			Cd(C₂H₃O₂)₂

* Slightly soluble is said to be less than one part in 100.

that a pair of molecules are oriented end-to-end with their carboxyl groups held in contact *via* hydrogen bonding.[75] Such an arrangement brings the electric moments of the single molecules into opposition with resultant cancellation of each other's effect. It seems likely that certain solutes may promote dissociation of these dimers; others may not. This behavior makes understanding of the nature of solutions particularly difficult and the literature filled with contradictions. In view of the small dielectric constant, however, it is probable that strong electrolytes in acetic acid do not exist, and where experiments appear to suggest their existence, some unwarranted assumption will have been found to have been made. Salts appear to exist almost exclusively in solution in the form of undissociated (and neutral) ion pairs [76] and acids ordinarily thought strong actually have very small dissociation constants. $HClO_4$ has a value, $K = 9 \times 10^{-7}$, and HCl, $K = 5 \times 10^{-10}$, for the constant in question.[77]

Many salts are soluble in acetic acid. A qualitative presentation [78] is given in Table 3.10.

[75] R. M. Morrow, *Phys. Rev.* **31**, 10 (1928); J. J. Trillat, *Ann. Phys.* **6**, 5 (1926); A. Muller, *J. Chem. Soc.* **123**, 2043 (1923); A. Muller and G. Shearer, *ibid.* **123**, 3156 (1923).

[76] A. A. Vernon, W. F. Luder, and M. Giella, *J. Am. Chem. Soc.* **63**, 862 (1941); E. Griswold, M. M. Jones, and R. K. Birdwhistell, *ibid.* **75**, 5701 (1953); M. M. Jones and E. Griswold, *ibid.* **76**, 3247 (1954).

[77] T. L. Smith and J. H. Elliot, *J. Am. Chem. Soc.* **75**, 3566 (1953).

[78] A. W. Davidson, *J. Am. Chem. Soc.* **50**, 1890 (1928).

The table immediately suggests various precipitation reactions which might be carried out in acetic acid. It is noted that all sulfates are insoluble in acetic acid, contrary to water, and that some substances soluble in water are insoluble in acetic acid. Some precipitation reactions of this kind have been carried out [79] as follows:

$$BaI_2 + 2NaNO_3 \rightarrow Ba(NO_3)_2 \text{ (insol.)} + 2NaI$$

$$FeCl_2 + NH_4(SCN) \rightarrow \text{(red color)}$$

$$Cu(NO_3)_2 + 2NaC_2H_3O_2 \rightarrow Cu(C_2H_3O_2)_2 \text{ (insol.)} + 2NaNO_3$$

$$Cd(C_2H_3O_2) + H_2SO_4 \rightarrow CdSO_4 \text{ (insol.)} + 2HC_2H_3O_2$$

$$ZnCl_2 + H_2S \rightarrow ZnS \text{ (insol.)} + 2HCl$$

$$Na_2C_2O_4 + ZnCl_2 \rightarrow ZnC_2O_4 \text{ (insol.)} + 2NaCl$$

$$2H_3PO_4 + 3ZnCl_2 \rightarrow Zn_3(PO_4)_2 \text{ (insol.)} + 6HCl$$

If the last three insoluble salts are treated with a solution of hydrogen chloride in acetic acid they dissolve exactly as they do in water.

Various cryoscopic studies on acetic acid have been made, but some anomalies appear. The solutes, SO_2, H_2S, $SnCl_4$, $AsCl_3$, and S_2Cl_2, have all been described as not ionized while $Mg(CH_3COO)_2$, HCl, and H_2SO_4 were described as ionized.[80] However, in view of the low dielectric constant for the solvent, measured values for the conductance of HCl,[81] and the small dissociation constant for HCl in acetic acid,[82] it appears that this conclusion must be modified.

From the freezing point and the heat of fusion one calculates the freezing point constant to be 3.74 deg per mole solute per kg solvent. The measured value [83] is in agreement. From this cryoscopic constant one can compute the extent of dissociation of various solutes in acetic acid. Sulfuric acid is found to be very slightly dissociated in a solution approximately $\frac{1}{10}$ molal,[84] and to increase in dissociation as the dilution increases.[85]

[79] A. W. Davidson, *J. Am. Chem. Soc.* **50**, 1890 (1928); A. W. Davidson and W. H. McAllister, *J. Am. Chem. Soc.* **52**, 519 (1930).

[80] M. Raoult, *Ann. chim. et phys.* (6) **2**, 66 (1884).

[81] I. M. Kolthoff and A. Willman, *J. Am. Chem. Soc.* **56**, 1007 (1933).

[82] T. L. Smith and J. H. Elliot, *loc. cit.*, p. 180.

[83] E. Beckmann, *Z. phys. Chem.* **57**, 129 (1906).

[84] Estimated from values reported by W. C. Eichleberger, *J. Am. Chem. Soc.* **56**, 799 (1934).

[85] In direct contradiction to this statement, G. Oddo and G. Anelli, *Gazz. chim. ital.* **41** (I), 552 (1911), have reported that sulfuric acid associates into a dimer, $(H_2SO_4)_2$. They likewise offer cryoscopic evidence. In the absence of further experimental evidence it is not possible to decide with complete confidence between these views.

The determination of the molecular weight of various quaternary ammonium salts, of which tetraethylammonium chloride is representative, by freezing point and boiling point measurements,[86] led to the conclusion that these salts are highly associated in acetic acid. For the salt, tetrapropylammonium iodide, four molecules of salt are associated into one "particle," at a concentration of 0.0316 mole per 100 ml of solvent acetic acid. It is extremely likely that this interpretation is incorrect, for it has been shown that the association of ions into triplets (plus-minus-plus or minus-plus-minus) is extremely unlikely in a medium of dielectric constant 6 and a concentration of about 0.3 molar.[87] It will probably be found that certain solutes can promote breakup of the solvent dimer, as mentioned earlier, and that in favorable cases linear polymers may form. In such a case, four (or more) salt molecules may serve as couplers in such a polymer. In this connection it is of interest to recall the unprecedented increase in viscosity observed when acetic acid and tin(IV) chloride(anh.) are mixed. Much heat is evolved on mixing, a very large volume contraction occurs, and the viscosity increases by an enormous factor. For a mole fraction of 0.25 for $SnCl_4$ in the mixture, the viscosity is nearly 300 times what it is for either pure component. Moreover a change in the temperature from 25° to 0°C produces a 23-fold increase in the viscosity, an unparalleled effect.[88] Aniline and acetic acid also are unusually viscous in mixtures with each other.[89]

Long chains of acetic acid molecules, cross-linked by $SnCl_4$, might account for the increase in viscosity, the heat effect, the temperature effect, and the volume change, in a manner faintly reminiscent of the melting of sulfur, which, as is well known, increases in viscosity markedly as the temperature is raised above the melting point only to diminish again as the temperature is raised still further. Sulfur rings, S_8, readily mobile, become viscous linear polymers as the temperature is raised, and in turn become mobile dimers as the temperature is raised still further.

The strengths of acids in acetic acid have been determined on a number of occasions [90] and these acids likewise are found to be weak, some

[86] W. E. S. Turner and C. T. Pollard, *J. Chem. Soc.* **105**, 1751 (1914).

[87] R. Fouss and C. A. Kraus, *J. Am. Chem. Soc.* **55**, 2387 (1933) and *ibid.* **57**, 1 (1935).

[88] J. D. Stranathan and J. Strong, *J. Phys. Chem.* **31**, 1420 (1927).

[89] F. B. Thole, A. G. Mussell, and A. E. Dunstan, *J. Chem. Soc.* **103**, 1114 (1913).

[90] T. L. Smith and J. H. Elliott, *J. Am. Chem. Soc.* **75**, 3566 (1953); H. Lemaire and H. J. Lucas, *ibid.* **73**, 5198 (1951); D. S. Noyce and P. Castelfranco, *ibid.* **73**, 4482 (1951); N. F. Hall and F. Meyer, *ibid.* **62**, 2493 (1940); N. F. Hall and W. F. Spengeman, *ibid.* **62**, 2487 (1940); M. A. Paul and L. P. Hammett, *ibid.* **58**, 2182 (1936); I. M. Kolthoff and A. Willman, *ibid.* **56**, 1014 (1934); V. K. LaMer and W. C. Eichelberger, *ibid.* **54**, 2763 (1932); A. W. Hutchison and G. C. Chandlee, *ibid.* **53**, 2881 (1931); N. F. Hall, *Chem. Revs.* **8**, 191 (1931).

being weaker than others. The strength of several acids decreases in the series, $HClO_4$, HBr, H_2SO_4, and HCl. The dissociation constant for $HClO_4$, estimated from conductance data and a Fuoss-Kraus plot, is only $K = 9 \times 10^{-7}$; that for HCl is $K = 5 \times 10^{-10}$, with the others at intermediate values.[91] Much earlier it had been noted that the effect of "pH"[92] upon the rate of inversion of sucrose in 98% acetic acid (2% water) corresponded to the aqueous hydrolysis, *i.e.*, as the "pH" went up, the rate went down, decreasing about three-fold for a change of half a "pH" unit.[93] Mixtures of H_2SO_4 and "weak" bases, such as hexamethylene tetramine, urea, benzamide *et al.*, were used as "buffers" in acetic acid. That the base was "weak" was decided by comparison with an equimolar mixture of pyridine and pyridinium acetate, this latter being assigned an arbitrary "pH" of 4.4. These "buffers" then were used to catalyze the sucrose inversion. In view of the limited dissociation of solutes in acetic acid it must be concluded that the catalytic effect resides in some other species than the (solvated) proton, although this conclusion appears not to have been tested.

A variety of studies on solvates in acetic acid have been made. Acetates of silver, zinc, lead, and iron are not solvated in acetic acid, but those of lithium, sodium, potassium, calcium, and copper form monosolvates. Sodium and potassium acetates also form a disolvate; barium acetate forms both a disolvate and a trisolvate.[94] Perchloric acid forms a disolvate[95] and nitric acid a monosolvate.[96]

The isolation of a solvate of zinc and lithium acetates, $Zn(CH_3CO_2)_2 \cdot 2Li(CH_3CO_2) \cdot 4CH_3CO_2H$, provides evidence for the amphoteric character of zinc acetate in acetic acid.[97] Zinc acetate is not soluble in acetic acid, but is taken into solution by HCl and also by lithium acetate. Lithium nitrate "salts in" (*i.e.*, increases the solubility) zinc acetate, but the effect is much less than that for lithium acetate.[98] Zinc acetate is thus the counterpart of zinc hydroxide in the water system in its ability

[91] T. L. Smith and J. H. Elliott, *loc. cit.*

[92] The term "pH" is put in quotation marks to indicate that it is here an arbitrary number in the acetic acid system.

[93] J. B. Conant and N. F. Hall, *J. Am. Chem. Soc.* **49**, 3062 (1927).

[94] A. W. Davidson and W. H. McAllister, *J. Am. Chem. Soc.* **52**, 507 (1930).

[95] T. Sumarokova and M. Usanovich, *Acta Physicochim. U.R.S.S.* **21**, 841 (1946); M. Usanovich and T. Sumarokova, *Zhur. Obshchei Khim.* **17**, 1415 (1947).

[96] S. P. Miskidzh'yan and N. A. Trifonov, *J. Gen. Chem. (U.S.S.R.)* **17**, 1033 (1947); *ibid.* **17**, 2216 (1947); *idem, Zhur. Obshchei Khim.* **19**, 441 (1949); A. S. Naumova, *ibid.* **19**, 1228 (1949).

[97] E. Griswold and W. Van Horne, *J. Am. Chem. Soc.* **67**, 763 (1945).

[98] E. Griswold *et al.*, *J. Am. Chem. Soc.* **67**, 372 (1945).

to play an amphiprotic role:

$$Zn(C_2H_3O_2)_2 \text{ (insol.)} + 2HCl \rightarrow ZnCl_2 + 2HC_2H_3O_2$$
$$Zn(C_2H_3O_2)_2 \text{ (insol.)} + 2NaC_2H_3O_2 + 4HC_2H_3O_2 \rightarrow Na_2Zn(C_2H_3O_2)_4 \cdot$$
$$4HC_2H_3O_2$$

Copper acetate behaves similarly:

$$Cu(C_2H_3O_2)_2 \text{ (insol.)} + 4NH_4C_2H_3O_2 + 4HC_2H_3O_2 \rightarrow$$
$$(NH_4)_4Cu(C_2H_3O_2)_6 \cdot 4HC_2H_3O_2$$

It will be noted that the soluble form of the complex is itself a solvate.

Some polarographic studies using acetic acid as solvent have been carried out [99] which showed that Cd(II), Ni(II), Pb(II), and Zn(II) ions are reducible at the dropping mercury electrode. Oxygen exhibits a maximum in the polarographic curve, requiring solutions to be de-gassed carefully, just as in aqueous polarography, before measurement. The use of methyl cellulose, *etc.*, to eliminate the oxygen maximum is without effect in acetic acid.[100] Unfortunately the hydrogen ion wave appears very early and interferes with substances having half-wave potentials more negative than -1.7 volts.

HYDROGEN CYANIDE

Although there are obvious disadvantages in the use of liquid hydrogen cyanide as a medium for chemical reactions, they have not deterred several investigators from research on it.

The table below sets forth some of the properties of this substance.

TABLE 3.11. SOME PHYSICAL PROPERTIES OF HYDROGEN CYANIDE

Normal boiling point	25.6°C
Freezing point	−13.4°C
Dielectric constant	123 (at 15.6°C)
Conductivity	4.5×10^{-7} mho (at 0°C)
Dipole moment	2.8
Viscosity	0.00201 dyne sec/cm² (at 20°C)
Density	0.681 g/ml (at 25.6°C)
Heat of vaporization	6.027 kcal/mole
Heat of fusion	2.009 kcal/mole

Hydrogen cyanide has a higher dielectric constant than any other substance, being approached only by hydrogen fluoride. As has been mentioned earlier, the dielectric constant is a measure of a solvent's

[99] G. B. Bachman and M. J. Astle, *J. Am. Chem. Soc.* **64**, 1303 and 2177 (1942).
[100] Some earlier work indicating no oxygen interference appears to have been in error. D. MacGillavry, *Trans. Faraday Soc.* **32**, 1447 (1936).

TABLE 3.12. SOLUBILITY AND CONDUCTANCE OF SUBSTANCES IN HCN

Readily Soluble Nonelectrolytes	Soluble but Very Poor Conductors	Soluble and Fair Conductors
I_2	acetic acid	$BiCl_3$
H_2O	cyanoacetic acid	$AgNO_3$
methanol	trichloracetic acid	$POCl_3$
ethanol	pyridine	$SOCl_2$*
glycerine	quinoline	SO_2Cl_2*
$CHCl_3$	phenylhydrazine	CH_3COCl
picric acid	$AsCl_3$	strychnine
benzene	$SbCl_3$	brucine
aniline		
urea		
$CNCH_2CH_2CN$		
$SnCl_4$		
$SnBr_4$		
SnI_4		
S_2Cl_2		

* Reacts violently with HCN.

TABLE 3.12—*Continued*

Soluble and Good Conductors	Sparingly Soluble	Insoluble
KI	NaCl	$CaCl_2$
KSCN	KCl	$BaCl_2$
$KMnO_4$	NaBr	$Ba(NO_3)_2$
KOCN	NH_4Cl	$Ca(NO_3)_2$
$K_2[Pt(CN)_6]$	KNO_3	$Sr(NO_3)_2$
$FeCl_3$	$NaNO_3$	PbF_2
$SbCl_5$	K_2SO_4	$PbBr_2$
HCl	K_2CrO_4	PbI_2
H_2SO_4	"borax glass"	$PbCrO_4$
SO_3	sodium oleate	Hg_2Cl_2
amylamine*	$K_2[PtCl_6]$	HgI_2
	$CoCl_2$	HgO
	CdI_2	$Cd(NO_3)_2$
	$HgCl_2$	$CdSO_4$
	$HgBr_2$	$CuSO_4$
	$Cu_3(AsO_4)_2$	copper oleate
	$Cu_3(AsO_3)_2$	$AlCl_3$
	Hg_2SO_4	$SnCl_2$
	AgCN	AgCl
	AgOCN	$CNCH_2COOAg$
	H_3BO_3	Cr_2O_3
	tartaric acid	P_2O_5
	biuret	HIO_3
	quinine sulfate	paraffin oil
	brucine hydrochloride	petroleum ether
		levulose
		sugar

* Reacts violently with HCN.

ability to separate charged bodies (ions) placed in it—the larger the dielectric constant the greater is this capacity.   The expectation would be, therefore, that hydrogen cyanide should be able to dissolve and dissociate the same sort of substances that water dissolves and dissociates, and should do so to a much greater degree.   Contrary to expectations, hydrogen cyanide is not exceptional among solvents, but is in fact inferior to water in many respects.[101]   In Table 3.12, some of the data on solubility and conductance are given, more or less qualitatively.

Triethylammonium chloride, triethylammonium picrate, potassium hydrogen sulfate, and potassium dichloracetate are readily soluble in HCN and conduct well.[102]   Propylamine is easily soluble but is a nonconductor.   Dichloracetic acid is likewise readily soluble but conducts poorly (*cf.* water).   Benzophenone, normal propyl ether, and normal butanol are easily soluble but no investigations have been made of their conductances.   The solubility of iodine decreases sharply with decreasing temperature.

The behavior of hydrogen cyanide with special regard to conductance phenomena and dissociation has been studied [103] and it is found that KBr, KI, LiCl, and KNO_3 [104] are nearly 100% dissociated, as evidence by freezing point measurements.   The conductance of alkali metal and tetralkylammonium salts, the chloride, bromide, iodide, nitrate, perchlorate, thiocyanate, and picrate, at increasing dilutions, shows that the Kohlrausch relation, $\Lambda = \Lambda_0 - X\sqrt{C}$, holds in many of these cases.   Here Λ is the equivalent conductance at concentration C, Λ_0 is the equivalent conductance at infinite dilution, and X the Debye-Huckel-Onsager "slope."   This slope, compared with the plotted slope, corresponds in most cases.   For some of them, however, large negative deviations occur. It is possible [105] to calculate, from the relation above, a value for α, the fraction of molecules of a solute which is dissociated into ions.   In Table 3.13, values of this quantity for the solute, tetraethylammonium picrate, at two different concentrations and for a number of different solvents, are given.   From the circumstance that this solute is more nearly completely dissociated in HCN than it is in water, it can be concluded that the Nernst-Thomson rule in general holds for HCN.

[101] L. Kahlenberg and H. Schlundt, *J. Phys. Chem.* **6**, 447 (1902).

[102] Jander & Scholz, *vide infra*, p. 187.

[103] J. E. Coates and E. G. Taylor, *J. Chem. Soc.* **1936**, 1245 and 1495, and *Nature* **134**, 141 (1934).

[104] R. Lespieau, *Compt. rend.* **140**, 855 (1905).

[105] R. M. Fuoss and C. A. Kraus, *J. Am. Chem. Soc.* **55**, 476 (1933) and *ibid.* **57**, 488 (1935).

TABLE 3.13. DISSOCIATION OF TETRAETHYLAMMONIUM PICRATE

Solvent	Dielectric Constant	α (0.001 molar)	α (0.0001 molar)
HCN	116	0.985	0.993
H_2O	81	0.965	0.992
CH_3OH	35	0.933	0.978
CH_3COCH_3	21	0.835	0.946

The mobilities of ions in HCN are some three times larger, at infinite dilution, than in water, at the same temperature. However, a comparison is better made at corresponding temperatures, *i.e.*, at a temperature roughly three-quarters of the way from freezing to boiling point.[106] When this adjustment is made, mobilities in the two solvents become concordant.

The freezing-point constant for HCN has been determined with the use of picric acid, urethane, urea, benzophenone, *n*-propyl ether, *n*-butanol, and pyridine. Each of these substances gives a freezing-point depression (in degrees per mole per kg solvent) of very nearly 1.78, the mean value being 1.786. This value has been used to calculate α for a number of solutes from the relation

$$\frac{M_{theor} - M_{obs}}{M_{obs}} = \alpha$$

Here M_{theor} is the molecular weight of the solute obtained by adding the atomic weights; M_{obs} is the molecular weight found in the familiar Beckmann experiment. It is of especial interest that neither sulfuric acid, dichloracetic acid, nor sulfur trioxide is dissociated in hydrogen cyanide. However, the SO_3 solution is slightly conducting.

Triethylamine and propylamine are not themselves dissociated; however they appear to be dissociated in HCN, and their dissociation must result from combination with one of the ions produced by auto-ionization of the solvent:

$$HCN \rightleftharpoons H^+ + CN^-$$

followed by

$$H^+ + Et_3N \rightleftharpoons Et_3NH^+$$

It is doubtful if unsolvated protons exist in any solvent. Hence it is better to write

$$2HCN \rightleftharpoons HCN \cdot H^+ + CN^-$$

than

$$HCN \rightleftharpoons H^+ + CN^-$$

[106] G. Jander and G. Scholz, *Z. physik. Chem.* **192**(A), 163 (1943).

TABLE 3.14. RESULTS OF TITRATING HCN SOLUTIONS

Solute	Titrant	Products formed
KCN	H_2SO_4	$KHSO_4$, K_2SO_4
$C_3H_7NH_2$	H_2SO_4	$C_3H_7NH_3HSO_4$, $(C_3H_7NH_3)_2SO_4$
Pyridine	H_2SO_4	$C_5H_5NHHSO_4$, $(C_5H_5NH)_2SO_4$
KCN	$Cl_2CHCOOH$	$Cl_2CHCOOK$, $Cl_2CHCOOK \cdot Cl_2CHCOOH$, $Cl_2CHCOOK \cdot 2Cl_2CHCOOH$
$(C_2H_5)_3N$	$Cl_2CHCOOH$	$Cl_2CHCOO(C_2H_5)_3NH$, $Cl_2CHCOO(C_2H_5)_3NH \cdot Cl_2CHCOOH$
H_2SO_4	KCN	$KHSO_4$, K_2SO_4
H_2SO_4	$(C_2H_5)_3N$	$(C_2H_5)_3NHHSO_4$, $2(C_2H_5)_3NH \cdot SO_4$
SO_3	$(C_2H_5)_3N$	$SO_3 \cdot (C_2H_5)_3N$
Picric acid	$(C_2H_5)_3N$	$C_6H_2(NO_2)_3O(C_2H_5)_3NH$
$Cl_2CHCOOH$	$(C_2H_5)_3N$	$Cl_2CHCOO(C_2H_5)_3NH$
HCl	$(C_2H_5)_3N$	$(C_2H_5)_3NHCl$, $(C_2H_5)_3NHCl \cdot HCl$
HCl	Pyridine	C_5H_5NHCl

This equilibrium indicates that the same substances which are acids in water should be acids in hydrogen cyanide, while cyanides should be bases. Table 3.14 shows the results of titrating various substances according to this idea, the titrations being followed conductometrically. The pairs, potassium cyanide—dichloracetic acid, triethylamine—dichloracetic acid, and hydrogen chloride—triethylamine, form acid salts which have no counter-parts in water.

Potentiometric titrations have been carried out [107] using triethylamine as the titrant against the solutes, dichloracetic acid, sulfur trioxide, hydrogen sulfate, and iron(III) chloride.

The first of these titration curves when plotted in the usual way of potential against moles of titrant per mole of solute shows an inflection point in the titration curve at the 1:1 molar ratio, indicating the formation of a substituted ammonium salt of dichloracetic acid.[108]

The second curve, that of sulfur trioxide whose solution had been allowed to "age" for thirty minutes or so, showed two inflections, corresponding to molar ratios of amine to SO_3 of 1:1 and 2:1.

Hydrogen sulfate shows three discontinuities in its titration curve, at molar ratios of amine to acid of 1:1, 2:1, and 3:1. The acid is assumed to undergo solvation,

$$H_2SO_4 + 2HCN \rightarrow (HO)_4S(CN)_2$$

and to have three especially labile hydrogen ions; thus its behavior is comparable to that of orthophosphoric acid in water. For the previous

---

[107] Jander and Scholz, loc. cit.
[108] Jander and Scholz, loc. cit.

case of sulfur trioxide, it is supposed that it too undergoes solvation: [109]

$$SO_3 + 3HCN \rightarrow (HO)_3S(CN)_3$$

Thus the titration curves appear to show that the former substance is tribasic while the latter is dibasic.

The curve for the potential titration of iron(III) chloride shows an inflection at a molar ratio for amine to salt of 3:1 and another at 6:1. Iron(III) chloride is soluble in HCN, and when triethylamine is added, a blue salt precipitates. Addition of excess amine redissolves the salt. The precipitation process ends with the first inflection in the titration curve, and the re-solution ends with the second. Accordingly, the reactions are

$$FeCl_3 + 3(C_2H_5)_3NHCN \rightarrow Fe(CN)_3 + 3(C_2H_5)_3NHCl$$

and

$$Fe(CN)_3 + 3(C_2H_5)_3NHCN \rightarrow [(C_2H_5)_3NH]_3[Fe(CN)_6].$$

It is not known whether the addition of acids would reverse the course of these reactions, although reversal would seem likely.

Few solvates in HCN are known, but the formation and constitution of one of aluminum chloride is of interest.[110] The compound, $AlCl_3 \cdot 2HCN$, is best described as an iminoformylcarbylamine, $AlCl_3 \cdot NHCHNC$, since the substance prepared from aluminum chloride and HCN is identical with that prepared from aluminum chloride and iminoformylcarbylamine. This last substance does not decompose to hydrogen cyanide on passage through a hot tube. Its compound with aluminum chloride, however, yields HCN when warmed to 100°C. In this connection it should be pointed out that a slow reaction occurs between sulfur trioxide and HCN. This reaction has been followed conductometrically with the finding that the conductance of sulfur trioxide changed six-fold in half an hour or less. Since both aluminum chloride and sulfur trioxide are similar substances in the Lewis sense of acids and bases, it may be that a reaction producing the SO_3 analogue of the compound, $AlCl_3 \cdot NHCHNC$, is occurring. It was found that the reaction is of the first order, based on the change of conductance with time. If the reaction here envisaged actually is occurring, the titrations involving SO_3 (and probably H_2SO_4) need to be reinterpreted.

A few examples of solvolysis are known in liquid HCN, corresponding to hydrolysis in water. Silver sulfate is solvolyzed according to the

[109] *Cf.* the work of Hinckel and Watkins reported later in this connection.
[110] L. E. Hinckel and T. I. Watkins, *J. Chem. Soc.* 1940, 407.

equation

$$Ag_2SO_4 + 2HCN \rightarrow 2AgCN + H_2SO_4.$$

This reaction is practically complete since silver cyanide is insoluble in HCN.

SULFUR DIOXIDE

Although sulfur dioxide is a gas under room conditions, it is nevertheless easily liquefied and as a liquid has served extensively for chemical investigations.

The table below sets forth some of the properties of this solvent.

TABLE 3.15. SOME PHYSICAL PROPERTIES OF SULFUR DIOXIDE

Normal boiling point	$-10.02°C$
Freezing point	$-75.46°C$
Dielectric constant	17.27 (at $-16.5°C$)
Conductivity	1×10^{-7} (at $0°C$)
Dipole moment	1.61 D
Viscosity	0.0039 dyne sec/cm^2 (at $0°C$)
Density	1.46 g/ml (at $-10°C$)
Heat of vaporization	5.96 kcal/mole
Heat of fusion	1.77 kcal/mole

Table 3.16 gives the solubilities of a variety of salts in sulfur dioxide.[111]   In general the iodides are the most soluble among inorganic salts, followed by thiocyanates.   The solubilities of a number of other substances in sulfur dioxide have been determined at various temperatures and under various pressures.[112]   The substances $AsCl_3$, Br_2, BCl_3, CCl_4, CS_2, ICl, PCl_3, $POCl_3$, and SO_2Cl_2 are all miscible with the solvent. Compounds with ionic lattices tend to be insoluble, while compounds with molecular lattices tend to be soluble or miscible.   Because of the inverse order of solubility for the alkali halides in liquid ammonia and sulfur dioxide, successive recrystallization from these two solvents can be used to separate cesium and rubidium from lithium, sodium, and potassium.

The auto-ionization of sulfur dioxide has been described according to the scheme [113]

$$2SO_2 \rightleftharpoons SO^{++} + SO_3^{=}$$

Thionyl chloride and cesium sulfite are said to react to produce cesium chloride and sulfur dioxide.   Thus thionyl chloride should be considered

[111] G. Jander, *Naturwissenschaften* **26**, 793 (1938).

[112] A. I. Shatenshtein and M. M. Viktorov, *Acta Physicochim. U.R.S.S.* **7**, 883 (1937).

[113] D. H. Puffett, *General Conception of Acids and Bases*, M.S. Thesis, U. of Kansas (1923).

TABLE 3.16. SOLUBILITY OF SALTS IN LIQUID SULFUR DIOXIDE *

	F^-	Cl^-	Br^-	I	CN^-	SCN^-	SO_3^-	SO_4^-	CO_3^-	CH_3COO^-	ClO_4^-
Li^+	23.0	2.82	6.0	1490	—	—	—	1.55	—	3.48	—
Na^+	6.9	i.	1.36	1000	3.67	80.5	1.37	i.	—	8.9	—
K^+	3.1	5.5	ca. 40	2490	2.62	502	1.58	i.	—	0.61	—
Rb^+	—	27.2	—	—	—	—	1.27	—	—	—	—
NH_4^+	—	1.67	6.0	580	—	6160	2.67	5.07	—	141	2.14
Be^{++}	—	5.8	—	—	—	—	—	—	—	—	—
Mg^{++}	—	1.47	1.3	0.50	—	—	—	—	—	—	—
Ba^{++}	—	i.	i.	18.15	—	i.	i.	—	—	—	—
Zn^{++}	—	11.75	—	3.45	—	40.4	—	—	—	i.	—
Cd^{++}	—	i.	—	1.17	—	—	—	—	—	—	—
Hg^{++}	—	3.80	2.06	0.265	0.556	0.632	—	0.338	—	2.98	—
Pb^{++}	2.16	0.69	0.328	0.195	0.386	0.371	—	i.	—	2.46	—
Co^{++}	—	1.00	—	12.2	—	i.	—	—	—	—	—
Ni^{++}	—	i.	—	i.	—	—	—	i.	i.	0.08	—
Al^{+3}	—	v.s.	0.60	5.64	—	—	—	—	—	—	—
Tl^+	i.	0.292	0.60	1.81	0.522	0.915	4.96	0.417	0.214	285	0.43
Ag^+	i.	<0.07	0.159	0.67	1.42	0.845	i.	i.	—	1.02	—
Sb^{+3}	0.56	575	21.8	0.26	—	—	—	—	—	—	—
Bi^{+3}	—	0.36	3.44	—	—	—	—	—	—	—	—

* i. (insoluble), v.s. (very soluble), — (no observation). Figures in millimoles per kg solvent, at 0°C

an acid in sulfur dioxide.[114]   An acid may be defined as being a substance which produces a solvent cation. These ideas have been adopted and widely promulgated.[115]

It will be noticed that according to this hypothesis ions are created in sulfur dioxide by the transfer of an oxide ion ($O^=$) from one solvent molecule to another, much as ions are created in water by the transfer of a proton from one molecule to another. Sulfites and hydrogensulfites are often referred to as "base-analogues" and thionyl compounds as "acid-analogues," the thionyl "ion" (SO^{++}) being thought the equivalent of the hydrogen ion in water. Indeed, the thionyl ion is supposed to function in sulfur dioxide even as the hydrogen ion does in water. Two arguments support this theory.

[114] H. P. Cady and H. M. Elsey, *J. Chem. Educ.* **5**, 1425 (1928).

[115] G. Jander and K. Wickert, *Z. physik. Chem.* **A178**, 57 (1936); K. Wickert and G. Jander, *Ber.* **70B**, 251 (1937); G. Jander and D. Ullmann, *Z. anorg. u. allgem. Chem.* **230**, 405 (1937); G. Jander, H. Knoll and H. Immig, *Z. anorg. u. allgem. Chem.* **232**, 229 (1937); G. Jander and W. Ruppolt, *Z. physik. Chem.* **A179**, 43 (1937); G. Jander and H. Immig, *Z. anorg. u. allgem. Chem.* **233**, 295 (1937); G. Jander, *Naturwissenschaften* **26**, 779 and 793 (1938); G. Jander and H. Mesech, *Z. physik. Chem.* **A183**, 121 (1938); *ibid.* **255** and 277 (1939); G. Jander and H. Hecht, *Z. anorg. Chem.* **250**, 287, and 304 (1943); G. Jander, H. Wendt, and H. Hecht, *Ber.* **77B**, 698 (1944); G. Jander, *Naturwissenschaften* **32**, 169 (1945).

The first rests upon the general reaction between thionyl compounds and sulfites:

$$SOCl_2 + Cs_2SO_3 \rightarrow 2CsCl + 2SO_2$$

It is of interest to note that the reaction between thionyl chloride and sodium sulfite does *not* lead to the formation of sodium chloride and sulfur dioxide. In spite of the considerable amount of work published on this reaction, further study is needed.[116]

The second argument rests on the reaction of amines with the thionyl ion of the solvent to form a product equivalent to the ammonium ion in water. By using triethylamine as an example, the reactions in water and sulfur dioxide are, respectively,

$$Et_3N + H_2O \rightarrow Et_3NH^+ + OH^-$$

and

$$2Et_3N + 2SO_2 \rightarrow (Et_3N)_2SO^{++} + SO_3^=$$

The coefficient 2 enters the second reaction because the thionyl ion is treated as bivalent, as opposed to the univalent proton.

These two arguments and the hypothesis which rests on them have been very strongly criticized.[117] The first argument,[118] based on the reaction between thionyl compounds and sulfites, does not make necessary the auto-ionization scheme for sulfur dioxide into thionyl ions and sulfite ions, as the nature of the ultimate products of the reaction does not establish the mechanism. Furthermore, in some organic reactions with thionyl chloride, it is possible to distinguish a first stage in which only one chlorine atom of the two in thionyl chloride becomes liberated as a chloride ion, the other product being an organic chlorosulfinate, R—OSOCl. And even for this case it is not known whether the first stage is a single process or a composite one. It thus seems reasonable to suppose that the reaction between thionyl chloride and the sulfite ion is separable into two stages, each corresponding to the liberation of a single chloride ion. If this mechanism is once assumed, then the entity with which the sulfite ion interacts is first thionyl chloride itself and secondly the ion, $SOCl^+$. It cannot be the ion, SO^{++}.[119]

If the second argument were upheld by experimental facts, it would establish the thesis. However, the evidence of the literature supporting

[116] J. Cornog and V. Lamb, *Proc. Iowa Acad. Sci.* **40**, 97 (1933).
[117] L. C. Bateman, E. D. Hughes, and C. K. Ingold, *J. Chem. Soc.* **1944**, 243.
[118] Puffett, *op. cit.*
[119] Bateman *et al.*, *loc. cit.*

the argument,[120] as well as the previous literature on amine-sulfur dioxide systems, make it very probable the conclusions were in error.

Thus, when triethylamine is dissolved in sulfur dioxide and the excess solvent is evaporated, a colorless salt melting at 73°C is obtained.[121] The composition, $(Et_3N \cdot SO_2)_n$, is stated to have been established by an analysis. However, it has been pointed out that an independent appraisal of the only analysis even partially quoted is impossible, as the weight of substance which gave the stated weight of sulfur dioxide is not given, nor is the percentage of sulfur dioxide given.[122]

In addition, experimental evidence shows that no colorless, crystalline solid having a melting point above room temperature is formed by the combination of triethyl amine and sulfur dioxide alone, although various salts can be obtained from mixtures of triethylamine and sulfur dioxide by allowing them to come in contact with moisture and oxygen, as in ordinary damp air.[123]

Triethylamine and sulfur dioxide in the absence of moisture and air form an orange-red liquid which sets to a colorless solid at $-80°C$, and remelts to the same orange-red liquid well below 0°C. The composition corresponds to $(Et_3N \cdot SO_2)_n$. The molecular complexity, found in freezing-point measurements, n, was found to be one.

When the colored compound, $Et_3N \cdot SO_2$, is exposed to moist air, it changes to a mass of colorless crystals having a melting point of 74–75°C and a composition, $Et_3N \cdot SO_2 \cdot H_2O$, or triethylammonium hydrogen sulfite, $Et_3NH^+HSO_3^-$. This salt undergoes further change whereby hydrogensulfite is progressively oxidized to hydrogensulfate, which melts above 115°C.

The compound, $(Et_3NBr)2SO$, was supposed to be prepared by treating triethylamine in sulfur dioxide with potassium bromide:[124]

$$(Et_3N)_2SO^{++}SO_3^{=} + 2KBr \rightarrow (Et_3N)_2SO^{++}Br_2^{=} + K_2SO_3$$

This compound is described as being a white solid melting at 230°C. On the other hand, it has been pointed out that such a formulation is untenable on grounds described above [125] and on evidence consisting of two estimations of the composition of the compound in question, $(Et_3N)_2SOBr_2$. One estimation is of the sulfur content: a quantity of compound corre-

[120] G. Jander, *loc. cit.*
[121] G. Jander and K. Wickert, *Z. physik. Chem.* **A178**, 57 (1936).
[122] Bateman *et al.*, *loc. cit.*
[123] Bateman *et al.*, *loc. cit.*
[124] K. Wickert and G. Jander, *Ber.* **70B**, 251 (1937).
[125] Bateman *et al.*, *loc. cit.*

sponding to a triethylamine content of 0.2968 g is said to have a sulfur content of 0.0128 g as compared with a calculated quantity of 0.0129 g. The quantity has been recalculated as 0.0470 g.[126]   The second estimation is of the bromine content but no analysis is given, merely the statement that the bromine content corresponds to the calculated amount.[127]   It is suggested that the compound analysed was probably impure triethyl-amine hydrobromide (mp 248–250°C).

Similar criticism exists for the formation of the compound, $Et_3N \cdot SO_2$, as $(Et_3N)SO^{++}SO_3^=$.[128]   Iodine is supposed to react as follows:

$$I_2 + 2(Et_3N)_2SO \cdot SO_3 \rightarrow (Et_3N)_2SO \cdot SO_4 + (Et_3N)_2SOI_2 + SO_2$$

The amount of iodine absorbed by a solution of triethylamine in sulfur dioxide depends simply upon how much water and how much oxygen the solution has taken up from the air, i.e., upon the amount of triethyl-ammonium hydrogen sulfite which was formed by hydration but not destroyed by (air) oxidation.   Thus all the evidence supporting the original ionization scheme fails to establish it conclusively.   In this con-nection recent isotope exchange experiments are of interest.   It has been shown that the isotope, ^{35}S, exchanges very slowly (half-time about two years) between SO_2 and $SOCl_2$ and between SO_2 and $SOBr_2$.[129]   The exchange of this isotope between SO_2 and SO_3 (either dissolved in the other as solvent) was likewise extremely slow.[130]   The exchange of the isotope, ^{18}O, between SO_2 and SO_3, has been shown to be very rapid; [131] while the exchange of the same isotope between SO_2 and $SOCl_2$ was found to be very slow.[132]   Consequently, it cannot be that sulfur dioxide under-goes auto-ionization, or that thionyl chloride ionizes to yield a thionyl ion.

The reaction between triethylamine and hydrogen chloride

$$Et_3N + HCl \rightarrow Et_3NHCl$$

takes place in sulfur dioxide.[133]

Acid strengths in sulfur dioxide have been determined in a qualitative way for a few substances, the order being somewhat similar to that

[126] Bateman et al., loc. cit.
[127] Wickert and Jander give an analysis of an analogous quinoline compound, formu-lated here as Qu_2SOBr_2, setting forth the weights of bromine and sulfur found, but neglecting to give the weight of Qu_2SOBr_2 taken.
[128] G. Jander and H. Immig, Z. anorg. u. allgem. Chem. 233, 295 (1937).
[129] R. E. Johnson, T. H. Norris, and J. L. Huston, J. Am. Chem. Soc. 73, 3052 (1951).
[130] J. L. Huston, J. Am. Chem. Soc. 73, 3049 (1951).
[131] S. Nakata, J. Chem. Soc. Japan 64, 635 (1943).
[132] E. C. M. Gregg and I. Lander, Trans. Faraday Soc. 46, 1039 (1950).
[133] K. Wickert and G. Jander, Ber. 70B, 251 (1937).

TABLE 3.17. INDICATOR COLORS IN SULFUR DIOXIDE

Indicator	Color in SO_2	Acid Color in SO_2	Base Color in SO_2
Methyl orange	red-orange	red	yellow
Tropaeolin 00	yellow	raspberry	yellow
Neutral red	violet-red	raspberry to blue	—
Malachite green	green-blue	green	green-blue
Methyl violet	violet	green-yellow	violet [a]
			green [b]
Thymol blue	colorless	violet-red	yellow
Bromthymol blue	yellow	violet	yellow
Bromcresol purple	red-orange	red	yellow

[a] By transmitted light.
[b] By reflected light.

for water: [134]

$$HCl > picric > Cl_3CCOOH > H_2O > Et_2NH$$

A number of indicators in water, liquid ammonia, and sulfur dioxide with their solvent colors, acid colors, and base colors are given in Table 3.17. Common acids, as trichloracetic acid, and nitrogen bases, as pyridine, were used.[135]

Not many oxidizing and reducing reactions have been studied in sulfur dioxide. One is indicated by the equation: [136]

$$6KI + 3SbCl_5 \rightarrow 2K_3[SbCl_6] + 3I_2 + SbCl_3$$

The potassium hexachloroantimonate(III) is insoluble. It is stated [137] that the following reaction occurs:

$$3KSCN + 3ICl + 2SO_2 \rightarrow 3KCl + I_2 + I(SCN)_3 \cdot 2SO_2$$

This last compound has not been hitherto reported.

A number of reactions in sulfur dioxide involving acetyl fluoborate have been reported.[138] Boron trifluoride reacts with acetyl fluoride as the equation

$$CH_3COF + BF_3 \rightarrow CH_3COBF_4$$

[134] K. Cruse, *Z. Elektrochem.* **46**, 571 (1940).
[135] A. I. Shattenshtein and M. I. Urizko, *J. Phys. Chem. U.S.S.R.* **10**, 776 (1937) and *Acta Physicochim. U.R.S.S.* **7**, 401 (1937).
[136] G. Jander and H. Immig, *Z. anorg. u. allgem. Chem.* **233**, 295 (1937).
[137] J. Cornog and V. Lamb, *Proc. Iowa Acad. Sci.* **40**, 97 (1933).
[138] F. Seel, *Z. anorg. Chem.* **250**, 331 (1943).

indicates.   The acetyl fluoborate reacts as follows:

$$CH_3COBF_4 + CH_3COOK \rightarrow (CH_3CO)_2O + KBF_4$$
$$CH_3COBF_4 + KCl \rightarrow CH_3COCl + KBF_4$$
$$CH_3COBF_4 + NaNO_2 \rightarrow CH_3CONO_2 + NaBF_4$$
$$CH_3COBF_4 + CH_3CONO_2 \rightarrow NOBF_4 + (CH_3CO)_2O$$
$$CH_3COBF_4 + (C_6H_5)_3CCl \rightarrow CH_3COCl + (C_6H_5)_3CBF_4$$

The last compound is a yellow powder melting with decomposition at 215°C.   The same product is obtained if triphenyl carbinol is used in place of triphenylchloromethane.

A number of solvates in sulfur dioxide have been reported.   The vapor pressure-composition diagrams for various solutes in sulfur dioxide show that the following solvates exist: $KSCN \cdot 2SO_2$; $KSCN \cdot SO_2$; $KSCN \cdot \frac{1}{2}SO_2$; $RbI \cdot 3SO_2$; $KBr \cdot 4SO_2$; $Me_4NBr \cdot SO_2$; $Me_4NBr \cdot 2SO_2$; $Me_4NCl \cdot SO_2$; $Me_4NCl \cdot 2SO_2$; $(Me_4N)_2SO_4 \cdot 3SO_2$; $(Me_4N)_2SO_4 \cdot 6SO_2$; quinoline $\cdot SO_2$.   No solvates were found for Me_4NClO_4, $SbCl_3$, or iodine.[139]

A temperature-composition diagram shows the compound between dimethylaniline and sulfur dioxide [140] to have the composition, $Me_2C_6H_5N \cdot SO_2$.

Aniline reacts with sulfur dioxide to give a monosolvate:

$$C_6H_5NH_2 + SO_2 \rightarrow C_6H_5NH_2 \cdot SO_2$$

This solvate is yellow, melts under three and one-half atmospheres at 65°C and sublimes at 52°C under one atmosphere.

The solvate reacts with water to form phenylammonium hydrogen sulfite, $C_6H_5NH_3HSO_3$, and phenylammonium sulfite, $(C_6H_5NH_3)_2SO_3$.[141]

The temperature-composition diagram for the system, $SO_2:BF_3$, shows a monosolvate of boron trifluoride.[142]   Boron trichloride however is only slightly soluble in sulfur dioxide and no compound between them is observed.[143]

Temperature-composition diagrams showing addition compounds between sulfur dioxide and various oxygen-bearing molecules have been reported [144] such as ethylene oxide:SO_2, dioxane:SO_2, dioxane:$2SO_2$,

[139] G. Jander and H. Mesech, *Z. physik. Chem.* **A183**, 121 (1938).
[140] J. R. Bright and W. C. Fernelius, *J. Am. Chem. Soc.* **65**, 637 (1943).
[141] A. E. Hill, *J. Am. Chem. Soc.* **53**, 2598 (1931).
[142] H. S. Booth and D. R. Martin, *J. Am. Chem. Soc.* **64**, 2198 (1942).
[143] D. R. Martin, *J. Am. Chem. Soc.* **67**, 1088 (1945).
[144] N. Albertson and W. C. Fernelius, *J. Am. Chem. Soc.* **65**, 1587 (1943).

anisole:SO_2, and diethyl sulfide:SO_2. Methylaniline does not form a complex with SO_2, although aniline and dimethylaniline do.

The formation of an addition compound between hydrogen acetate and sulfur dioxide, $HAc:SO_2$, is reported,[145] as are the solvates, $2TiBr_4 \cdot SO_2$, $2TiCl_4 \cdot SO_2$, and $2SnBr_4 \cdot SO_2$.[146]

The preparation and properties of an addition compound between trimethylamine and sulfur dioxide, $Me_3N \cdot SO_2$ are described.[147]

One-to-one addition compounds between sulfur dioxide and pyridine, and sulfur dioxide and each of the three isomeric picolines have been found.[148]

Solutions of triarylhalomethanes are good conductors in sulfur dioxide.[149] When triphenylchloromethane is electrolyzed, the free radical triphenyl methyl forms. This radical is also a conductor, a rare example among hydrocarbons as they are characteristically nonconductors.[150] It was formerly believed[151] that two triphenylmethyl radicals (or hexaphenylethane) dissociated in such a way as to give a positive and a negative ion:

$$2(C_6H_5)_3C \rightarrow (C_6H_5)_3C^+ + (C_6H_5)_3C^-$$

However, absorption-spectra measurements show[152] that virtually no anions, $(C_6H_5)_3C^-$, are present. It is thus believed that triphenylmethyl donates an electron to a solvent molecule (SO_2) in much the same way an alkali metal atom donates an electron to ammonia:

$$(C_6H_5)_3C + SO_2 \rightarrow (C_6H_5)_3C^+ + SO_2^-$$

It is reported that a hydrate of SO_2 and snow, formed at $-8°C$, is able to hold radon[153] and argon.[154] It is supposed that a hydrate of the inert gas makes possible this "holding."

A comparison of the *emf*'s of concentration cells with thermal data[154a] shows that in sulfur dioxide the silver-silver chloride electrode is most

[145] W. Scheub and C. R. McCrosky, *J. Am. Chem. Soc.* **66**, 841 (1944).

[146] P. Bond and W. Belton, *J. Am. Chem. Soc.* **67**, 1691 (1945).

[147] *Inorganic Syntheses*, Vol. II, p. 159, by J. R. Bright and W. C. Fernelius, McGraw-Hill, New York, 1946.

[148] K. Hoffman and C. VanderWerf, *J. Am. Chem. Soc.* **68**, 997 (1946).

[149] P. Walden, *Z. physik. Chem.* **43**, 385 (1903).

[150] M. Gomberg, *Ber.* **36**, 3929 (1903); M. Gomberg and L. H. Cone, *ibid.* **37**, 2045 (1904).

[151] M. Gomberg, *Ber.* **35**, 2406 (1902); A. Hantzch, *Ber.* **54**, 2607 (1921).

[152] L. C. Anderson, *J. Am. Chem. Soc.* **57**, 1673 (1935).

[153] B. A. Nikitin, *Z. anorg. Chem.* **227**, 81 (1936).

[154] *Idem, Nature* **140**, 643 (1937).

[154a] K. Cruse, *Z. Elektrochem.* **46**, 571 (1940).

satisfactorily reversible, with the silver-silver bromide electrode less so. The calomel electrode alters with time. The hydrogen electrode is reliable, but the oxygen electrode is unsuited to work in sulfur dioxide.

It is reported that 0.02 molar solutions of nitrosyl chloride, benzoyl chloride, and thionyl chloride are very poor conductors, their specific conductances being around 0.5×10^{-6} mho. The solvent conductance is given as 0.1×10^{-6} mho. Acetyl chloride is a feeble conductor in sulfur dioxide, the conductivity being 1.4×10^{-6} mho.[155]

LIQUID PHOSGENE

Liquid phosgene is a solvent of some interest because of the absence of hydrogen in it. Its poisonous character has not deterred investigations of its solvent properties.

A bibliography on phosgene, up to 1920, cites standard reference books, production, purification, liquefaction, properties, reactions with other substances, products formed by its reaction, and various miscellaneous facts regarding it.[156]

A review of the use of phosgene in organic chemistry as a reagent [157] and a résumé on the use, detection, protection, etc., of phosgene as a war gas [158] have been prepared.

Phosgene is a comparatively poor solvent for inorganic molecules as might be supposed from its small dielectric constant. The substances I_2, ICl_3, $SbCl_3$, $SbCl_5$, S_2Cl_2, and SCl_2 are all soluble or miscible, while red phosphorus, As, As_2O_3, B_2O_3, Sb, Bi, $SnCl_2$, Se, $SeCl_2$, $SeCl_4$, S, Na, K, Ca, $ZnCl_2$, $FeCl_3$, $Fe_2(SO_4)_3$, $CrCl_3$, $HgCl_2$, HgI_2, CuCl, $CuCl_2$, $PbCl_2$, AgCl, $PbCrO_4$, and the thiocyanates, sulfates, and sulfides of the alkali and alkaline earth metals are all insoluble.[159] Aluminum fluoride is insoluble in phosgene, $AlCl_3$ is readily soluble, $AlBr_3$ reacts, giving COClBr, and AlI_3 is soluble with reaction, forming iodine.

Several phosgenates of aluminum chloride have the following compositions: $2AlCl_3 \cdot 5COCl_2$, $2AlCl_3 \cdot 3COCl_2$, and $4AlCl_3 \cdot COCl_2$.[160] The density of $AlCl_3$ solutions up to 46% of the solute increases with concentration and decreases with increasing temperature.[161] The vapor pressures of aluminum chloride solutions at 0°C and 25°C fall with increasing con-

[155] F. Seel, *Z. anorg. Chem.* **252**, 24 (1943).
[156] D. D. Berolzheimer, *Ind. Eng. Chem.* **11**, 263 (1919).
[157] G. M. Dyson, *Chem. Revs.* **4**, 109 (1927).
[158] K. E. Jackson, *J. Chem. Educ.* **10**, 622 (1933).
[159] E. Beckmann and F. Junker, *Z. anorg. Chem.* **55**, 371 (1907); A. von Bartal, *ibid.* **55**, 152 (1907); **56**, 49 (1907).
[160] E. Baud, *Compt. rend.* **140**, 1688 (1905).
[161] A. F. O. Germann, *J. Phys. Chem.* **29**, 139 (1925).

centration as would be expected, appearing to meet the vapor pressure-axis (vp = 0) at 58% $AlCl_3$.[162] This percentage is the composition corresponding to $AlCl_3 \cdot COCl_2$, although this phosgenate is apparently not known. Crystals appear at 0°C for the 55% composition, presumably a phosgenate.

A number of solvates between chlorine and phosgene, ranging from $16COCl_2 \cdot Cl_2$ to $COCl_2 \cdot 10Cl_2$, have been found by cryoscopic measurements.[163]

There are a number of solvents for phosgene.[164] Benzene and ethyl acetate dissolve phosgene without reaction (benzene reacts if a catalyst such as aluminum chloride is present); carbon tetrachloride and chlorocosane are solvents but poor ones. Gasoline and chloroform give a positive heat of solution and a change of boiling point on standing, as does toluene. Acetic acid reacts with phosgene, while paraffin oil does not dissolve it.

The supposed COF_2, obtained by treatment of phosgene with fluorine at 200°C,[165] appears to be carbonyl fluorochloride, COFCl, as in both cases −42°C is given for the boiling point.

The preparation of $BeCl_2$ from beryllium oxide and phosgene shows this method of preparing volatile chlorides is in general superior to the well-known method of using S_2Cl_2.[166]

The reaction between ammonia and phosgene gives urea, biuret, ammelide, and other products [167] and takes place in steps, the first one being the formation of HOCN.[168]

It has been observed [169] that liquid phosgene does not attack aluminum unless the latter is amalgamated, and that neither copper nor zinc amalgams are attacked at all. If aluminum in phosgene is exposed directly to sunlight, not through glass, the aluminum is converted to the chloride. Ultraviolet light brings about dissociation of phosgene into carbon monoxide and chlorine; the chlorine attacks aluminum. Potassium is not attacked in the dark, but solutions of aluminum chloride attack potassium at any time, to form a salt, $KAlCl_4$, and carbon monoxide. It is found that calcium, magnesium, strontium, and barium,

[162] A. F. O. Germann and G. H. McIntyre, *J. Phys. Chem.* **29**, 102 (1925).

[163] A. F. O. Germann and V. Jersey, *Science* **53**, 582 (1921).

[164] C. Baskerville and P. Cohen, *Ind. Eng. Chem.* **13**, 333 (1921).

[165] B. Humiston, *J. Phys. Chem.* **23**, 572 (1919); J. H. Simons, D. F. Herman, and W. H. Pearlson, *J. Am. Chem. Soc.* **68**, 1672 (1946).

[166] C. Matignon and J. Cathala, *Compt. rend.* **181**, 1066 (1925).

[167] E. A. Werner, *J. Chem. Soc.* **1919**, 113, 694.

[168] R. Fosse, P. de Graeve, and P. Thomas, *Compt. rend.* **202**, 1544 (1936).

[169] A. F. O. Germann, *J. Phys. Chem.* **28**, 879 (1924).

all behave likewise.[170]   When calcium is used, a phosgenated salt is formed:

$$Ca + 2AlCl_3 + 3COCl_2 \rightarrow CaCl_2 \cdot 2AlCl_3 \cdot 2COCl_2 + CO$$

The phosgenate loses phosgene when heated, and can be formed from the salts alone without the oxidation of the metal.   It is also observed [171] that phosgene solutions of aluminum chloride take up lithium halides, as well as those of potassium, strontium, magnesium, and lead, to form similar phosgenates.   The sodium, strontium, and barium salts are associated in phosgene solution, that of barium being colloidal.

This behavior suggests [172] that aluminum chloride in phosgene solution is an acid in the Lewis [173] sense.   This acid is formed as follows:

$$2AlCl_3 + COCl_2 \rightarrow COAl_2Cl_8$$

It reacts with calcium to yield carbon monoxide:

$$COAl_2Cl_8 + Ca \rightarrow CaAl_2Cl_8 + CO$$

It is neutralized by the chloride ion:

$$COAl_2Cl_8 + CaCl_2 \rightarrow CaAl_2Cl_8 + COCl_2$$

It is supposed that in a medium of such low dielectric constant as phosgene, the likelihood of finding a strong acid would be very small, that all acids would be weak, and that salts of these weak acids would be stronger electrolytes than the parent acids.   To test this idea [174] the conductance of aluminum chloride solutions was determined by the Kohlrausch method, a Freeland oscillator being used for the a. c. source. Then [175] the vapor pressure, density, and conductance of $CaAl_2Cl_8$ were determined in phosgene at various temperatures.   For correlative conditions of concentration and temperatures, the salt, $CaAl_2Cl_8$, was found to be a better conductor than the acid, $AlCl_3$.

When aluminum chloride solution of phosgene is electrolysed, both carbon monoxide and chlorine are evolved.[176]   Electrolytic evolution of carbon monoxide is very uncommon.   The conductance of saturated $AlCl_3$ solution, 0.7×10^{-3} mho, is 10^5 times that of the parent solvent,

[170] A. F. O. Germann and K. Gagos, *J. Phys. Chem.* **28**, 965 (1924).

[171] D. M. Birosel, *Proc. Iowa Acad. Sci.* **33**, 174 (1926).

[172] A. F. O. Germann and C. R. Timpany, *J. Am. Chem. Soc.* **47**, 2275 (1925).

[173] G. N. Lewis, *J. Franklin Inst.* **226**, 293 (1938).

[174] A. F. O. Germann, *J. Phys. Chem.* **29**, 1148 (1925).

[175] A. F. O. Germann and C. R. Timpany, *J. Phys. Chem.* **29**, 1423 (1925).

[176] A. F. O. Germann, *Science* **61**, 70 (1925).

0.7×10^{-8} mho. It is possible that phosgene dissociates slightly:

$$COCl_2 \rightarrow COCl^+ + Cl^-$$

If an acceptor for chloride ions, such as aluminum chloride, is introduced the equilibrium between the solvent and its own ions is disturbed in such a way as to promote ionization of more solvent molecules in accordance with the Le Châtelier-Braun principle.

Some of these ideas may at some time be tested unambiguously [177] by the use of radioactive phosgene, which has been synthesized from $Ba^{14}CO_3$ by reducing the evolved $^{14}CO_2$ with hot zinc and then combining the resulting ^{14}CO with chlorine.[178]

SELENIUM OXYCHLORIDE

Selenium oxychloride has been described as the parent of a system of acids and bases in much the same way that water is the parent of a system of acids and bases.[179]   Particular interest attaches to selenium oxychloride in view of the fact that, like sulfur dioxide and phosgene, it contains no hydrogen and hence no protons.

Moisture very drastically modifies the solvent properties of $SeOCl_2$ [180] as it introduces selenium dioxide and hydrogen chloride into the solution. A simple test for the presence of moisture makes use of $CoCO_3$, which remains pink in contact with selenium oxychloride so long as the latter is dry but immediately becomes blue under other conditions.   Tantalum metal is unattacked by solutions of selenium oxychloride, and titanium and tungsten are practically inert towards them.   A number of substances form solvates with $SeOCl_2$. When ammonia is passed into a solution of selenium oxychloride in dry ether, the addition compound, $SeOCl_2 \cdot 4NH_3$, forms.[181]

Each of the compounds $TiCl_4$, $SnCl_4$, $SbCl_5$, and $FeCl_3$ forms a solvate with two molecules of $SeOCl_2$ per molecule of chloride; rubidium and potassium chlorides form a monosolvate, and magnesium chloride forms a gel of indeterminate composition.[182]   Arsenic(III) chloride is miscible with $SeOCl_2$ in all proportions; $SbCl_4$, $FeCl_3$, and $SnCl_4$ are very soluble; $MgCl_2$, $CaCl_2$, $BaCl_2$, and $SrCl_2$ are sparingly soluble; $ZnCl_2$, $CdCl_2$,

[177] *Vide supra*, SO_2.
[178] J. L. Huston and T. H. Norris, *J. Am. Chem. Soc.* **70**, 1968 (1948).
[179] G. B. L. Smith, *Chem. Revs.* **23**, 165 (1938).
[180] V. Lenher, *J. Am. Chem. Soc.* **44**, 1664 (1922).
[181] W. Strecker and L. Claus, *Ber.* **56B**, 362 (1923).
[182] C. R. Wise, *J. Am. Chem. Soc.* **45**, 1233 (1923).

$HgCl_2$, and $TiCl_4$, are slightly soluble; and $CuCl_2$, $AgCl$, $PbCl_2$, and $CrCl_3$ are insoluble.

The solvate of water, $SeOCl_2 \cdot H_2O$, and Ditte's compound, $SeO_2 \cdot 2HCl$, have been shown to be identical.[183]

Pyridine, quinoline, and isoquinoline form the two series of solvates with selenium oxychloride, $R \cdot SeOCl_2$ and $R_2 \cdot SeOCl_2$.[184]

Selenium oxychloride is without action on SO_2 or CO; H_2S reacts, giving SeS and HCl; I_2O_5 and also KIO_3 first evolve chlorine and then ICl_3.[185]   The behavior in general of the solvent is a combined chlorinating and oxidizing one.   Copper, silver, lead, nickel, cobalt, iron, bismuth, antimony, and tin, and their oxides are all converted into chlorides by the solvent.[186]

When a solution of KCl in selenium oxychloride is electrolyzed, chlorine is formed at the anode and SeO_2 at the cathode.   When $SnCl_4$ solution is electrolyzed, chlorine appears at the anode and both SeO_2 and Se_2Cl_2 at the cathode.   From these facts it is concluded [187] that the solvent undergoes auto-ionization,[188]

$$2SeOCl_2 \rightleftharpoons SeOCl \cdot SeOCl_2^+ + Cl^-$$

and that the following reactions occur on electrolysis:

$$2Cl^- \rightarrow Cl_2 + 2e^- \qquad \text{(at anode)}$$
$$2SeOCl^+ + 2e^- \rightarrow (Se_2O_2Cl_2) \qquad \text{(hypothetical)}$$
$$3(Se_2O_2Cl_2) \rightarrow 2SeO_2 + Se_2Cl_2 + 2SeOCl_2 \quad \text{(at cathode)}$$

The action of the solvent on copper is as follows:

$$3Cu + 6SeOCl^+ \rightarrow 3Cu^{++} + Se_2Cl_2 + 2SeO_2 + 2SeOCl_2$$

Then a precipitate forms:

$$Cu^{++} + 2Cl^- \rightarrow CuCl_2 \text{ (insol.)}$$

Magnesium, calcium, lead, mercury, copper, zinc, and sodium are all more readily soluble in tin(IV) chloride solutions than in the solvent alone. This behavior compares with H^+ solutions in water, and $AlCl_3$ solutions

[183] C. W. Muehlberger and V. Lenher, *J. Am. Chem. Soc.* **47**, 1842 (1925).

[184] J. Jackson and G. B. L. Smith, *J. Am. Chem. Soc.* **62**, 544 (1940); B. Edgington and J. Firth, *J. Soc. Chem. Ind.* **55**, 192T (1936).

[185] V. Lenher, *J. Am. Chem. Soc.* **44**, 1664 (1922).

[186] W. L. Ray, *J. Am. Chem. Soc.* **45**, 2090 (1923).

[187] G. B. L. Smith, *Chem. Revs.* **23**, 165 (1938).

[188] It should be pointed out that alternate explanations are possible.

in phosgene.   It will be recalled that tin(IV) is a Lewis acid, even as are aluminum chloride and the proton.   It is observed that calcium chloride is readily dissolved by $SnCl_4$ solutions.   A solid phase, probably $CaSnCl_6 \cdot SeOCl_2$, separates on evaporation of the solvent.   It is said that potassium chloride behaves likewise.[189]

Pyridine can be titrated with tin(IV) chloride, when both are in selenium oxychloride solution; the course of the reaction may be followed conductometrically.   There is a discontinuity in the curve of resistance *versus* moles $SnCl_4$ per mole pyridine at the 0.5 mark, indicating the formation of $(C_5H_5N)_2 \cdot SnCl_4$.   Other conductance titrations are described.[190]   Also NaCl, KCl, NH_4Cl, $HgCl_2$, $FeCl_3$, and $BaCl_2$ are all electrolytes in selenium oxychloride.[191]

The potentiometric titration of the bases, potassium chloride, pyridine, quinoline, and isoquinoline with SO_3 (all in selenium oxychloride) has been carried out.[192]   The Müller electrode [193] or a reference electrode of 0.1 molar KCl (in $SeOCl_2$) in a chamber communicating with the body of the titration liquid *via* a ground glass joint was used.   Either of these electrodes shows a measurable potential against a platinum wire dipping into the body of the titration liquid.   No account is taken of the junction potential as it cannot be estimated.   When *emf* is plotted against moles of SO_3 per mole of base, curves are obtained which show the same shape as corresponding curves for bases of various strengths against a strong acid in water.   Potassium chloride is found to be the weakest base, followed by pyridine, quinoline, and isoquinoline.   In another set of titrations SO_3 is found to be a stronger acid in selenium oxychloride than is $FeCl_3$, and that in turn stronger than $SnCl_4$, when all are titrated against quinoline.

[189] Smith, *loc. cit.*
[190] Smith, *loc. cit.*
[191] A. P. Julien, *J. Am. Chem. Soc.* **47**, 1799 (1925).
[192] W. S. Peterson *et al.*, *J. Am. Chem. Soc.* **65**, 2403 (1943).
[193] E. Müller, *Z. Elektrochem.* **31**, 323 (1925).

INDEX

Acetic acid, 179–184

as a solvent, 179; dimer, breakup by solutes, 182; ionization constants of acids in, 180; ionization of solutes in, 181; molecular chains of, broken by tin(IV) chloride, 182; molecular weight determination in, 182; molal freezing constant for, 181; physical properties of, table, 179; precipitation reactions in, 181; solubility of salts in, table, 180; strength of acids in, 182

Acids:

acetic, 179; aminocarbonic, 46; aminonitric, 46; aminophosphoric, 144; antimonic, 146, 149; arsenous, 127; azidothiocarbonic, 49; azidosulfuric, 49; bismuthic, 135, 149; fluophosphoric, 129; hexafluoantimonic, 135; hydrazoic, 41, 46, 172; hydrobromic, 183; hydrochloric, 183; hydronitrous, 70; hyponitrous, 52; hypophosphoric, 128; hypophosphorous, 117; metaphosphoric, 137; nitric, 88; nitrohydroxylamic, 70; nitrous, 71, 73; nitroxylic, 70; orthophosphoric, 137; perchloric, 180, 183; pernitric (peroxynitric), 101; pernitrous, 101; peroxydiphosphoric, 152; peroxymonophosphoric, 152; peroxyphosphoric, 152; phosphoric, 137 (meta, 137); phosphorus, 126 (meta, 127); triphosphoric, 137; pyrophosphoric, 138; rhodozonic, 167; sulfuric, 181, 183; thioantimonic, 152; thioantimonous, 152; thioarsenic, 152; thioarsenous, 152; triphosphoric, 137; pyrophosphoric, 137

Acids, strengths of, in sulfur dioxide, 194

Actyl fluoborate, 193; reactions of, in SO_2, 196

Alkali hydrides, ammonolysis of, 174

Alkali metal amides, 30

Alkali metals, nature of their solutions in ammonia, 161

Alkali metals, reactions, with compounds in liquid ammonia, 164; with elements in liquid ammonia, 163

Alkali metals, stability of their solu- in liquid ammonia, 161

Alkali nitrites, 77

Alkaline earths, reaction with $AlCl_3$ in phosgene, 200

Alkali oxides, reactions with liquid ammonia, 174

Aluminum, anodic oxidation of in NH_3, 178

Aluminum chloride:

conductivity of, in liquid phosgene, 200; Lewis acid in $COCl_2$, 200; reduction of, by potassium in liquid ammonia, 178

Amides, 29; as monoacidic bases, 170; of alkali metals, 30; of alkaline earths, 30; of heavy metals, solubility of, 30

Ammelide, 199

Ammonia, 15–27, 158–184

abnormal physical properties of, 15; as electron donor, 19; as solvent, 129, 159–184; auto-ionization of, 19, 161, 170, 177, constant for 177; chemical properties, analogous to those of water, 19; complexes with alkaline earths, 18; ammonium compounds, analogous to those of water, 24; formation of addition compounds by, 20; heat of neutralization of, 178; hydrates, 21, crystal structure of, 21; hydrogen bonding in, 15; ionization constant of, 21; molecular structure of, 15; oxida-

205

DATE DUE

MAY 7	2004		
GAYLORD			PRINTED IN U.S.A.